THE ORIGIN OF
VERTEBRATES

THE ORIGIN OF
VERTEBRATES

BY

N. J. BERRILL

F.R.S.C., F.R.S.

PROFESSOR OF ZOOLOGY
McGILL UNIVERSITY
MONTREAL

OXFORD
AT THE CLARENDON PRESS
1955

Oxford University Press, Amen House, London E.C.4
GLASGOW NEW YORK TORONTO MELBOURNE WELLINGTON
BOMBAY CALCUTTA MADRAS KARACHI CAPE TOWN IBADAN
Geoffrey Cumberlege, Publisher to the University

———

PRINTED IN GREAT BRITAIN

PREFACE

FOR various reasons much of my time as a biologist has been given to the study of ascidians and other tunicates. It was inevitable that sooner or later they would begin to talk back and try to tell their own story. To the extent I have been able to understand, the following account is the part they seem to have played in the far distant prechordate and prevertebrate past of our own lineage. What I have presented is far from being the whole truth and some of it may be mistaken, but the facts do speak for themselves to a very great extent, and in general outline I believe the early chordate phase of vertebrate evolution to have been more or less along the lines I have suggested. I am indebted personally to D. M. S. Watson for a point of view, and to three biologists of an older vintage, now no longer alive: to E. J. Allen for introducing me to a rich ascidian fauna and for being patient when patience was most needed; and to Walter Garstang and Arthur Willey who each in his turn directed my thoughts toward the problems of early chordate evolution. Above all, perhaps, I am indebted to a decidedly vegetative, often beautiful, and generally obscure group of marine animals, both for their intrinsic interest and for the enjoyment I have had in searching for them.

N. J. B.

McGill University
January 1955

CONTENTS

INTRODUCTORY

1

INTRODUCTION

MEN have speculated concerning their origins since time immemorial and have been making more or less inspired guesses in the light of the knowledge of each particular place and period right up to the present. At the moment the interest is focused more on our immediate emergence from an anthropoid past. Speculation on the infinitely more remote origin of the vertebrates as a whole from a non-vertebrate source, so fashionable during the last half of the nineteenth century, is more of less in abeyance. The reasons for the shift of interest are clear enough. New facts are pouring in concerning fossil anthropoids, while all the evidence we are ever likely to get concerning the origin of vertebrates as a whole seems to have been garnered long ago and discussions of it have gone on interminably. The topic now appears to be unduly academic, and it is with somewhat of the feeling of a voice speaking from the wilderness that I present in this book what is in part a new theory and in part the extension of ideas that have been crystallizing slowly and quietly for two or three generations.

For nearly a century and a half, ever since the idea of evolution, with its concept of life transforming through the ages, first took definite form, the question of vertebrate origins has loomed large; and from the beginning an assumption has been made that vertebrates have arisen from one or another of the invertebrate groups. As long ago as 1818 St. Hilaire conceived a relationship between vertebrates and insects in which one was considered to be the reverse of the other—the insect was in effect a vertebrate lying upon its back. From the first the inverse position of the nerve cord in vertebrates as compared with most invertebrates has been recognized as one of the greatest differences to be explained in assuming an invertebrate origin of vertebrates.

We go on to find almost every major type of invertebrate put forward as the ancestral form of the vertebrates, in particular those various types that have a segmented body, a ventral nerve cord, and a dorsal heart. Turn them over and you have the basic plan of a vertebrate, more or less. Dohrn (1875), Semper (1875–6), Minot (1897), and Delsman (1922) have all upheld the annelids as the ancestral stock; Hubrecht (1883) the nemerteans; while the arachnoid Limulus has been offered, in amazing detail and in different ways, both by Gaskell (1895–1910) and by Patten (1912). An origin of vertebrates that does not go outside the chordate phylum for its source has been proposed relatively lately, and only after the more general interest in the subject has died down. It is a theory that has had a slow growth, and rests upon the labours of Bateson (1884–6), Brooks (1893), Willey (1894), and Garstang (1894–1928). To these I add my own, with full recognition that what, to me, have become my own ideas are only the logical development of concepts long in the making. Meanwhile, before I launch upon my theme, the older theories merit a brief presentation and some discussion. They have their own intrinsic interest, and, by closing one avenue after another, they have progressively narrowed the search until, as chordates ourselves, we are virtually forced to look within our own group for our beginnings, for lack of any real alternative.

The annelid theory took its roots in the general comparison, made by St. Hilaire and others, between the vertebrate and arthropodan pattern. At a later time Semper and Dohrn, in the same year (1875), although independently, transferred the comparison from the arthropods to the annelids, and the annelidan theory of vertebrate descent held a dominant position for a considerable period. Dohrn was led to it by general considerations concerning the organization of the nervous system, its relationship to the mouth and intestine, neuromuscular segmentation, &c.; while Semper by the discovery that in vertebrates the first rudiment of a kidney arises as a number of separate, segmentally arranged tubules that show a remarkable resemblance to the so-called segmental organs of annelids. In fact, the general correspondence between annelids and vertebrates in the excretory system and its relation to the genital products and the segmented coelom has been one of the strongest arguments put forward in favour of the annelidan theory. Further support came from the discovery by Boveri (1892) and Goodrich (1902) of the peculiar flame-cell type of nephridia in Amphioxus, found elsewhere only in flatworms, rotifers, and some polychaetes. The theory finally was put forward in book-length form by Delsman in 1922. The major difficulty previously recognized was that when an annelid is inverted so as to obtain the typical dorsoventrality of a vertebrate, only the nerve cord proper assumes the dorsal position—the brain becomes relatively ventral and is pierced by the oesophagus so that the mouth opens above it. This was the situation or problem to which Delsman gave most of his attention, namely, how to evolve a vertebrate-type head and brain from that of an annelid in such a way that the digestive tube lies ventral to it throughout its length. The gist of his theory, which he presented with great elaboration, is that the neural tube of the vertebrate was at one time the stomodaeal part of the alimentary canal, and that this became cut off during early embryonic development and underwent a change of function. A new mouth and stomodaeum developed in a more ventral position; while the old mouth survives in vertebrate embryos as the neuropore. The transformations as a whole are conceived for the most part in terms of embryological processes and morphogenetic movements, and in many ways Delsman reflects a combination of the older and purely morphological outlook with that of an emergent analytical and experimental embryology. The result is a highly ingenious argument, although so intricate and in some ways fantastic, that one of Delsman's colleagues in Amsterdam announced that the book should be confiscated and burned. As it stands, it seems to have become a fitting epitaph to those who laboured to make vertebrates out of worms.

Annelids and arthropods are built along the same general lines, and all who have sought to derive the vertebrates from the arthropods have had the same obstacles to overcome as have the proponents of the annelidan theory. According to Patten (1912), who compares vertebrates with the arachnoid Limulus and derives them from the more primitive limuloid eurypterids, the original mouth became closed as the result of pressure produced by a rapidly enlarging brain and by the backward growth of the anterior borders of the carapace. The new mouth broke through, he thought, on the original ventral side between the bases of the diverging paired appendages. These, he supposed, lost their locomotory function and emphasized their respiratory function, and became the branchial skeleton and apparatus of the vertebrates. This theory, like Delsman's, was worked out in great detail and rested heavily on a comparison of the oldest fossils of both groups, the eurypterids and ostracoderms. Patten demonstrated how a primitive arachnoid *might* be transformed into a vertebrate, but he brought forward no evidence that such a transformation ever took place. The almost overwhelming evidence against it is well summarized by Gregory (1951) in his general introduction to *Evolution Emerging*.

Gaskell's theory starts with the same general base as Patten's, as a comparison between Limulus, scorpions, and other arthropods on the one hand and the vertebrates on the other, but his assumptions, arguments, and conclusions are widely different. Like Patten, he was impressed with the resemblances between the fossil eurypterids and ostracoderms, but his theory rested mainly upon a detailed comparison of the cranial nerves of the ammocoete larva of lampreys with those of the arachnoids. It is unique in that he derives the vertebrate from the arthropod without turning the latter upside down, although once again the original digestive tube loses its primary function and becomes the cavity of the brain and spinal cord, connecting with the new gut at the hypophysis.

None of these theories has received any wide acceptance, no matter how skilfully they have been presented. Their value is a negative one inasmuch as they show fairly conclusively that neither annelids nor arthropods can be regarded as the ancestral source from which the vertebrates have arisen. The effort to make such a derivation has been pushed to the limit and has failed monumentally, both in the case of annelids and of arthropods, and shows the fallacy in attempting to derive any one highly differentiated animal type from another of comparable complexity. Similarities in such cases are almost inevitably the result of parallel evolution.

On the basis of early developmental patterns the majority of the animal phyla can be formed into two superphyla, the teloblastic arthropods, annelids, nemerteans, flatworms, &c., comprising the Trochozoa, and the enterocoelic echinoderms, brachiopods, pterobranchs, prochordates, Amphioxus, and vertebrates. This, in all likelihood, is a natural grouping, and bio-chemical studies tend to confirm it. With the tacit abandonment of annelids and arthropods as the possible ancestral vertebrate stock, and the recognition of a vague but possibly real relation-ship between chordates and echinoderms, there has been a natural tendency to try and fit the ancestral garment upon this group. The attempt has been made in two ways, the one in-volving for the most part a consideration of larval organisms, which I will discuss later, and the other a direct comparison of the fossil vertebrate ostracoderms and fossil echinoderms of extinct types of an even earlier period.

The carpoid echinoderms of the Cambrian and Ordovician periods appear to be the most primitive known members of the group, a type of sea lily attached to the sea floor by a stalk and possessing an exoskeleton or calyx of many plates, together with a water-pore system formed from ciliated grooves. Gislén (1930) has pointed out that one of these, Cothurnocystites Elizae, of the lower Silurian, has a markedly asymmetrical calyx perforated by a series of sixteen small openings reminiscent of the asym-metry and gill slits of a young Amphioxus, and suggests that carpoid echinoderms are closely related to the ancestral chor-dates. The carpoid stalk becomes the chordate tail. Whether or not the echinoderms and the chordate-vertebrate stock have some dim and distant affinity with one another, I feel that con-necting the heavily armoured, bottom-crawling, fully differen-tiated ostracoderms with the complexly organized, heavily armoured, and more or less coextant echinoderms is on a par with the attempt to equate a vertebrate with an annelid. To find our sources we need to go much farther back than the Ordovician and even the Cambrian periods, to evolutionary times that have left us no fossil evidence of any kind; our clues can come for the most part only from the study of living organ-isms, the manner of their development, and the nature of their adaptations.

II

As the more prominent invertebrate types one by one failed or showed signs of failing to meet the requirements for qualification as the ancestral form of vertebrates, more and more attention has been given to the lesser lights, particularly to those that share

certain significant features with the vertebrates. The pterobranchs, Cephalodiscus and Rhabdopleura, possess a nerve
centre or 'brain' that is situated dorsal to the mouth, and one
of them, Cephalodiscus, has a single pair of gill slits. The
Enteropneusta are equally well endowed with a nervous system
which is at least dorsal in part, and with a series of gill slits
equipped with tongue bars comparable with those of Amphioxus.
Only the notochord, the crowning insignia of the chordates,
appears to be lacking. Ascidians in adult form possess the dorsal
neural ganglion and gill slits, and a true notochord in the larva.
Yet the segmentation of the neuromuscular locomotory system
characteristic of vertebrates seems to be absent, and here again
much effort has been put forward to find some trace of it. Only
Amphioxus among the so-called non-vertebrate chordates possess
all the qualifications—the segmental muscular system, dorsal
nerve cord, notochord, and series of gill slits. Yet in other ways
Amphioxus itself is anomalous, particularly in the absence of
sense organs and any brain worthy of the name. These various
types have been regarded as primitive or as degenerate forms
according to the changing fashions of the times, but in a general
way they have become increasingly regarded as the bridge
between vertebrates and some simpler, non-vertebrate, non-
chordate kind of animal.

Comparative anatomy alone, however, with or without more
of the same kind of information obtained from fossils, is inadequate to give us much insight into the manner and means by
which one kind of animal may have evolved from another.
Every organism, living or extinct, has developed as an individual
from a relatively small and simple egg or from a tissue bud of
comparable size and simplicity. It becomes what it is as the
result of a complex process of development that is difficult to
comprehend and becomes in many ways the more mysterious
the more it is subjected to analysis. Yet the general concept of
the organism as a four-dimensional continuum undergoing continual change at all levels of organization is one that is currently
dominant, and it is one that seems to reflect the reality better
than the older, more static points of view. It is essential, I think,
to understand how an organism, vertebrate or otherwise, develops, if we are to understand much concerning its evolution;
for every individual organism develops as a whole and not in bits

and pieces, and while we are inclined to think of mutational changes either in terms of genes and chromosomes or of adult character, the effective innovations are essentially small changes in the nature of early developmental processes of growth or organization. It was inevitable that embryology should play an increasingly important role in efforts to unravel the evolutionary past, but its application is beset with difficulties inherent in the understanding of developmental processes itself.

The Tunicates, in particular the ascidians, enter the story early, when Kowalewsky in 1869 discovered the chordate nature of the tadpole larva. The immediate effect of this discovery was to remove the ascidians from their previous grouping with molluscoid invertebrates and to place them in association with the chordate animals. And probably more than any other single observation it caught Haeckel's imagination and evoked the basic concept contained in the theory of recapitulation, namely, that adult stages of ancestors are repeated during the development of their descendants, although crowded back into early developmental periods; in short, that the course of development is a brief recapitulation of the evolutionary past. In this light the ascidian tadpole larva became a relic or reflection of a past free-swimming chordate ancestor of the ascidians, and adult ascidians became generally regarded as secondarily sessile and degenerate descendants of a more ancient chordate stock. Even Willey (1894), who studied ascidians and the manner of their development almost as intensively as he did Amphioxus, says, in his introduction to his *Amphioxus and the Ancestry of Vertebrates*, 'that the ascidians are degenerate animals, to the extent that they have become adapted to a fixed habit of life, is of course obvious'. Yet he himself was the first to make a serious attempt to trace out the course of chordate evolution by studying the embryos and larvae as well as the adults of Amphioxus, ascidians, and protochordates in general. Amphioxus was taken as the prototype of the chordates and Willey's chief purpose was to reconstruct its hypothetical chordate ancestors with the aid of the recapitulatory theory. He considered Amphioxus to be on the main line of chordate ascent leading to the full vertebrate type, an assumption that is of very doubtful validity. His final conclusion was:

that the proximate ancestor of the vertebrates was a free-swimming animal intermediate in organization between an ascidian tadpole and Amphioxus, possessing the dorsal mouth, hypophysis, and restricted notochord of the former; and the myotomes, coelomic epithelium, and straight alimentary canal of the latter. The ultimate or primordial ancestor of the vertebrates would, on the contrary, be a worm-like animal whose organization was approximately on a level with that of the bilateral ancestors of the Echinoderms.

The links briefly are, according to Willey, as follows: echinoderms are descended from bilaterally symmetrical pelagic ancestors, represented in their development by such larval forms as the Bipinnaria and Auricularia; the general likeness between the echinoderm Auricularia and the Tornaria larva of Balanoglossus is so great that it 'can only be accounted for on the ground of genetic affinity'; Balanoglossus is a protochordate supplied with gill slits and a dorsal tubular nervous system, and requires only the notochord and segmental myotomes to approximate the amphioxid type. Larval forms represent past ancestral forms, and the evolutionary sequence is worked out accordingly. Throughout the whole discussion Willey makes much of the pre-oral lobe, a feature common to all the forms he discusses. Garstang, in the same year (1894), made the suggestion that the endostyle of Amphioxus and ascidians is derived from the adoral ciliated band of the echinoderm larva. Many years later (1928) he formulated his own theory of chordate evolution along lines which take obvious origin in his own and Willey's ideas of this early period. To quote:

The ancestry of Chordata must be consistent with the systematic sequence: Echinoderm—Hemichordate (i.e. Pterobranchia and Enteropneusta)—Protochordate—Vertebrate, which, at bottom, implies an evolutional progress of plankton-feeding organisms from a fixed condition with external ciliated tentacles and food grooves to an eventually free and motile state with endopharyngeal apparatus of gill-slits and endostyle. This implication is corroborated by the secondary character of the coelomic (locomotive) metamerism of Amphioxus, by the association of an external lophophore with the simplest known condition of gill-slits (Cephalodiscus), and, negatively, by the absence of proof that pelagic larvae necessitate pelagic ancestors.

Garstang on the one hand conceived the sessile adult form of the ascidian as evolving from a sessile pterobranch ancestor somewhat like Cephalodiscus, and on the other a progressive evolution of larval organisms as such, taking place independently of changes or the absence of change in the nature of the adult organism. The larval sequence is seen as follows: echinoderm-auricularia → hemichordate-tornaria → protochordate-ascidian tadpole → permanently free-swimming chordate. On this theory the ascidian tadpole becomes essentially an interpolation in the ascidian life cycle; and by suppression of metamorphosis and through further evolution it gives rise to the vertebrates as a whole. This is the general thesis, with which I am in agreement, although not with the manner in which Garstang supposes the changes to have taken place. It places the ascidians in the main line of chordate ascent, as larvae at least, although not necessarily as the basic stock in other ways. It puts them in a position far removed from that given them by Gregory (1951), who expresses the relationship between ascidians and Amphioxus in two alternative ways:

basic chordate → Amphioxus → primitive fishes
                    ↓   (ostracoderms)
                 ascidians

or more likely

basic chordate → primitive fishes → Amphioxus
                  (ostracoderms)   ↓
                                     ascidians

Thus in the first alternative an hypothetical chordate ancestor gives rise to Amphioxus, which in turn gives rise to primitive vertebrates in one direction and to the ascidians, by retrogressive evolution, in another. In the second alternative both Amphioxus and the ascidians evolve from primitive vertebrates as two successive steps in retrograde evolution, with the main line evolving in another direction.

Obviously there are various ways in which the data derived from the study of the lower chordates and other organisms can be organized so as to give a plausible picture of evolutionary relationships. The question is which arrangement is the most satisfactory; that is, which concept makes use of the greatest number of apparently relevant facts and at the same time leaves the smallest number unaccounted for. The discussion which follows is less an attempt to justify a particular interpretation than it is to bring into an hypothetical evolutionary story as much of the more or less superabundant provertebrate data as possible, with a minimum of exclusion; and at the same time to envisage each step of the transforming organisms in terms both of their embryological development and in relation to their environment. There is no direct proof or evidence that any of the suggested events or changes ever took place; what strength the argument may have comes only from whatever wealth of circumstantial detail I have been able to muster. In a sense this account is science fiction, but I have myself found it an interesting and enjoyable venture to speculate concerning the Cambrian and Precambrian happenings that may have led to my own existence. In these days of projected travel to the moon and Mars, I find a speculative journey into time a more comfortable and less nightmarish form of escape from the inquietude of our present civilization. In this mood I have put two and two together in the hope that the total will be greater than the sum of its parts.

2

THE ORIGIN OF VERTEBRATES

THE theory I hope to establish in the following pages requires a wealth of detail to give it substance and involves a discussion of many debatable topics. Consequently, rather than enter at once upon this undertaking, I believe it is desirable here to present a brief outline of the principal assumptions and conclusions.

The assumptions in a sense are negative, and are in effect a simplification of the material to be considered. These are, first, that the hemichordates represented by the pterobranchs and enteropneusts together are not in any direct way relevant to the story and may exhibit no more than a convergent resemblance to chordate organization in so far as gill slits and a dorsally placed nerve centre may have been independently acquired; and, second, that Amphioxus is a degenerate form in no sense ancestral to ascidians and not even a satisfactory vertebrate prototype. On the other hand, ascidians have never been taken fully at their face value. This I propose to do, not so much as an evangelical protagonist of their ancestral role as with the belief that it is the one approach to the problem that has yet to be made whole-heartedly, and that it is in essentials a simpler and more direct approach than any other.

The thesis in brief is as follows.

1. Ascidians are primarily a primitive sessile, marine group of organisms which may or may not be related to the hemichordates. On one or more occasions they have given rise to pelagic forms. The derivative questions are what has been the early history of the ascidians themselves, and at what stages in their internal evolution have they given rise to the pelagic types.

2. The tadpole larva of ascidians (and of tunicates as a whole in so far as the tadpole form is recognizable) has evolved within the group to meet specific ascidian needs, and has not been inherited from any other source.

3. At some time the tadpole larva became neotenous, ceasing to metamorphose into a mature ascidian and maturing sexually as a free-swimming organism. This took place as an exploitation of the rich pasture of oceanic surface waters, particularly that of shallow continental seas, and the thaliacean and appendicularian tunicates are the direct but modified descendants of this original neotenous form.

4. At an early period of the pelagic evolutionary phase, before the thaliacean specializations had been initiated, some forms exploited the rich detritus descending from the river systems and entered the estuaries and river mouths to the extent that their locomotory power enabled them. Through elaboration of their sensory and locomotor equipment, and above all through increase in size and by acquisition of a segmented muscle system, they finally ascended the rivers themselves. Segmentation of the body was called forth by the need to maintain or improve position in the face of down-flowing freshwater currents. The derivative problem is the origin of segmentation in terms of developmental mechanics.

5. At first the rivers were ascended only by partly grown or adult organisms intent solely upon feeding. They returned to the sea to breed, where they shed innumerable small pelagic eggs typical of their ancestors. Without such use or retention of the common ante-room of the sea the general exploitation and long-phase evolution from a primitively marine to a specialized and highly differentiated freshwater type could hardly have been possible.

6. Amphioxus is a relic of this intermediate phase and survives as the result of having become a backslider in an almost literal sense, that is, as a representative of the early chordates that ascended the rivers to feed but returned to the sea to breed. Amphioxus rediscovered certain advantages of marine life, probably from necessity, became readapted to feeding in the same general territory as the ancestral ascidians, and eliminated any tendency to move away and migrate up rivers by the comparatively simple device of suppressing the development of its navigational sense organs and associated brain.

7. Within the river systems the chordates evolved directly to a relatively simple, unarmoured type of ostracoderm. As such they also evolved the comparatively large freshwater vertebrate

type of egg of the kind still laid by lampreys, dipnoans, crosso-
pterygians, and most amphibians.

8. Such an ostracoderm is the vertebrate prototype, and gave
rise to the heavily armoured and specialized ostracoderms, and
to the true fishes. At this point the conception of vertebrate
evolution becomes that of current palaeontological thinking and
extends beyond the scope of this discussion.

The general validity of the foregoing depends primarily upon
the nature and origin of the ascidian tadpole larva. If the tadpole has been inherited from a non-ascidian source, the ascidians
become merely an offshoot of the main chordate growth. On
the other hand, if the ascidian tadpole can be shown to be of
ascidian origin, the ascidians themselves, at least in their original
form, become ancestral to the chordates as a whole and assume
pedigree importance. The crucial points first to be established
therefore are the nature of the typical, least modified tadpole
larva, the survival value of the tadpole larva to the ascidian, its
origin as a developmental interpolation in the life cycle, and the
manner in which the tailed tadpole originated, in terms of
developmental mechanics. If these can be substantiated, then
the conclusion follows that the chordates as a whole have arisen
from such a larval organism; the only alternative, that the
tadpole larva has arisen independently of the chordates and is
no more than a parallel evolution without genetic affinity, puts
a much greater strain upon credulity.

Ascidians then take on a greater interest as the actual, although
now specialized, stock from which the chordates have emerged,
and the early evolutionary phases of the ascidians as such become part of our own ancestry. The questions which arise are:
to what extent, if at all, are ascidians related to pterobranchs,
enteropneusta, and echinoderms; and how much of the basic
ascidian organization, apart from that of the tadpole larva, is
carried through into the chordate and vertebrate structure? On
the other hand, what evidence is there that ascidian tadpoles
have given rise through neoteny to permanently free-swimming
forms and what developmental problems were involved in the
formation of larger, pre-vertebrate types? These and other questions will be taken up in sequence in the following chapters.

ASCIDIANS

3

THE ASCIDIAN TADPOLE

TADPOLE larvae of ascidians vary in detail considerably, yet a basic type does appear to exist, from which various derivative forms have evolved. Taxonomically the ascidians were at one time divided into two groups, the simple or solitary forms and the social or compound forms; the distinction still has value although not in the sense it was originally made. In the present connexion the significant fact is that almost all solitary kinds are oviparous and shed innumerable small, more or less translucent, eggs into the surrounding water, where they become fertilized. This seems to be a primitive condition. Compound forms on the other hand, that is, those ascidians that reproduce by budding to form colonial organisms in which the individual is inevitably small, are with one or two exceptions viviparous and produce comparatively small numbers of relatively large and yolky eggs. This I believe to be a secondary condition and, while the changes in the nature of the eggs and in their developmental circumstances result in certain changes in the nature of the tadpole larvae, these seem to me to be of immediate interest only as indications of a certain plasticity in the development of the tadpole. They will be discussed later.

Oviparous species produce eggs having a diameter varying only within certain narrow limits, between 0·12 and 0·18 mm. Their course of development is essentially uniform: cleavage rates and patterns are virtually the same in all, and so are the size and shape of the tadpole larvae. Only in certain details of sensory equipment do the larvae differ significantly, but even these differences appear to be simply degenerative, and we find a fairly standardized type common to the families Cionidae, Diazonidae, Corellidae, and Ascidiidae of the order Enterogona, and essentially similar larvae in the Pyuridae of the order

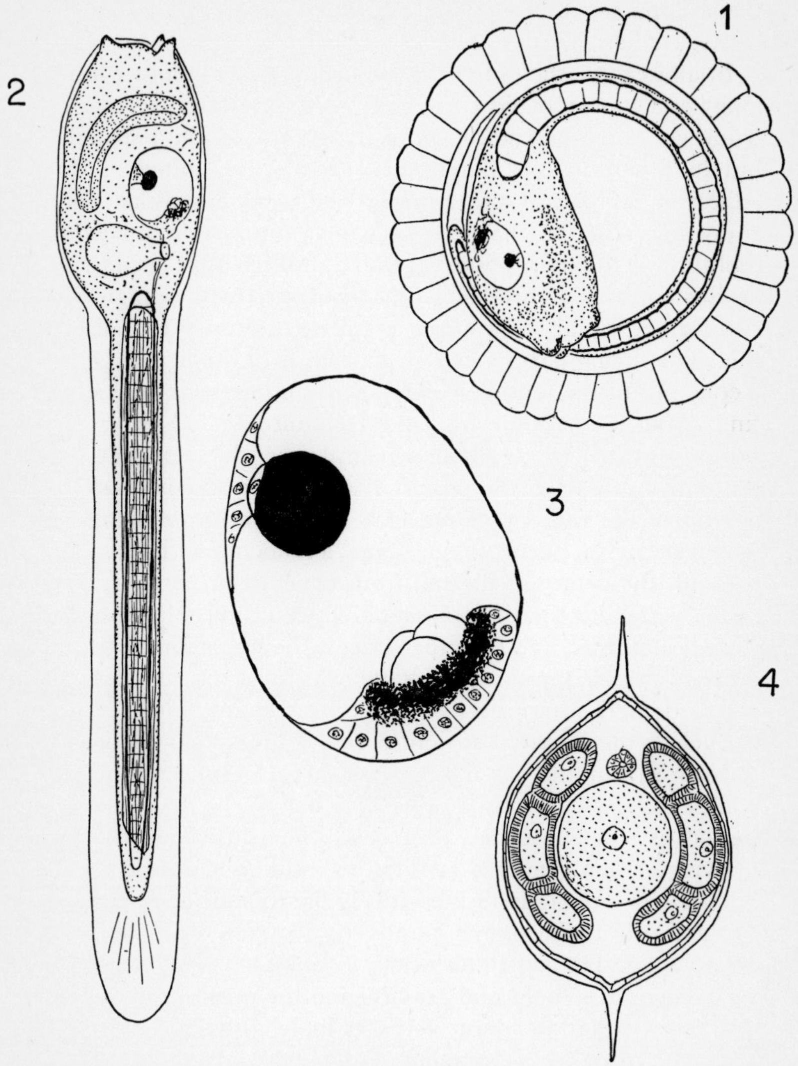

FIG. 1. The ascidian tadpole (Ascidia or Ciona type). 1, tadpole ready to hatch, showing sensory vesicle and about forty notochord cells, with flotatory follicle cells attached to the egg membrane. 2, tadpole with anterior adhesive organs, tail with muscle band, notochord, and cuticular fin. 3, sensory vesicle showing unicellular otolith, and ocellus with three lens cells, pigment, and about a dozen retinal cells. 4, cross-section of tail to show central notochord, bands of muscle cells, and dorsal neural tube.

Pleurogona (for a general account of ascidians, including taxo-
nomy, cf. Berrill, 1951).

In all of these the tadpole is uniformly small (about 1·0 mm.
long) and has an ovoid trunk and a slender tapering tail. The
trunk contains the rudiments of the future ascidian structure,
but its functionally differentiated tissues are limited to three
adhesive papillae at the anterior end, and a sensory vesicle
consisting of a sac the floor of which supports a unicellular
otolith and the dorsoposterior wall a multicellular ocellus. The
ocellus consists of three lens cells associated with a pigmented
cup formed by about a dozen pigmented sensory retinal cells,
the whole being part of a local thickening of the neural wall.

The tail of the tadpole consists of a simple epidermal sheath
supporting a cuticular fin, and contains the following three
component structures: a hollow neural tube which extends along
the dorsal side from the posterior wall of the sensory vesicle to
the tip of the rail, consisting of a large number of small cells
which are neither neurons nor fibres; a notochord which extends
through the centre of the tail from beneath the posterior wall
of the vesicle to the tip, consisting of 40–42 vacuolated cells in
a single column; and on either side of the notochord a band of
striated muscle tissue, each band consisting of eighteen cells
and activated anteriorly as a single contractile unit.

Such is the essential structure at the time of hatching. The
tadpole is a motile but non-feeding larval organism which becomes active some considerable time before the developmental
period as a whole comes to an end. The duration of tadpole
activity as such generally lasts for several hours, during the first
part of which the tadpole is positively phototactic and negatively
geotactic, later becoming positively geotactic and negatively
phototactic. The net result of the locomotory activity, the sensory reactions to light and gravity, and the presence of adhesive
organs is the attachment of the tadpole to what may well be
a suitable spot for permanent settlement and continuation of
post-larval growth.

The all-important question is whether the ascidian has exploited for the purpose of habitat selection a type of larval
organism inherited from some non-ascidian and possibly higher
chordate ancestral type, or whether the total organization just
described is essential for survival and has been evolved within

the ascidian group as an innovation of its own. If the second alternative holds, then the general nature of the tadpole, particularly in relation to environmental circumstances, requires a much more detailed analysis. In any case the question of value, and its implications concerning origin, need to be determined at the outset.

4

THE SURVIVAL VALUE OF THE ASCIDIAN TADPOLE

No matter how different in size or structure ascidians may have been at the time other chordate groups may have started to evolve from them, we have to begin with a study of ascidians as they now exist. For the most part they are inhabitants of the littoral and are exclusively marine; they do not effectively penetrate the intertidal zone, while those ascidians which inhabit very deep water are usually obviously and highly specialized.

Ascidians of a kind that possess the more or less standard type of tadpole described in the last chapter range through depths anywhere from low-tide level down to several hundred metres. All are associated with a sea floor that is either rocky, hard clay with stones, or gravel; all attach to shell, stone, or rock and are not equipped to find a footing in either sand or mud. All, excepting Diazona species, are solitary, non-budding forms, and all, including Diazona, are comparatively large massive types generally bathed by the surrounding water except for a restricted area of attachment. They are not imbedded in either mud or sand, and their protective case of tunicin is relatively clean. Some sort of selection of the settling site is clearly important and of great survival value.

Suitable locations must be advantageous for all stages. They must be of a texture clean enough for the microscopic tadpole to settle on without danger of suffocation by mud or other debris, and stable and extensive enough to permit growth to proceed to the size of sexual maturity. The sides of ledges, rocks, and even small stones if they are firmly anchored meet the requirements, since they afford a firm footing and at the same time do not tend to become matted over by falling detritus or become too heavily settled by algae, &c. Undersurfaces are equally desirable if there is sufficient space above the sea floor for a sweep of current.

All oviparous ascidians liberate eggs in fairly large numbers,

and such eggs all have a considerable perivitelline space between the ovum and the chorion or egg membrane; the chorion
supports a layer of more or less buoyant, vacuolated follicle
cells on its outer surface. In two species only, Ciona intestinalis
and Ascidiella aspersa, are the follicle cells large enough to
cause the eggs to float in still water; those of Corella parallelo-
gramma do so doubtfully, while the rest do not. But all are
buoyant enough to be well dispersed in moving water. Inasmuch as the eggs develop freely in the water for one or two or
more days according to the temperature, dispersal to a considerable extent is assured without the intervention of swimming
larvae. When the tadpoles hatch from the egg membranes their
responses to light and gravity cause them to swim upward toward the surface. Since this first phase of activity usually lasts
for several hours, the distance covered is adequate to ensure
not only further dispersion but a sufficient elevation to permit
a downward scattering at the time of settling. And in so doing
their negative reaction to light now prevailing causes them to
turn toward shaded surfaces, that is, towards those surfaces of
rock or shell which do not face directly upward.

This degree of selection of habitat may not appear to be
great enough to account for the existence of the typical tadpole
larva. Yet if it were not so we should find ascidians which
possess this type of larva occurring in a greater variety of situations than we do. The very great majority are found attached to
vertical or under surfaces of rock, weed, or wood the common
feature of which seems to be comparative cleanliness. It is true
there are exceptions such as Phallusia mammillata, but as these
large individuals are usually found attached to stones barely
submerged in mud, we cannot be sure that they were exceptions
at the time of settling, when they were microscopic. As Wilson
(1950) and others have shown, the settling upon the sea floor
by pelagic larvae of more or less sedentary animals is an event
that is in all probability the most crucial in their whole life
cycle. The surface upon which they settle must be viewed on the
scale of the organisms at the stage at which settling occurs.
The particular admixture of sand, mud, and shell gravel, and the
size and nature of the particles, for instance, are all-important
in connexion with the metamorphosis and successful settling
of the larvae of marine polychaetes. And this appears to be

equally true for ascidians, except that the particular conditions required are very different. Stability as well as cleanliness is necessary; the shifting medium of gravel, sand, and mud is entirely unsuitable for the relatively primitive kinds of ascidians now under discussion. Only the more specialized kinds, with particular adaptive devices for anchoring in unstable ground, are found to construct their houses upon the sand.

It is important, obviously, that a site must be selected which permits the individual attaching to it to grow to the size of reproductive maturity. It is equally important that the microscopic tadpole larva finds the site suitable for the initial attachment. The question is whether the degree of site selection involved requires an organization of the kind represented by the tadpole larva under discussion.

Two phases of larval life are involved. The first is the ascent of the larvae towards the sea surface, from whatever level the eggs may be at the time of hatching. For this a positive phototropism or a negative geotropism is necessary, though not both; while any simple ciliary locomotor mechanism would presumably suffice. Most larvae of marine invertebrates are of this general type. The chordate tail seems to be an unnecessarily difficult means of attaining the same end, unless external ciliary mechanisms suitable for locomotion have from the first been inhibited by a tendency to secrete an external cuticle. In any case the upward migration is primarily dispersive and non-selective. The second phase is very different. The reversal of the tropistic reactions, a commonly occurring phenomenon among marine larval organisms, brings the larvae close to the sea floor in most instances, and away from the surface light even if there is no complete descent. This again can be accomplished by ciliary mechanisms, without requiring an organ such as a tail.

The terminal reaction is the vital one. A tadpole, descending from the upper zone of greater light intensity, turns toward any dark or shaded surface it may be passing. That surface is likely to be hard and clean compared with horizontal surfaces in general. The relatively sudden turning toward one side seems to be essential for possible attachment to such locations, and for such sudden directed turnings the tail appears to be a far more efficient mechanism than any ciliary girdles or bands could possibly be.

Accordingly we get the following picture. The majority of the ascidians of what is generally regarded as the least specialized group are species which typically attach to clean, hard surfaces characteristic of sites which are more or less vertical or overhung, or at least swept bare by relatively strong currents. The species are oviparous, the eggs more or less buoyant and around 150 microns in diameter. Fertilization and development take place in the water external to the parent organisms and the tadpole larvae hatch from the egg membrane after one or two days development at commonly prevailing temperatures. An otolith and ocellus direct the hatched tadpole towards the surface at first and later, usually after several hours, direct it downward toward the sea floor by virtue of a reversal of tropistic reactions. The muscular, chordate tail serves as the organ of locomotion throughout, is probably no more efficient during the ascent and descent than the various ciliary locomotor mechanisms found among the larvae of marine invertebrates, but is decidedly more efficient as a propulsive organ for directing the tadpole towards its preferred attachment site during the final phase of the free-swimming period. The immediate attachment is effected by the sticky secretions of three glandular epidermal papillae situated at the tadpole's anterior end. The importance of the final selection of a settling site seems to justify the existence and nature of the tailed tadpole; but there is a suspicion that the alternative locomotory mechanisms of ciliated epidermal bands may have been inhibited or prohibited by epidermal cuticular secretion in general.

In a general way therefore the ascidian tadpole appears to fulfil a vital function which could be served by other kinds of larvae only with less efficiency. How vital the tadpole is as a site-selector remains to be shown, for there appears to be a close relationship between the particular nature of the tadpole larva and the nature of the habitat of the species concerned.

5

COMPARATIVE LARVAL ECOLOGY

THE ascidians so far discussed are all of one general kind, all belonging to the somewhat heterogenous order Phlebobranchiata of the order Enterogona. All forms within the group grow to a relatively large size as individuals, the body in most instances being more or less ovoid and growing in a comparatively uniform manner in the three dimensions. The individuals of most species characteristically anchor themselves by a limited basal area. Their habitat is consequently restricted to places where they can grow more or less freely out into the surrounding water. Hard vertical surfaces therefore are at a premium, for they afford both the necessary spatial freedom for growth and protection from silt; at the same time protection from wave action is almost as necessary. The nature of the tadpole larvae of these forms seems to be closely related to selection of this sort of location.

Of the remaining ascidians, those of the enterogonid suborder Aplousobranchiata consist of a number of families of compound forms, that is, consisting of species all of which multiply asexually to form colonial organisms or communal aggregations. In consequence much, if not most, of growth as a whole is diverted into asexual reproduction; the individual ascidiozooids remain small and also remain more or less embedded in a common tunic. The general result is the conversion of a solitary single individual of typical three-dimensional proportions into compound or colonial forms consisting of many very small individuals united together as a more or less two-dimensional encrusting sheet. Such a form has a relatively enormous area of attachment often co-extensive with the exposed free surface. And as a type it is admirably adapted to living and growing attached to the under surface of rocks and ledges, &c., where there is abundance of clean hard surface for attachment but restricted free space for outward growth. Most members of this suborder are found in such places, or on sites where the encrusting type of growth is essential for permanent attachment. All locations occupied by the ascidians constituting this suborder require at least as much as and usually considerably more selective action by the larvae than is necessary for the first described. The larvae need to turn even more sharply and powerfully toward a shaded or darkened surface in order to reach a suitable site for attachment. Accordingly genetic selection pressure must be even greater in the direction of maintaining and increasing the efficiency of the tadpole as a selector of a suitable anchorage than in the case of those that need to deflect their vertical descent to a lesser degree.

That this is so seems to be borne out by the structure and activity of the tadpole larvae. All species of this suborder are viviparous, and all produce eggs which are relatively large and yolky. Eggs vary in diameter, according to the species, from 2 to 5 times that typical of oviparous forms, and usually contain relatively much more yolk per unit mass. To what extent this is a consequence of reduction in parental size—a compensatory response to an inevitable reduction in egg number—is difficult to decide. But it is probable that both the viviparity and increase in egg size and content are related to the nature of the habitat, quite apart from the question of the mutual interdependence of the presence of large eggs and the viviparous condition. The effect of viviparity alone is to curtail drastically the pelagic developmental phase by limiting it to the free-swimming period of the fully differentiated tadpole; the result of increase in egg size, apart from increase in yolk content, is the formation of a correspondingly larger tadpole which is in consequence a more powerful and faster swimmer (tadpole speed varies directly with tadpole size, a topic that will be discussed later); while increase in relative amount of yolk delays attainment of the functional tadpole phase in relation to development as a whole, and as a consequence greatly shortens the length of the free-swimming period (Berrill, 1935). In short, tadpoles are produced as late as possible in the course of development, are liberated as such at the parental site, and have an abbreviated free-swimming phase. Dispersal is reduced to a minimum and comparatively powerful tadpoles are produced capable of a more decisive selection of a site than are those of oviparous forms. Not only do the body and tail constitute a relatively better locomotory structure, but the sensory equipment is unimpaired and even improved inasmuch as it exists on a larger scale. More than this, the anterior adhesive papillae are reinforced by surrounding epidermal cups which greatly increase their efficiency as adhesive organs. There is no doubt that the tadpole as tadpole is a much improved edition of that which develops from the smaller oviparous eggs, or that the improvement relates almost exclusively to the final phase of selection of a site for anchorage. In other words, the greater the importance of habitat selection, the greater the general efficiency of the tadpole larva as a chordate type of site selector. This is borne out again in the family Perophoridae, which stands somewhat alone although placed within the Phlebobranchiata, in which the larger species attach to vertical and underhung surfaces and the smaller ones beneath the rocks; the tadpoles are large, are produced viviparously, are short-lived, and as fully equipped as the best.

The proof of the matter is to be found, however, in the associations found within the order Pleurogona (or Stolidobranchiata). This order is clearly set apart as a natural group derived at some time from an oviparous enterogonid stock with a habitat like that of Ciona or Ascidia. Diversification, however, has proceeded within the order to a very great extent, and both habitat and larvae show a much greater range of character than in the other order. The order consists of three families, the Pyuridae, Molgulidae, and Styelidae, each of which merits separate discussion.

The Pyuridae

The pyurid ascidians serve as the best point of departure since they are mostly moderately large, solitary forms typically attached to rocks and stones at various depths from low tide to the beginning of the continental slopes. They are highly evolved in general structure, although not in the sense of specialization. They attach to their anchorage surface much as do the phlebobranch ascidians, usually by a restricted basal area. Their outer tunic, however, is not only of a fibrous, leathery texture, but is usually differentiated on its outer surface to form a layer of small fibrous extensions. In some species these have a tendency to adhere to particles of sand or shell gravel. Consequently it is possible for certain species, such as Microcosmus species, to become anchored finally in coarse sand or gravel.

Altogether the family ranges in its habitat from attachment to the rocks and ledges of the littoral to attachments to small stones and finally in gravel itself. The nature of the larva, however, is known only for a few species. Pyura squamulosa is typically attached to stones in relatively shallow water, is oviparous, and produces tadpole larvae of typical structure with regard to tail, sense organs, and adhesive papillae. The ocellus is normal in size and cellular constitution (Millar, 1951). Tethyum pyriforme is a large form attached to exposed sides of rocks in shallow to moderate depths. Eggs may develop oviparously or viviparously; the free-swimming period, like that of Pyura, lasts for several hours at least, and the tadpole larvae are well formed and perfect in every respect (Berrill, 1929). The only other example known is Boltenia echinata, a viviparous form that attaches to a wide variety of surfaces, from rocks to other ascidians, and produces a typical tadpole except that the three ocellar lens cells are some-what smaller than the standard (Berrill, 1948). Accordingly we may regard this family as relatively primitive both in its general habitat and in the character of its tadpole larvae; and therefore the whole order to which it belongs must have shared these characters with it at one time. With this situation in mind we can now profitably examine the state of affairs in the remaining two pleurogonid families.

The Molgulidae

Molgulid ascidians in all likelihood have evolved from a more or less pyurid stock. The two families are clearly closely related, and molgulids exhibit derivative specializations in internal structure; in any case they may be regarded as descendants of a more generalized type with habitat and tadpole larvae similar to those of the pyurids.

Yet molgulids as a group appear to have ventured farther from the typical ascidian habitat than almost any other kind. In most cases they have tunics covered with adhesive filaments and in consequence are able to adhere all over to surrounding shell gravel, sand, or even mud particles; they are able to acquire a secure anchorage in submerged sand and mud flats, the more so if they settle close together so that they become anchored finally side by side. Typically the individuals of such species become completely embedded in the sand except for the distal region where the two siphons are located, and, as is fitting, are usually of ovoid or even globular shape. Species adapted to such a habitat have relatively enormous areas of the sea floor available to them for colonization, compared with those able to find security only on hard rock surfaces. In suitable locations,

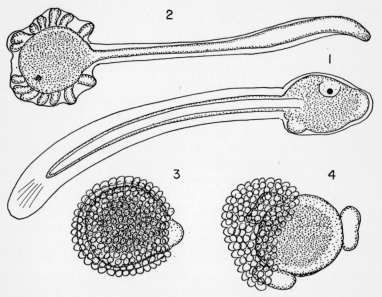

Fig. 2. Development of molgulid ascidians. 1, active tadpole larva of sessile species of Molgula, with sensory vesicle containing an otolith but no ocellus. 2, the same after metamorphosis and attachment, showing clusters of short and one very long anchoring ampulla. 3, 4, stages in hatching of anural species of Molgula, in which tadpole has been suppressed and the tailless larva anchors directly to sand grains.

from low-tide level downward and throughout the continental shelf, the sea floor may become matted with molgulids embedded in close contact with one another, a factor which in itself greatly increases the stability of the area and increases the security of its molgulid inhabitants.

Many molgulid species, however, remain attached to more secure foundations, although in general they appear to be none too selective in their choice of site; and a fair percentage of these have the coat of tendrils that serve their kind for anchorage in the sand flats. There is considerable evidence in fact to indicate that such species have secondarily reattached to rocks and weeds, and that the family as a whole evolved in the first place as an adaptation of originally rock-fastened pyurid-like ascidians to the shifting, unstable medium of the sandy or shell-gravel sea floor. Garstang and Garstang (1928), for instance, were of this opinion 'in spite of numerous secondary readaptations, these ascidians, from their entire organization, appear to be essentially and primarily inhabitants of spacious sand flats in which they live immersed, loosely anchored by their coating of adhesive hairs'. While in my own account (1931) of the family, of fifty-two species under consideration, thirty-one were described as free and unattached. The advantage of such an evolutionary venture is great and obvious, simply in terms of territory which can be occupied, and there is no doubt that molgulids, as individuals, far outnumber all other ascidians in consequence.

If this view is correct, then the situation should be reflected in the character of the larvae, for it is they that determine in the first place the colonization areas to be exploited.

The development of the egg and the nature of the larva are recorded for only a small proportion of the known molgulid species (Berrill, 1931). Eight of these produce tadpole larvae which appear to be typical in structure in all but one respect: they lack an ocellus. It is assumed that the ocellus has been lost, rather than the alternative that it was never present, for this last assumption raises taxonomic difficulties which are insurmountable. The otolith remains as the sole directive sense organ of the larva. Caswell Grave (1926) studied the reactions of the tadpoles of Molgula citrina and found that they were completely insensitive to changes in light intensity. Even 'the response, so characteristic of ascidians larvae that possess an "eye", to shadows that pass momentarily across their path is also lacking in the Molgula larva'.

The tadpole still swims toward the surface of the water, in consequence of its negative response to gravity, although the greater part of its swimming movements are at random and have the effect of exploring relatively extensive horizontal and vertical surfaces to which attachment may be made. Thus the absence of the ocellus does not seem to limit dispersal as such, either vertically or horizontally, and the otolith appears to function primarily in connexion with the upward drive from the sea floor during the early phase of the free-swimming larval period. The important point is that the absence of the ocellus,

whether or not it has any influence upon dispersal, results in
the elimination of the shadow response and thus prevents the
tadpoles from turning selectively toward those shaded rock
surfaces favoured by the tadpole larvae of other families.

The loss or developmental suppression of the ocellus may in fact
well be or have been a necessary condition for the exploitation
of the more open spaces on the sea floor, not only by removing
the restrictions of the negative phototactic response characteristic of the late phase of activity, but also encouraging the
exploitation of areas where no shadows fall. Moreover, in water
of considerable depth, lack of the larval ocellus may well reduce
the extent of upward migration and so tend to keep the larvae
in the stratum adjacent to the settling grounds. However this
may be, I believe that the suppression of the ocellus was the
first and essential larval mutation necessary to permit colonization of the open sea floor on an unrestricted scale, although this
in itself naturally would depend upon the ability of the attached
and metamorphosing larvae to succeed in holding their place
and subsequently growing in the unstable sand, which is another
matter.

From this initial explorative venture the molgulids appear to
have followed two very different directions. Many have become
even more adapted to the sand-flat habitat. Others have rediscovered and readapted to the rocks and weeds of the shallow
waters along the shore. The latter have tended to become very
small as sexually mature forms, occupying in particular those
places on exposed rocky surfaces that afford no more than a very
restricted basal anchorage. For such as these extensive dispersal
becomes too great a luxury; too few eggs and larvae can be produced. With one exception these are viviparous species which
liberate their larvae as fully formed tadpoles; while the free-
swimming period of the tadpoles is restricted on an average to
one hour or less. Settlement is usually on exposed rock or weed
surfaces, but only where there is little water disturbance or
where natural contours afford protection. The extensive areas
of undersurface of rocks, eminently suitable for such species, are
apparently unattainable. Without their ocellus and shadow
reflex these locations are rarely found, for all is dark to the
blind, and recolonization of the rocks is accordingly a limited
success.

Submerged sand flats, whether pure sand or mixed with mud or shell gravel, require no selective action on the part of settling larvae. The sea floor is broadly extensive and only texture and consistency are important (leaving aside qualities of the water itself). It seems unimportant whether larvae settling upon the sea floor generally have been swimming as tadpoles or not. The tadpole as a tadpole has no choice to make. In the case of oviparous species horizontal dispersal is extensive in any event, while the closer the larvae remain to the sea floor the better. There is undoubtedly vigorous natural selection from the moment of settling onwards, but not before, and the tadpole, blind or not, has obviously little value. This is borne out by the character of the larvae, for the majority of free-living molgulid species do not develop a tadpole larva at all. Their development is anural.

Accordingly, of those species of which the development is known at all, seven of the free-living species are without a tadpole larva and only one species is so supplied; while among attached species, thirteen produce tadpoles (though without ocellus) and only two are anural. The single free-living urodele species is otherwise as well adapted to sand-flat life as any other. The two anural attached species show obvious structural descent from free-living forms.

It might be argued that the urodele and the anural species comprise two natural genetic groups, but taxonomic studies fail to bear this out (Berrill, 1931). Whether we adopt the intra-family classification of Huntsman (1922), of Hartmeyer (1923), or of Arnback-Christie-Linde (1928), three classifications which are based upon three very different structural features, the urodele and anural species remain haphazardly distributed among the subdivisions of the family. If we assume that the tadpole larva was once universally present among ascidians and that those species now without it have lost it, then we cannot avoid the conclusion that it has disappeared on at least several occasions within the Molgulidae.

I believe therefore that we have to conclude that a typical tadpole larva persists only as long as there is genetic selection pressure; that when this pressure is lessened or removed, as it appears to be when the habitat is changed from restricted rock sites to virtually unlimited sand flats, the tadpole tends to de-generate and even disappear. In other words, the tadpole larva exists among ascidians because in the great majority of cases it is vitally necessary for the location of a suitable site for settlement, and not because it is in anyway an inevitable ancestral relic retained in the course of development. It exists because it is needed for the performance of delicately controlled locomotor responses at a critical moment in the life cycle. Where there is no such need, there is usually no tadpole.

The means by which the tadpole organizations is suppressed in anural species of molgulid ascidians is significant in relation to the manner in which the tadpole larva may possibly have been evolved. An analysis of the developmental basis of suppression does not, however, fit into the present ecological level of the discussion, and accordingly will be left until later.

Meanwhile, in a different way, a study of the family Styelidae strongly supports the conclusions just reached, and, since it is vital to our whole argument to establish the functional value and significance of the ascidian tadpole beyond any doubt, a fairly exhaustive account is merited.

The Styelidae

The Styelidae as here considered includes the solitary styelids, the budding polystyelids, and the botryllids, a taxonomic discussion of which has been given elsewhere (Berrill, 1951). Whatever their relationship may be with the pyurid stock, there is on structural grounds alone little doubt that the solitary, attached styelids of genera such as Styela and Katratopa are relatively primitive. These attach to hard, more or less vertical surfaces of rocks, mangrove roots, &c. They are rarely found beneath rocks. In other words they occupy sites generally characteristic of the more primitive enterogonid genera of the kind first discussed.

The tadpole larvae are known and have been studied in only two species of this sort, in Styela partita (Conklin, 1905, 1931; Berrill, 1929; and Grave, 1944), and in Katratopa yakatutensis (Berrill, 1948). The tadpoles of both are typical except in one respect: they possess an ocellus of apparently degenerate form, consisting of a single small lens cell and a small number of non-pigmented sensory cells. Apart from habitat, there is no reason to regard these styelids as being primitive in any way except in relation to other members of the styelid family; one can only consider the ocellus as having undergone considerable degenera-

tion from the standard three-lens, pigmented sensory cup constitution typical of the pyurid members of the order and ascidians
as a whole. Grave investigated the larvae responses, in addition
to larvae structure, and found the usual upward-swimming
migration occurs in either the light or dark, and presumably
controlled by the otolith. The tadpoles react to sudden changes
in light intensity by increased or renewed activity, but appear to
be neither as strongly positive to light to start with nor as strongly
negative to light later on as, for instance, tadpoles of Amaroucium. As these and most of the solitary styelids are oviparous,
dispersal is extensive; but effective employment of the larval
ocellus for the final selection of site for attachment seems to be
of doubtful efficiency.

The interest here relates to the condition found in other
styelid groups, for this degenerate larval eye seems to be a point
of departure; and, so to speak, one feels that the parental
organisms with this kind of tadpole appear to have been hesitat-
ing on the brink of solidarity, poised between safe anchorage to
rocks, &c., and life in the shifting sands that lie beyond.

The majority of solitary, i.e. non-budding, styelids are inhabitants of the great territories of the continental shelf to much
the same extent as the molgulids; some species extend into considerable depths of the continental slope. Most of them live
embedded in soft mud or sand, some only where sand is mixed
with stones to which they can become attached. All show adaptations of body form and surface-coat relating to the embedded
position in which they live, elongated in the case of Pelonaia
corrugata, more or less globular in the various species of Cnemi-
docarpa and Polycarpa. Two or three species of Polycarpa
inhabit shallow water attached to the upper surface of stones,
the rest are embedded in sand or mud without any other
anchorage. The overall situation therefore is comparable to that
of the Molgulidae. What of the larvae?

Information is lacking in most cases, particularly those we
would like most to know something about, those species which
occur abundantly in comparatively deep water. All that is certain is that they are oviparous. The larvae are known, however,
for three species of Polycarpa (Berrill, 1929, 1951). One of these
species is invariably attached to stones, the other two are found
both attached to stones and embedded free in sand. All three

species produce tadpoles of the small size typical of small oviparous eggs, and in all three cases the tadpoles possess an otolith
as their only sense organ. There is no trace of an ocellus what-
soever. Thus in species which are not so extremely adapted to
sand-embedded life in offshore waters as most, we find the same
type of tadpole as we do in those molgulid species that possess a

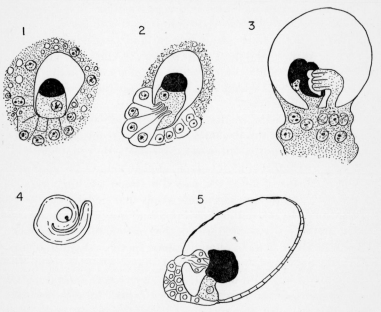

Fig. 3. Development of the Photolith in botryllid tadpole larvae. 1, 2, 3, three stages
of Botryllus showing development of a typical unicellular otolith and its conversion
into a photolith by the invasion of photosensory neurons (after Gravé). 4, young
stage in development of tadpole of the botryllid Stolonica showing unicellular
otolith. 5, final stage of same with otolith converted into a photolith.

tadpole larva of any kind. Whether or not the tadpole larva is
absent altogether in the more fully adapted Polycarpa species
remains to be seen. At least the first step appears to have been
taken by those of marginal habit. Accordingly once again the
suppression of the ocellus and the loss of its dependent shadow
response is correlated with colonization of the wide open spaces
and failure to settle on vertical rock, weed, or other surfaces.
The combined equipment of otolith plus ocellus seems to be
necessary for settlement in such places. In the case of the
solitary or simple styelids, Dendrodoa (Styelopsis) grossularia

appears to be the exception which proves the rule. Its tadpole larvae possess the otolith alone, yet the species is found characteristically attached to the sides of rocks, often in enormous aggregates. But the tadpoles, which are relatively large, are produced viviparously, and many settle and metamorphose alongside the parents immediately upon liberation.

It seems to me, however, that the most spectacular case of readaptation of a free type to an attached existence is to be seen in the botryllids, using this term to denote all styelids with a capacity for budding. And it is all the more striking inasmuch as we are able virtually to pin-point the origin of this subfamily as a whole. Were it not for the capacity to reproduce asexually by budding, certain species would undoubtedly be classified as species of Polycarpa. As it is these are assigned to the genus Polyandrocarpa. The close relationship is recognized and discussed at length elsewhere both by Van Name (1945) and Berrill (1951).

The styelids which are able to reproduce by budding to form colonial or compound aggregates comprise a natural group, in spite of extreme structural variability within it in certain respects. All of them, including Botryllus itself, produce buds by forming local outpushings of the atrial body wall. The details are not important to the present discussion, except that the method of budding is fundamentally the same in all these styelids and is of a type unknown among other ascidians. And all those species of this subfamily for which we have information possess tadpole larvae which have a unique type of sense organ. The group is a natural one and can be discussed as such. Variation within the group must be regarded as the result of evolutionary and adaptive changes that have occurred since the subfamily itself arose from a solitary, sand-adapted, polycarpid stock.

The capacity for budding probably arose before any associated modification of the larva. The two changes could hardly have been simultaneous and the alternative sequence makes little sense. The genus Polyandrocarpa is, as already stressed, indistinguishable from the solitary Polycarpa apart from the capacity to form buds. It is divided into two subgenera (cf. Van Name, 1945), the typical subgenus Polyandrocarpa and the subgenus Eusynstyela. Species of the former occupy the same sort of territory as do most species of Polycarpa, and remain typically adapted to submerged sand flats. It is not recorded whether they are oviparous or viviparous, and nothing is known concerning the nature of the larvae, although it is of extreme interest to discover. Species of the other subgenus are individually smaller and are typically attached as flat encrusting colonies on the sides and undersurfaces of rocks, occasionally on algae or on other ascidians.

This in general is the habitat of the remaining genera of budding styelids. Some genera or species attach to more or less exposed rock or algal surfaces, others tend to occupy the undersides of rocks and weeds, depending to a great extent upon the size of individual zooids and the thickness of the encrusting colonial sheet. Taken as a whole, therefore, the subfamily has clearly re-exploited the hard-surface locations typically occupied by ascidians in general, from a point of departure as one of those genera that had previously become secondarily adapted to an unattached life in sand or mud.

If this group did evolve from a Polycarpa stock, as I believe, then it inherited the Polycarpa type of tadpole, that is, a tadpole with all of the standard equipment except for the absence of an ocellus. On the other hand, if our previous argument is valid, the vertical and shaded surfaces of rocks and weeds, and particularly the undersurfaces of boulders and ledges, require light-sensitive tadpoles with a high degree of selective action.

This is what we find. So far as is known, all species of this subfamily are viviparous. The purely dispersal phase of drifting eggs and embryos is eliminated and larvae are liberated only as active organisms. All produce tadpoles, although tadpoles that vary greatly both in size and in duration of the active free-swimming period. And the tadpole larvae of all species so far recorded are unique in one respect. They have a light-sensitive sense organ of a remarkable kind, which has been called a photolith. It serves both as an otolith and as an ocellus, and the larvae react to gravity and to light in the manner similar to that of tadpoles equipped with the two senses as independent organs (Grave, 1934). There is no doubt whatever that functionally the tadpoles react as do those that belong to the enterogonid families that occupy a similar habitat. Nature of tadpole and nature of site are closely correlated.

The question which arises is, how has the function of the lost ocellus become replaced? The answer seems clear enough. The photolith of the tadpole larva of Botryllus is typical and has been carefully studied developmentally by Grave and Riley (1935); photolith development in others such as Polyandro-carpa, Distomus, Stolonica, and Symplegma appears to be essentially the same. In all of these the tadpole develops to an almost fully formed stage, with full-grown tail; to a stage, in fact, remarkably like that of a completely developed tadpole of a Polycarpa species. Development continues beyond this stage, however, to some extent in Polyandrocarpa species and others, and to a very considerable extent in species of Botryllus and Botrylloides. In all, however, the otolith first appears in typical form as pigmented granules within a single otolith cell which soon fuse together as a relatively large pigmented intracellular mass. It attains its full size without showing any sign of an ocellus (in standard-type tadpoles that have both an otolith and an ocellus, the pigment of the two organs appears approxi-mately at the same time during the course of development). Then, when one would think it was almost too late for any such event, neurosensory cells grow out into the cavity of the sensory vesicle from a site corresponding to that of the ocellus in other forms, and the cluster of cells together enter an invagination of the pigmented otolith. The otolith cell serves as a pigmented ocular cup and also continues to function as an otolith, while cells which appear to be the homologues of the neurosensory elements of the lost ocellus become light-orienting agents once again in co-operative association with otolithic pigment. There is no recovery or redevelopment of lens cells, but the combined organ appears to function as efficiently as the original set of two. That such a situation should have arisen can be interpreted, it seems to me, only as the response once again to a genetic selec-tion pressure. If surviving neurosensory cells in the original ocellar region of the sense vesicle had failed to respond in this way and had failed to take advantage of the shadow formed by the adjacent otolith, shadow reflexes would not have been re-established and re-exploitation of the protected undersurfaces of rocks and weeds would not have become possible.

The general conclusion therefore is that the ascidian tadpole is a vitally important type of larval organism for those ascidians that live a typically attached existence, whether to vertical sides of rocks and weeds or to the more difficultly attained under-surfaces. The tadpole structure degenerates under other circumstances, and in one group has been subsequently restored as a condition for the reoccupation of the original habitat. Both its sensory and motor equipment is rigorously maintained in relation to certain specific requirements for the selection of suitable sites for attachment. Apart from preconceived notions concerning ascidian relationships with other forms, there is every reason to regard the typical ascidian tadpole as a unique type of larval organism evolved by the primitive ascidian stock in response to opportunities for settling in certain habitats.

Note: According to Millar, in a paper which appeared after these pages went to press, the eggs of the sand-dwelling Petonaia corru-gata develop directly without including a tadpole stage of any kind (Millar, R. H., 1954, 'The breeding and development of the ascidian Pelonaia corrugata Forbes and Goodsir.' *Jour. Mar. Biol. Assoc. U.K.* 33: 681).

6

GARSTANG'S THEORY CONCERNING ORIGIN OF THE ASCIDIAN TADPOLE

THE problem of origin of the ascidian tadpole is both an evolutionary and a developmental one. If, in view of the evidence given in the preceding chapter, we provisionally accept as valid the conclusion that the typical tadpole larva is essentially an ascidian creation evolved to meet certain rigid requirements involved in the selection of a restricted type of habitat, it should be possible to conceive how the tadpole has come into being. It is important that the evolving larva should have been functionally valuable at all stages in its evolution, otherwise we fall into one of the impasses inherent in the older theories of vertebrate origin.

Garstang (1928) has already put forward the thesis 'that the Tunicate tadpole may have been an interpolation within the life-history of a line of sedentary organisms, and that it does not necessitate "a former free-swimming ancestor" to account for it'. His is mainly an evolutionary approach based upon the comparative study of larval and adult organisms, which conceives the chordate tadpole of the ascidian as a terminal stage of a long progressive evolutionary transformation of a much simpler type, brought about primarily in order to prolong the pelagic larval life. His argument runs as follows, commencing with an analogy:

When Annelids became changed into Molluscs, the Trochosphere was succeeded by the Veliger, which is simply a Trochosphere with Molluscan characters of shell and foot superadded, and with the circular prototroch produced laterally into a powerful bilobed velum. This velum is plainly no relic of adult ancestry, but a larval development to sustain the weight of additional structures carried during the pelagic phase. The bigger the velum, the more fully can the adult organization be developed in the larva without jeopardizing the larval function of distribution.

We assume, from the evidence of comparative embryology, that

the pelagic larvae of these ancestors (of the Chordata) were simple
Dipleurulae, of the Echinoderm-Enteropneust type, provided with
apical eye-spots and a circumoral ciliated band.

Our new theory invokes yet another example of prolonging the
pelagic phase. . . . Instead of adding new and more powerful ciliary
mechanisms, the larval body elongated, became increasingly muscular, with an increasing tendency towards a segmental arrangement, in consequence of resorting to lateral undulations as a means

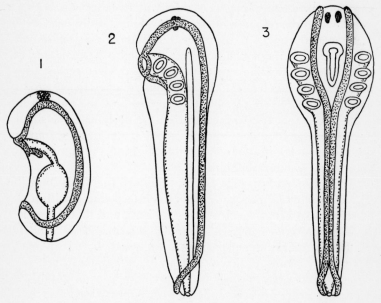

FIG. 4. Comparison between larva of an Echinoderm (1) and the hypothetical
primitive chordate (2, 3,) according to the theory of Garstang.

of locomotion. This had the effect of bringing the lateral halves of
the circumoral band, and its underlying nerve-tract, into closer
parallelism on either side of the mid-dorsal line. Subsequently, as a
result of additional yolk in the egg, the early ciliated Dipleurula
phase was relegated to the embryonic period, and the larvae were
hatched as muscular tadpoles, the circumoral band, with its underlying nervous system and its apical sense organs, having been rolled
up meanwhile beneath the surface as a neural canal. The result of
this process would be to bring together for the first time within a
single dorsal epithelial tube the rudiments of two nervous systems—
a mid-dorsal adult nerve centre, and a pair of lateral nerve-tracts

derived from the circumoral band, and connected with the apical sense-organs. If to these features we add the persistence of the larval adoral band and ventral loop as the beginnings of a peripharyngeal band and endostyle, this muscular Dipleurula, which may be distinguished as a 'Notoneurula', would lack only gill-slits and a notochord to transform it into a regular Chordate tadpole.

At the same time, however, that these changes were taking place in the larval form, the organization of the sessile adult was presumably changing from external tentaculate to internal trematic modes of collecting plankton. If we imagine the pelagic larval life prolonged until the rudiments of the adult gill-slits made their appearance (as happens, e.g. in Tornaria), the various organs which had hitherto had a purely larval value would come into possible working relations with the gill-slits, which hitherto had been organs only of the adult phase. This would be a real moment of creative evolution, and it is this way, as I shall hope to show, that the typical Chordate combination of characters has come into being. Certain features, especially the gill-slits and the beginnings of a notochord, have had their origin in the adult phase of sessile Pterobranch ancestors, while the endostyle and neural canal are the results of a further development and transformation of early larval characters. The neuro-muscular metamerism, which is merely incipient in the Tunicate larva, did not attain its complete expression until, by the abandonment of fixation, the larval type of organization was enabled to persist to maturity (paedomorphosis). That this, in part, has been the history of Appendicularians, and of Amphioxus more fully, will be shown in the sequel.

Garstang's general thesis that the ascidian (or tunicate) tadpole larva has been evolved from a simpler type of pelagic larva, all the time as larvae produced by sessile, non-pelagic, parents, is essentially that which is adopted in the present account. In detail, however, there is little in common. Garstang, for instance, conceives ascidians themselves as evolving from pterobranch organisms; the tadpole larva evolving from larvae similar to the dipleurula of echinoderms and the tornaria of enteropneusts, as a means of prolonging the pelagic phase, and dependent upon an accumulation of yolk within the egg; and a subsequent attainment of muscular segmentation, leading to a neotenous chordate form, which is gradually acquired. None of this is, I believe, either necessary or true; yet the sequence of events as postulated by Garstang is both plausible and coherent, and merits serious consideration.

Echinoderm—Pterobranch—Enteropneust—Tunicate—Relationships

Echinoderms, pterobranchs, enteropneusts, and tunicates are generally considered to be related upon the following grounds. Echinoderms and certain enteropneusts (species of Balanoglossus especially) are remarkably alike in their general manner of development and in the production of certain types of larval organisms. Both undergo a comparatively indeterminate type of cleavage and development, resulting in larvae that propel themselves by means of ciliated epidermal bands; both develop coelomic cavities by means of enteric evaginations; both develop one or sometimes two hydrocoels, coelomic sacs connecting with the external surface by way of a duct and hydropore. In certain forms, e.g. the Bipinnaria and Auricularia larvae of echinoderms and the Tornaria larva of certain species of Balanoglossus, the epidermal surface is expanded into folds bearing convoluted bands of powerful cilia as a means of prolonging the larval pelagic life of the larvae beyond the duration and capacity of simpler kinds. The resemblance is striking.

Pterobranchs and enteropneusts are rather clearly related to one another, and inasmuch as they possess gill slits and a supposedly dorsal nervous system, features elsewhere found only among tunicates and other chordates, the pterobranchs and enteropneusts supposedly link with the chordate phylum. The problem is a familiar one, that of distinguishing between convergent and related evolution.

The question of similarity between the Tornaria larva of Balanoglossus and the larvae of echinoderms has been discussed at length by Barraclough Fell (1948), in relation to the conception of an echinoderm-chordate connexion. His analysis is mainly of the echinoderms themselves, since the larval forms and their development is well worked out, and also the evolutionary history of echinoderms is known from the study of fossil forms as well as, if not better than, that of any other group of animals. In brief, it is this: that if on the one hand the echinoderms are arranged in a pattern or scheme to show their intra-phyletic relationships based on their known fossil history, and on the other according to the types of larval organisms, two schemes are obtained which are so absurdly different from each other that one of them must be rejected as a picture of echinoderm evolution. Fell's conclusion, which appears to be the only reasonable one, is that the scheme based upon palaeontological evidence must be accepted, and that in consequence the similarities which appear among the various echinoderm larvae, for instance between echinopluteus and ophiopluteus, and among the vitellaria of certain ophiuroids, crinoids, and holothurians, are the result of convergent or parallel evolution of larval forms. The more elaborate types of echinoderm larvae, including the bipinnaria and auricularia that figure in Garstang's hypothesis, are highly specialized larval adaptations for prolonging the pelagic phase of the particular echinoderms that give rise to them, and in no way represent primitive larval types within the group. In the same manner, the Tornaria larvae of enteropneusts such as Balanoglossus are equally an adaptation for prolonging the pelagic phase, but it is not universally present within the Enteropneusta and probably should be regarded as an innovation that is far from being primitive. It does not seem reasonable, therefore, to trace evolutionary connexions along a path that leads from a highly specialized and differentiated larval form of certain species or genera of one phylum to equally specialized larvae restricted to only certain members of another phylum, although what appears to be unreasonable is not necessarily impossible.

This discussion refers solely to the larval resemblances of a locomotory nature, in particular to the presence and character of ciliated epidermal bands. Inasmuch as these devices, with or without supporting calcareous rods, appear to have been evolved many times within the echinoderm phylum, the presence of a somewhat similar type among the enteropneusts may more simply be regarded as one more independent example, even though not within the same phylum. This conclusion is important in the present connexion in so far as it tends to eliminate the echinoderm-enteropneust larval type, at least in its more elaborate form, as the point of departure for the evolution of the ascidian tadpole.

The further question, whether the enteropneusts and the related pterobranchs are in any way antecedent to ascidians, is one which involves analysis of ascidian structure in general, and must accordingly be postponed, although in anticipation of this the conclusion is that they are not. I do not believe that such forms as Cephalodiscus, Rhabdopleura, and the balanoglossids

represent either separately or collectively the ancestral stock
from which the ascidians originated. The basis for this conclusion will appear later; but if meanwhile we provisionally accept
this as valid, and also accept Fell's conclusion that the ciliated
larval forms of echinoderms and enteropneusts portray parallel
or convergent evolution and are not themselves evidence of
relationship, Garstang's employment of these larval types as
indications of the way in which the ascidian tadpole, and therefore the chordate organism, came into being becomes an analogy
only. The tadpole might have evolved along the lines he suggests, but echinoderm and balanoglossid larvae offer no evidence
that it did; that is, the peculiar tubular, dorsal nervous system
of the chordates may have evolved as the result of a pair of
lateral, longitudinal, ciliated, epidermal larval bands coming
together at the mid-dorsal line to form an enclosed ciliated tube
with anterior and posterior neuropores; but echinoderm and
balanoglossid larvae merely suggest a possible starting-point and
are not themselves relics of that starting-point. On the other
hand, the manner in which the neural tube of chordates actually
is formed during individual development is almost exactly the
same as the way in which, according to Garstang, it evolved in
the course of evolution. If the course of development in general,
and that of the nervous system in particular, is recapitulatory,
then the evidence of vertebrate embryology strongly supports
this concept of neural-tube origin phylogenetically as well as
ontogenetically.

In the final analysis it seems to me that Garstang's thesis
rests too heavily upon the validity of the general theory of
recapitulation, although it was Garstang himself who first emphasized the possibility that new evolutionary ventures may
take larval stages, as distinct from adult, as points for new departures—what has been since termed clandestine evolution.

There are two other assumptions made by Garstang which
call for attention, namely, that the change from a ciliated larva
to a tadpole larva depended upon increase in the yolk content
of the egg, and that the adaptive motive was prolongation of the
pelagic phase. Neither of these contentions is valid. Ascidian
eggs of the pelagic type are no larger and no yolkier than the
pelagic eggs of echinoderms, and at the end of their process of
development have produced only about half the number of cells

as are produced by echinoderm eggs of equivalent size and yolk content. In other words there is no reason to suppose that the typical ascidian egg has ever been smaller or less yolky than it now is; size and yolk content are virtually minimal as they are. In somewhat like manner, the ascidian tadpole is hardly a device for prolonging a pelagic phase of embryonic and larval forms. Most simple ciliated larvae of other groups are pelagic for much longer periods, and the tadpole of the ascidian actually cuts short what may well have been a much longer drifting pelagic phase of existence. Its real value has already been discussed at length; it is a short-range habitat selector, not a dispersal mechanism nor a pelagic feeder.

The alternative to either the concept of a gradual transformation of an echinoderm-type larva into a tadpole larva, or the inheritance of the tadpole larva as a relic of a remote and more highly advanced chordate past, is that it arose more or less suddenly as a developmental innovation that had an immediate value. Inasmuch as a larval or an adult form of any organism is fundamentally an expression of developmental processes and must be interpreted dynamically, the plausibility of this third alternative can be determined only in terms of developmental analysis. It so happens that in ascidians such analysis is made easier and more profitable by the coexistence of several kinds of development, all culminating, though taking different paths, in the same general final form. In the Molgulidae, according to the species, an egg may develop directly to the final ascidian structure without producing a true larval form of any kind, or it may, like all other ascidians, attain the same final state by way of a swimming tadpole that must needs undergo a metamorphosis. While in six ascidian families the final form may be reached either as the consequence of the development of an egg, or as the development of a bud formed from parental somatic tissues. And to all this we can add certain significant facts derived from the study of other tunicates, both thaliacean and larvacean. The discussion immediately following, therefore, concerns problems relating to the development of organisms in general, as well as those relating to evolution, subjects that are controversial in both areas.

7

DEVELOPMENTAL ANALYSIS OF THE ASCIDIAN TADPOLE AND THE QUESTION OF ITS ORIGIN

A FULL understanding of the nature and significance of the tadpole larva of the ascidians can be obtained only from a detailed analysis of its structure in terms of the developmental processes which create it. No doubt much remains to be discovered but at least we have a great deal of information which seems to me to throw considerable light upon the subject. We have in fact so much detail and the problem as a whole is so complex that I think it expedient to treat it as a series of related topics, although all included under the general heading of this long chapter. These are as follows:

(a) The duality of development of the ascidian egg.
(b) The direct development of ascidian buds.
(c) The nature of an egg and an interpretation of gastrulation.
(d) The development of the tail of the ascidian tadpole.
(e) The neural tube.
(f) Suppression of tadpole organization among molgulid ascidians.
(g) The developmental origin of the tadpole larva.

(a) The duality of development of the ascidian egg

The conclusion which emerges at once from the discussion in the last chapter is that the chordate tadpole larva of the ascidian is not in any real sense a necessary stage of prerequisite for the development of the permanent or adult ascidian organism, and the questions arise: how much of the processes of development of the egg are concerned in the production of the final ascidian form, and how much are they concerned with purely tadpole organization? How much of what seems to be the process of development of the tadpole is, so to speak, inadvertent, and how much is exclusively tadpole and, from the viewpoint of final outcome, dispensable? Admittedly more questions are raised than answered, yet the tadpole organization seems unmistakably to be an interpolation in the developmental cycle, a conclusion which necessitates a detailed analysis of its development, both in the positive and negative sense.

The eggs of most ascidians develop to form a tadpole stage which subsequently undergoes a metamorphosis whereby all of the locomotory and sensory structure of the tadpole organism is destroyed, whereas the residual tissues proceed with the development of the permanent ascidian structure. Those molgulid ascidians the eggs of which develop without forming a swimming tadpole are to be interpreted as having suppressed the tadpole stage, the reasons for and nature of which will be discussed later. In general, therefore, the egg develops virtually as a dual system, one leading to tadpole formation and the other to attainment of sessile ascidian organization. And inasmuch as all ascidian and other tunicates buds, whatever their size and histological content, develop directly to form the permanent structure without passing through a tadpole phase of any kind, this type of development is correspondingly simple and serves to differentiate more clearly in the development of the egg what is basic and what has been added to yield a tadpole larva as a precocious and transient stage. Bud development is, in a manner of speaking, single-minded, and it emphasizes and clarifies the duality of the development of the embryo. The origin and nature of this duality is the key to our main problem.

(b) The direct development of ascidian buds

In the present connexion, the simplest types of ascidian buds are the most informative, and two examples must suffice, the pleurogonid Botryllus, and the enterogonid Distaplia. Whether reproduction by budding among the enterogonids is polyphyletic or not, these two examples undoubtedly represent independent attainments, and in each case the bud in its initial state is a remarkably simple developmental unit.

Buds of Distaphia, at their inception, consist of small spheres of epidermal epithelium enclosing an even smaller group of indifferent cells of epicardial origin. The outer envelope or vesicle is derived from parental epidermis and may consist of

as few as twenty cells, while the inner group may be as few as
eight or ten cells with a small central space in between. The bud
thus formed is entirely free from contact with its parental source,
and grows and develops within a nutritive matrix, the nature of
which is not relevant to the present discussion. Cells of both
layers are of minimal size to begin with, having been derived
directly from mature tissues, and development proceeds on a
basis of continual growth and proliferation of cells, as distinct
from the process of subdivision or cleavage of a non-growing
egg. Compared with even the small pelagic ascidian eggs, let
alone the somewhat larger and yolkier egg of its own species,
the bud is at first extraordinarily minute. Yet morphologically
it corresponds to the gastrula stage and consists of a double-
walled vesicle. The difference lies in the potentiality of the
inner and outer layers. The ectodermal layer of the gastrula,
whether of a chordate or invertebrate, is multipotent like the
inner archenteric layer. In all chordates the embryonic ectoderm gives rise to sensory and nervous tissues as well as to
epidermis, and this is as true of the developing ascidian egg as
it is of any other chordate egg. The outer layer of ascidian buds,
however, is not embryonic ectoderm, nor even indifferent tissue,
but is a direct descendant of parental epidermis, and in consequence has the restricted potentiality of that tissue. Its cells can
grow and proliferate to form more epidermis, but the tissue is
unipotent and can differentiate into no other kind. The formative burden is accordingly thrown upon the indifferent cells of
the inner layer.

The bud of Botryllus is essentially the same, although of independent origin. It does not, however, separate from its parent
until comparatively late. The bud is first recognizable as a disk
of relatively thick tissue of the parental body wall, and consists
of an outer disk of epidermis and an inner and thicker disk of the
inner or atrial epithelium. As the cells within the disk area continue to grow and divide, and the double-layered disk as a whole
expands, the disk becomes hemispherical and finally becomes a
double-layered vesicle similar to the initial Distaplia bud except
that it remains for a while attached by a narrow stalk to the
parent organism. And again the outer layer is unipotent and
contributes only to the epidermis of the developing ascidian;
the inner vesicle is the formative component.

In each case, therefore, there is an inner vesicle, initially composed of a very small number of cells, which progressively evolves or exhibits the ascidian organization. The inner vesicle

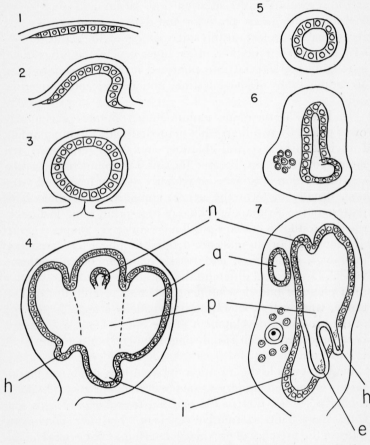

FIG. 5. Direct development in the buds of two types of ascidians. 1 to 4, development of double-layered disk of Botryllus bud into stage showing six primary organizational divisions by invaginative and evaginative foldings. 5 to 7, comparable stages of bud of Distaplia. *a*, atrial chamber; *e*, epicardium; *h*, heart; *i*, intestine; *p*, pharynx.

is at first only a hollow sphere of simple cubical epithelium, which slowly enlarges as cell growth and cell division continue, but always as an expanding sheet of tissue of one-cell thickness.

This is essentially the stage the subsequent development of which we need to compare with that of the egg.

In Distaplia, by the time the original bud has grown a little and consists of two or three hundred cells, the inner vesicle already exhibits differentiation into atrial and pharyngeal divisions, with antero-posterior and dorso-ventral axes already recognizable. In fact, at this stage, simply as the result of constrictions and evaginations of the inner vesicle, the future zooid is roughly marked out into pharynx, atrium, descending and ascending limbs of the intestine, and neural and pericardial units.

In Botryllus the same monumentally simple development takes place. By two ingrowing epithelial folds the inner vesicle is divided into a central chamber and two lateral ones. The lateral compartments become the atrial or mantle cavities, the central division evaginates proximally to form heart and intestine, distally to form the neural complex. The whole basic pattern of the ascidian, as a kind of blue-print, is marked out in the simplest form it seems possible to conceive. Shape, regional divisions, and organ units are defined simply as a succession of infoldings, outfoldings, and local expansions of an epithelial vesicle. Histological differentiation becomes evident only in the final phase of bud development, whether of Botryllus or Distaplia, when cell proliferation has virtually ceased. At the end of the process of development of the bud a small ascidian has been produced which is indistinguishable from one which develops from an egg and passes through a tadpole stage on the way. The tadpole organization apparently is in no way necessary or even contributory as such to the final structure; and it should be noted that in the original assemblage of cells that comprises the inner formative vesicle of a bud there is no possibility of the presence of organized determinative devices characteristic of so many types of eggs. With this asexual pattern of development in mind, we can proceed to the analysis of the developing ascidian egg itself.

(c) The nature of an egg and an interpretation of gastrulation

An egg, almost any egg, serves several ends. It is part of the mechanism whereby genetic variation is produced, which does not concern us here. It is also, possibly primarily, a unicellular protoplasmic mass large enough for the manufacture of a functional organism. If the final structural pattern is comparatively simple this may be attained directly by the substance of the egg alone, without any secondary complication, for example in the case of rotifers and many coelenterates. Or an excessively large and yolky egg may attain a very elaborate end point. Where the egg is small and the final pattern bulkily complex, as in echinoderms, the egg is materially incapable of expressing that pattern until it has already become an active organism capable of feeding and so adding to its mass. The terminal phase of egg development is then of necessity a larval organism markedly different from the final pattern, with differentiated tissues, whose primary function is planktonic feeding. Larval evolution among echinoderms is, as Fell points out, primarily a matter of prolonging this planktonic phase so that the final organization can be attained decisively and suddenly, with a corresponding chance of success; or, in contrast, increasing the material content of the egg so that the burden upon the larva, functionally and structurally, is greatly relieved.

The ascidian egg, while typically small and pelagic, has within itself sufficient substance for the production of cells numerous enough to establish a miniature ascidian. The egg, for instance, of Ascidia or Ciona, is able to subdivide to form from 2,500 to 3,000 cells before minimal cell sizes are reached and cleavage comes to an end (Berrill, 1935b); while the eggs of Asterias or Echinus, of about the same size and yolk content, produce 4,000 to 5,000 cells, individually a little smaller. The distinction lies in the fact that 3,000 cells suffice to make a small ascidian of more or less permanent pattern, if not in size, whereas 5,000 cells fall far short of what is necessary for the construction of the smallest possible recognizable starfish or sea-urchin.

The egg of the ascidian accordingly falls into the category of those that contain within themselves all the material necessary for the development of the permanent organization in miniature, and all ascidian eggs develop to this stage without gaining any additional substance on the way. The capacity to gain and digest food from external sources comes only after the development of the egg has run its course, when cells are no longer dividing and histological maturity has been attained. The tadpole larva is a transient, non-feeding stage that appears early in this developmental course. It represents something that has been added to or inserted into embryonic development as a whole, and our immediate task is to unravel the twisted thread, to determine which of the various developmental processes in the cleaving egg relate primarily to the formation of the tadpole, and which relate to the more protracted development of the young ascidian. In effect, two developmental procedures take place side by side within the framework of a single developing egg, although at different rates and with different outcomes.

An egg is a relatively very large cell which, in a variety of invertebrates at least, according to Whitaker (1937), is in a state of abnormal or atypical metabolism. Normal metabolism is restored at fertilization and the egg or cell responds by re-establishing normal or typical cell size; that is, it divides successively until constituent cells are of minimal size. Thereafter cells only divide following a period of individual cell growth.

Thus, comparing egg and bud development, the egg divides successively to produce a number of cells which at first form a hollow ball or sphere, the blastula, consisting of a single layer of cells. By invaginative gastrulation the single-walled blastula becomes the double-walled gastrula, an inner and outer vesicle comparable with the inner and outer vesicle of a bud. I believe we are dealing here with fundamentally the same process—employing this term in its broadest sense—and that in the case both of early bud development and egg development the first and basic step toward the expression of the typical organization of the individual is the establishment of a double-walled vesicle; that the organism is primarily a sac within a sac, and this condition is of necessity the precursor of all others. The Distaplia bud is launched upon its individual existence already in this state. The Botryllus bud starts as an inner and outer epithelial disk, which together arch and evaginate to become a two-walled hollow vesicle. The blastula, a single-walled vesicle to start with, invaginates to attain to the same condition. It is the simplest way of doing it. In other words, I hold the opinion that the process of gastrulation itself is simply the method by which the cleaving egg establishes the first essential organismic pattern—the tissue folds so as to produce a sac within a sac as the first step in a series of foldings and expansions of one kind and another that lead to the final elaboration, and that the invagination is no less and no more mysterious, significant, or reminiscent of an ancestral stage than the evaginations and invaginations which follow it. I am equally convinced, in the case of ascidian development, that gastrulation primarily relates to the final pattern of the ascidian organism, and only in an incidental or secondary way to the development of the tadpole. Gastrulation is a necessary event in any case, and the processes concerned with tadpole development have been superimposed upon it and in a sense have exploited it.

These remarks concerning the general significance of gastrulation may be little more than an expression of the obvious, but they lead the way to a similar approach to a much more controversial topic, namely, the manner in which the nervous system is developed, and its significance; for it is upon this, for instance, that Garstang's conception of the evolution of the chordate tadpole is based. A more detailed account of tadpole development is, however, desirable before this is attempted.

(d) The development of the tail of the ascidian tadpole

Conklin's classical account of the development of the egg of Styela partita (1905), which he extended to that of Ciona intestinalis and Phallusia mamillata, supplies by far the most detailed description available of the early phases of embryonic development, up to the stage at which the tadpole organization is first established. Experimental analytical methods have been applied to this and similar ascidian eggs and embryos by Conklin (1905, 1911, 1931) and others, notably Dalcq (1932), Chi-Tow-Tung (1934), Rose (1939), and Reverberi (1947). The events of normal, uninterrupted, development, however, are those that concern us most at the present time.

The eggs of Styela partita (Conklin, 1905), Boltenia echinata (Berrill, 1929), and Pyura squamosa (Millar, 1951), all of them pleurogonid species, are unique in possessing ooplasmic regions which are coloured in the living egg, a quality that has made the tracing of cleavage and embryonic patterns unusually informative.

When the germinal vesicle of an ascidian egg ruptures, which may be before or after fertilization, according to the species (in the case of Styela it is afterwards), certain events take place that are of the utmost significance in relation to subsequent development.

According to Conklin, with the rupture of the egg nucleus and the ensuing mixture of nuclear sap and cytoplasm, a polar cap of ectoplasm flows across the equator of the egg; and at the time of polar body formation a yellow crescent appears in the equatorial zone and extends half-way around the egg. The yellow colour is due to contained mitochondria. Two other substances were also recognized, a slate-grey substance which goes into the future endoderm, and a transparent cytoplasm which forms the general ectodermal layer. The same zones are also recognizable in the living eggs of Boltenia and Pyura, in which the crescent material is a vivid orange.

The first cleavage plane divides the egg into presumptive left- and right-half embryos, and subsequent cleavages proceed in an orderly, precise manner which results in highly distinctive cell patterns. Thus at the 64-cell stage, that is, after 6 cleavages, the so-called animal or presumptive ventral half of the cleaving egg consists of 26 ectoderm and 6 neural plate cells; the vegetal or presumptive dorsal half consists of 4 neural plate, 4 chordal, 10 mesenchyme, 4 muscle, and 10 endoderm cells. These categories are defined both by location, which determines the future position, and by ooplasmic and yolk content, which indicate future histological character in varying degree. Gastrulation, by invagination, is begun and completed in the interval between the sixth and seventh cleavage. Preceding this event, the yellow crescent substance is found to exist as a crescent of cells symmetrically placed around the future posterior side of the organism. The cells which comprise the chordo-neural plate are also symmetrically placed about the antero-posterior embryonic axis, only at the anterior side. During gastrulation the two arms of chordal cells are brought together in the middle line, and fit as a short column, four cells across and four in length, between the two arms of the posterior yellow crescent cells. In other words, two crescentic regions, originally widely separated in the egg and blastula, are brought together by gastrular movement to form a single dorso-posterior mass. The central core of chordal cells gives rise to the notochord, the cells of the yellow crescent from the two lateral bands of tail-muscle tissue. The process of determination is rigid. It commences with the onset of development itself, is closely geared with the process of gastrulation, and proceeds rapidly to a conclusion. The cells constituting the chordal group at the time of gastrulation undergo no more than two or three further divisions, so that a notochord is finally formed which consists of forty-two cells, perhaps one or two more or less. And it is remarkable that this is invariably the case in all ascidian tadpoles, no matter what the size and yolk content of the egg may be.

In the case of all tadpole larvae which develop from small

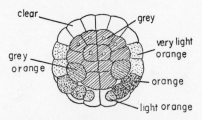

FIG. 6. Late cleavage stage of living egg of Boltenia echinata with natural colours indicated. Deep orange cells, rich in lipoids, give rise to tail mesoderm. Light orange and grey-orange give rise to trunk mesoderm. Grey indicates yolk inclusions and represents endoderm and notochord. Anterior clear zone is presumptive neural plate.

eggs, that is, in all oviparous and a few viviparous species, the bands of tissue corresponding to the yellow crescent of Styela are equally restricted. The total number of tail-muscle cells finally produced is 36 to 40, that is, each lateral band of muscle cells numbers no more than 18 to 20, and as a rule each band consists of three rows of six cells each. The presumptive tail-muscle cells divide only once following the completion of gastrulation.

Such are the tissues of locomotion, at least as regards origin and cell numbers. Both the presumptive notochord and tail muscle can be traced back to special localized regions of the undivided egg, which appear to be histogenetic determiners, although the mitochondria which are responsible for the yellow colour of the crescent of the Styela egg are not themselves the active agent (Conklin, 1931).

The actual process and final state of differentiation of the notochord and lateral muscle bands deserve closer attention, for, if our general thesis verges on the truth, here is the emergent propelling tail of the chordates, the beginnings, in a larval organism only 1 mm. long, of the locomotory structure of the greatest aquatic vertebrates. The nature of the tail, and of its development, of the ascidian tadpole may have changed markedly from what it was originally when this type of larva first came into existence. On the other hand it is equally possible that the

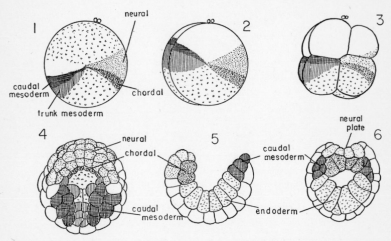

FIG. 7. Early development of ascidian Styela (after Conklin). 1, ooplasmic crescental regions of uncleaved egg. 2, 3, the first and second cleavage showing relationship of cleavage planes to plane of ooplasmic symmetry and presumptive body axis. 4, gastrula showing convergence of crescental groups of presumptive neural, chordal, and tail mesodermal cells. 5, section through plane of symmetry of gastrula. 6, cross-section through later neural stage to show neural plate and the final disposition of neural, chordal, and mesodermal tissue.

tadpole larva, once it became perfected for its particular function, has persisted without significant change, and that accordingly we can see in these developmental processes of notochord and tail muscle the original manner in which the chordate tail first made its appearance upon this planet.

In the first place, to take the Styela egg, the yellow crescent and blue-grey crescent of the opposite side contain histogenetic agents for muscle and chordal tissue. The ooplasmic or cytoplasmic regions involved undergo rapid histodifferentiation. At the same time these territories undergo regular cleavage or cell division in keeping with that of the egg as a whole, except that the enforced histological maturation process brings cell division to a premature close, since the two processes are apparently incompatible (cf. Berrill and Huskins, 1932).

The inclusive process of tail formation therefore consists of the following principal features:

(i) localized histogenetic ooplasmic regions in the egg prior to the onset of cleavage;

(ii) spatial convergence during gastrulation of the previously separated presumptive muscle and notochordal territories;

(iii) rapid histodifferentiation of muscle and notochordal regions, with consequent cessation of cell division preceding final differentiation; these tissues accordingly consist of small numbers of relatively large cells;

(iv) outgrowth of the tail in consequence of the activity of the notochordal cells;

(v) histodifferentiation of the muscle bands.

The last two items are of particular interest.

The actual force which causes the outgrowth of the tail derives from the swelling of the individual chordal cells. This commences after the completion of gastrulation and only after the full complement of chordal cells are present, and is the result of vacuolation; a single fluid-containing vacuole appears in each cell shortly after the final division, and progressively swells until the cell is several times the original size. At the same time the chordal cells not only adhere closely to one another, but as a group appear to be constrained within a continuous, enveloping protoplasmic coat of a more or less elastic nature. The expanding constituent cells accordingly progressively interdigitate, sliding among themselves, so that a single row of forty or so replace the original mass which were arranged four in cross-section. The extension of the tail is as much the result of this rearrangment as it is of individual cell expansion directly, although this last is in great part a cause of the other. In many ascidian tadpoles the vacuolated chordal cells, in single file, retain their individuality to a recognizable extent, but in many others, the vacuoles of adjacent cells expand until they fuse, so that finally there is but a single long vacuole extending the length of the notochord.

During the time the chordal cells swell, become rearranged and protrude as the core of the tail outgrowth, the pair of lateral groups of muscle cells undergo a comparable process of extension, only in this case the extension is relatively passive. Each lateral band of presumptive muscle tissue ceases cell division at about the same time as do the cells of the notochord, and thereafter undergo histological differentiation. Each band

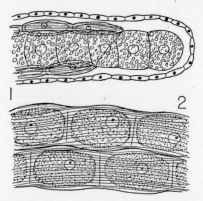

Fig. 8. Tail of tadpole of Stolonica. 1, to show epidermal sheath, yolky notochord cells, and muscle band, as seen in optical section. 2, part of muscle band to show continuity of myofibrillae from cell to cell, but cellular discreteness with regard to nucleus and endoplasm.

becomes tapered in width from the base to the tip of the tail, and is closely apposed to the surface of the notochord. There appears to be a marked extent of positive stretching exerted by the lengthening notochord upon the adhering muscle bands, and muscular twitching begins when full chordal length and turgidity is nearly attained. Each muscle band is to a significant extent a syncitial unit. Nuclei and endoplasmic territories retain their individuality, but the ectoplasmic or plasmagel layer, particularly of the surfaces running parallel with the tail axis, fuse to form a continuous layer. The myofibrils differentiate within this layer and run in a slightly spiral course from one end of the muscle band to the other, completely overriding the integrity of the individual cells that contribute to their existence (Grave, 1921; Scott, 1946; Berrill, 1947).

(e) *The neural tube*

Such are the essentials of tail outgrowth as distinct from tadpole structure as a whole. Leaving aside the nature and origin
of the adhesive organs of the tadpole, which are part of the
transient larval equipment, the remaining feature of importance
is the manner of development and nature of the larval nervous
system and sensory apparatus. This is possibly the most significant feature in the development of the ascidian tadpole, other
than the notochord itself, for the developmental pattern is
unmistakably the same as that of the vertebrates. In general
outline it is as follows.

At the close of gastrulation, when the blastopore has virtually
disappeared, and its ventral margin has brought the two arms
of presumptive muscle tissue alongside the chordal cells of the
dorsal region, the dorsal ectoderm assumes the typical shape
and character of a neural plate. A neural groove appears and
the lateral ectodermal margins approach the mid-dorsal line
and fuse in typical manner to form a neural tube. An anterior
neuropore forms, which shifts progressively anteriorly until the
wider anterior region of the neural plate becomes completely
closed. Posteriorly a neurenteric canal persists for a brief while.
The result, at the stage during which the tail is extending rapidly,
is a completely invaginated and closed neural tube which is in
the form of a wide vesicle anteriorly and an extremely narrow
tube overlying the notochord and extending the length of the
tail. Nothing could be more clearly homologous with the cerebral and spinal region of the vertebrate nervous system. Yet the
relationship is a peculiar one.

With regard to the ascidian tadpole itself, the nerve tube thus
formed may be divided into three parts according to their
nature and prospects: an anterior vesicle from the inner wall
of which develop the otolith and ocellus; a narrow neural tube
which extends mid-dorsally through the tail; and a residual
region of the posterior part of the vesicle, from which the adult
neural complex develops. Each has its own particular interest
and problems, but in the present context the last, together with
the general problem presented by manner of neural development as a whole, offers the sharpest challenge.

The nerve cord of vertebrates and other chordates is unique
in several respects. It is dorsal, it is hollow, and, although not so

distinctive, it is greatly extended along the antero-posterior axis. Of these, the dorsal position is a feature of organization, like the anterior position of a mouth; we can adduce reasons for such positions, but the locations, as distinct from the manner of development, are primarily part of the basic organizational pattern, and will be discussed later in relation to ascidian (or tunicate) evolution rather than that of the tadpole. The manner in which the nervous system develops and the shape it assumes, however, are developmental processes and products thereof, and concern us here.

In brief, I believe that the invaginative process that produces the nervous system is to be regarded as a developmental phenomenon exclusively; and that the elongated character of the cord and the retention of the hollow condition are consequences of tail formation. The distinction will be made clear.

Earlier in this section I have emphasized the point of view that gastrulation by invagination of a hollow blastula is no more and no less than the most direct and simple process whereby the single-walled blastula proceeds to exhibit the most fundamental feature of the inherent organization, namely, that of a tube within a tube; and that the process is comparable with the formation of the double-walled bud or with the subdivision of the inner vesicle of the Botryllus bud, for instance, by two invaginating folds, to form a central and a pair of lateral compartments. The invagination of a neural plate, whether of an ascidian tadpole embryo or of the embryo of a vertebrate, I believe to be a strictly comparable phenomenon.

If we disregard for a moment the particular shape of the neural plate and tube, neural invagination is once again the simplest and most direct way in which an outer epithelial layer of tissue can give rise to an inner mass or strand of tissue destined to assume a distinctive histological character. I do not think that this developmental process or folding, for such it is, has any ancestral or historical significance apart from being perhaps an old-fashioned way of making an old-fashioned structure; I do not believe it has any connexion with ciliated epidermal bands of ancestral larval or adult organisms. The process is simply a means to an end, and while the problem involved is profound, it concerns the nature of development rather than evolution.

In studying ascidians and other tunicates we have the advantage of being able to compare the development of the same structure as it is produced in embryonic development and as it is formed in the development of asexual buds of various sorts. In the present connexion the comparison is illuminating.

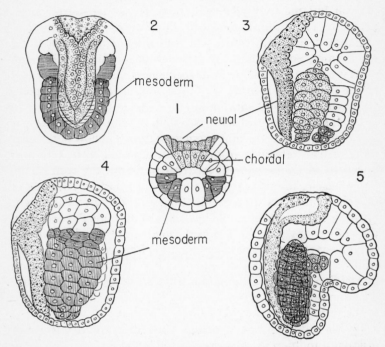

FIG. 9. Later stages in the development of embryo of Styela (after Conklin). 1, cross-section through anterior region of neurula. 2, 3, dorsal and median sagittal view of neurula with neural plate still widely open anteriorly. 4, lateral sagittal view of same stage to show tail and trunk mesoderm. 5, later stage from side with neuropore about to close, with both notochord and tail mesoderm superimposed.

In the buds of botryllids of perophorids (Perophora listeri, Ectemascidian Turbinata, &c.), of species of Clavelnia, Distaplia, and others, the wall of the inner vesicle gives rise to all structures and tissues except the epidermis. The outer, or epidermal, wall gives rise only to more epidermis; that is, it remains histologically epidermal, grows in pace with the growth of the bud as a whole, and merely conforms in shape to that of the inner developing component. The outer, epidermal, vesicle is formed from a unipotent tissue, the parental epidermis, which apparently is so far committed to its role of cuticle secretion and tunic formation that it cannot participate in any other activity, which is not surprising. On the other hand the tissue of the inner vesicle is derived from parental tissues of an unspecialized nature and is obviously totipotent inasmuch as it differentiates into all but the unneeded epidermis. Its actual source varies according to the family, and with the nature of bud formation, and may derive from tissues which themselves may be of either ectodermal, endodermal, or mesodermal origin. In all cases, however, the tissues serve as unspecialized limiting membranes in the parental organism, and their role in bud development, while vital, is almost incidental.

In all such cases, the nervous system develops as an evagina-tion of distal wall of the inner vesicle, to form a hollow outgrowth more or less segregated from its point of origin. If it were pro-duced in the same general location but from the wall of the outer vesicle, the process involved would necessarily be one of invagination rather than evagination, and the narrow transient opening to the exterior would be truly a neuropore. Accordingly, the embryo gives rise to a dorsal, hollow, more or less tubular nervous system by means of invagination from an outer epithelial wall (ectoderm), while the same hollow structure is produced in ascidian buds by evagination from an inner epithelial wall. The question which arises from this is, what is the significance of the difference in developmental procedure?

In chordate embryos a neural plate differentiates from an originally indifferent or unspecialized ectoderm. According to various experiments conducted on amphibian embryos, for instance, the flank ectoderm proceeds along a maturation path toward epidermal differentiation, and at a fairly early stage in this process loses its capacity to become neural plate and all that that in turn can lead to. It loses its competence to develop into anything but epidermal structures, and this apparently is the state that characterizes the epidermal wall of the ascidian bud. In other words, the ascidian chordate embryo invaginates a neural tube from its ectoderm because it can; the ascidian bud does not invaginate a neural tube from its epidermis because it cannot. This may sound trite, but it is important. The ascidian bud evaginates what is essentially a neural tube from its inner wall because that tissue is unspecialized and is able to do so; the chordate embryo experimentally bereft of its ectoderm cannot do so from the inner layer because this layer is anything but unspecialized.

The developmental plasticity implied in these statements is a startling phenomenon, but it lies outside our present discussion. Yet if the line of thought I have attempted to develop in

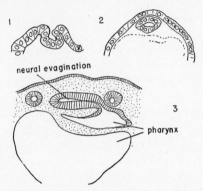

FIG. 10. Development of neural complex in tunicate budding. 1, 2, sections through basal and more distal region of salpa stolon to show origin of neural tube as an invagination of the stolon ectoderm. 3, evagination of neural tube from pharyngeal endoderm of bud of the botryllid Distomus (after Selys Longchamps).

the preceding paragraphs has any meaning, then it should be possible to show that, were the outer layer of a bud not so restricted in an epidermal sense, it could give rise to a nervous system in much the same manner as the dorsal ectoderm of an embryo.

This does not happen in the bud of any ascidian, but we do find it in the formation or development of buds in the thaliacean tunicates, to which the ascidians are related. The condition is most clearly seen in Salpa (Berrill, 1950). In this genus, as in other thaliaceans, buds are formed from a stolon which grows out from the body wall near the base of the pharynx. The stolon consists of an outer envelope, which is an extension of the ectoderm or epidermis of the parent zooid, of an inner tube which is an extension from the pharyngeal wall and is thus

endodermal, and of a solid strand of tissue lying between the
inner and outer layers so formed which is gonadial and of
mesenchymal origin. The stolon grows continually from its base,
that is, there is a zone of growth close to where it joins the
parental body. Distally, constrictions appear in the outer wall
which subdivide the tubular stolon into a series of transverse
sectional units, each of which eventually becomes a fully
developed, independent salp. No formative process or developmental unit could be farther removed in character from that of
an egg.

Leaving aside a general account of the formation and development of the Salpa buds, there are two points of immediate
interest: the nature of the outer wall of the stolon and the way in
which a nervous system is formed.

The stolon first forms in Salpa, not from a functional, histologically mature, individual, whether juvenile or not, but from
a rapidly growing embryo. There is no histological indication
that the embryonic ectoderm, at the time the stolon forms, has
passed from the originally indifferent ectodermal condition into
the final epidermal state. The outer envelope of the stolon, in
other words, is formed from embryonic ectoderm; and once
formed, the stolon ectoderm, at least in its zone of growth, never
loses its original plasticity. In Salpa, and apparently also in the
other thaliaceans, Pyrosoma and Doliolum, the outer wall of the
stolon base never becomes epidermis in the histological sense.
Here, then, if anywhere, we should find the outer layer playing
a more active formative role than it does in the buds of ascidians.

The outer envelope of the Salpa stolon is a single layer of
ectoderm. It is separated from the equally simple epithelial
tube of endoderm by a wide space, at least to begin with. The
cells of the ectoderm proliferate in such a way that a proximal
zone of growth persists and new tissue is continually being
shunted distally; in other words it grows from the base out-
wards and differentiates as it does so.

In cross-section the stolon corresponds closely to a cross-section
of a late gastrula stage of a developing egg, as an outer layer of
ectoderm surrounding an inner layer of endoderm. The inner
stolonic layer, as in the case of gastrular endoderm, gives rise
to the digestive canal and its derivatives, although much in the
same way as does the inner vesicle of an ascidian bud. It does

not, however, contribute to the formation of the neural complex. This is formed solely as the result of ectodermal activity.

Close to the base of the stolon, in the mid-dorsal position with regard to the stolon axes, the proliferating ectodermal cells crowd somewhat toward the middle line to form a recognizably distinct region. This is a continuing process, for simultaneously there is a progressive shifting distally as new tissue is formed in the growth zone. In short, there appears what can only be designated as a neural plate which is continually being added to at its proximal edge. At its distal edge the plate invaginates to form a neural groove, which continues to invaginate to become a tube lying beneath the ectoderm. A series of sections at intervals through this region shows neural plate, neural groove, and neural tube with overlying ectoderm just as though it were a series through a vertebrate embryo. A surface view shows a neuropore between neural plate and tube. A typical neural tube is formed from ectoderm in a manner almost identical with the way in which a neural tube is formed during the development of a chordate egg. The only important difference is that in the stolon there is rapid proliferation in a proximo-distal direction, whereas in the embryo it is not so polarized.

The point I wish to make here is that neural-tube formation occurs in fundamentally the same manner in the egg and in a stolonic structure that has no possible connexion with any hypothetical ancestral larval form. The stolonic processes are to be looked upon as strictly comparable to those of bud development in general, as asexual and of a generally regenerative character. When the outer layer of the developing unit is unspecialized, it gives rise by invagination to the structure most closely related to it, histologically and functionally. That is, where both inner and outer layers of the developing unit are histologically multipotent, or plastic, each contributes, by invaginative or evaginative folding, to the basic organizational components. This is obviously the case in the Salpa stolon. Here the neural tube, or that piece of it which is assigned to an individual bud, gives rise to a neural ganglion and associated structures, all of which are part of the adult Salpa organism. No chordate tadpole or any comparable stage is formed, the neural tube does not persist as such, and the neural plate, neural groove, and neural tube sequence refers only to the development of the final state.

Therefore, if this is so, it should apply equally to the development of the egg; that is, neural invagination in the ascidian embryo is fundamentally a developmental process connected with formation of the ascidian organization and is not primarily connected with tadpole development at all.

This conclusion is of vital importance in connexion with both the evolutionary and developmental origin of the tadpole larva. It is borne out further by the fact that the neural tube, whether it arises from the inner vesicle of an ascidian bud, from the mid-dorsal ectoderm of a Salpa stolon, or from the mid-dorsal ectoderm of an ascidian tadpole embryo, is destined to give rise not only to the central nervous system and sense organs, but to such non-nervous structures as the neural gland and hypophyseal duct. In the ascidian bud, the neural tube evaginates from the inner vesicle for the same reason that the pericardium does. Both evaginations represent tissue-organ complexes which in prospective histology, form, and location are to be sharply differentiated from other tissues and structures, and in each case an evagination is the simplest way by which a simple epithelial tissue can segregate a local region. The Salpa stolon performs the neural segregation by ectodermal invagination. The result is the same, and there is no reason to suppose that the difference in source is more than a developmental variant, although a profoundly interesting one. And by the same token, the invagination of the ectoderm of the ascidian embryo to form a neural tube is first and foremost a segregation of the neural complex as a whole and is not to be regarded as primarily taking place for the purpose of producing a tadpole larva. This is not to say that it is unnecessary for the development of the tadpole as such. Undoubtedly it is necessary; but I believe that a neural tube of some sort would still develop by ectodermal invagination even if a tadpole was not formed or had never been evolved, that the neural complex of the sessile ascidian is such that it would have to be formed either by ectodermal invagination, as in Salpa, or by inner layer evagination as in ascidian buds, and that in the case of a developing egg the outer ectodermal layer would necessarily be the source in any event. At the same time there is no doubt that the invaginating neural complex becomes intimately involved, both in time and in character, with the creation of the tadpole larva, and it will be discussed at the end of the present section. Meanwhile the development of the anural embryos of various species of Molgula and related genera is enlightening, for here we have examples of ascidian eggs which develop directly to the final ascidian state without passing through the tadpole form on the way.

(f) Suppression of tadpole organization among molgulid ascidians

When first discovered (by Lacaze-Duthiers in 1874) the anural type of development of certain species of Molgula was thought to be primitive, and the tadpole larva of others to be derived from it, an interpretation which would have made the molgulids, in their developmental form at least, our own ancestral stock. The evidence, however, appears overwhelmingly conclusive that this type of development, which we have already concluded is of polyphyletic origin within this family, is of a degenerative kind: that the molgulid eggs which now develop without passing through a tadpole stage at one time developed into more or less typical tadpole larvae; that the tadpole organization has in some way become suppressed, and that this has happened a number of times (Berrill, 1931). The early cleavage patterns, for instance, so distinctive of ascidian development and apparently linked with the development of the tadpole larva rather than the final condition, remain unchanged. Yet the absence of the tailed tadpole stage in these species of specialized sand-living ascidians, when analysed in terms of the developmental processes, does throw some light upon the general character of ascidian development, and in a negative sense upon the way in which a tadpole is produced.

The anural development of molgulid ascidians has been analytically examined only in the case of one species, Molgula bleizi (Damas, 1902; Berrill, 1931), but from what is known of the rest it appears to be typical.

Early cleavage patterns, as already stated, are no different from those of tadpole-forming eggs. Development proceeds in a typical manner until a gastrula is formed, the opening of which is more or less closed by the posterior growth of the anterior lip of the blastopore. At this stage, chordal cells form at least four rows, each of three or four cells, in the archenteric roof underlying a neural plate. The neural plate and notochordal plate together extend back to the anterior lip of the blastopore. The

ventral lip grows dorsally and lifts mesodermal cells to the level
of the notochordal cells. Neural folds appear and meet dorsally
to form a neural canal. In other words, a stage is reached which
is virtually identical with that which in other ascidians immediately precedes the outgrowth of the tail. But the chordal
cells do not thereafter increase in volume, either individually or
in aggregate, so that there is a negligible tendency to extend

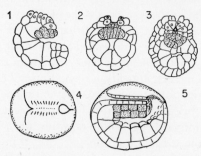

Fig. 11. Development of tailless embryos of
Molgula bleizi. 1, 2, 3, sections to show
presence of chordal cells and of invaginating
neural plate (after Damas). 3, 4, dorsal
surface and longitudinal half-embryo of same
to show anterior and posterior neuropores,
and presence of non-extended notochord
and neural tube (after Berrill).

posteriorly, to obliterate the neurenteric canal or allow neural
folds to extend and fuse above the residual blastopore. It is at
this stage, in fact, that tadpole development fails. The chordal
cells are present, but they do not mature histologically; no
posteriorly extending notochord forms, and no tail grows out.
Moreover, since the aborted chordal cells, and the neural plate
lying above them, form a broad edge at the anterior rim of the
blastopore, thereby putting the burden of closure of the blastopore upon the ventral and lateral rim, and so delaying it,
mesodermal cells lie at each side of the mass of small chordal
cells, and they likewise fail to undergo histological differentiation, at least with regard to tadpole organization.

Accordingly, the absence of a tadpole stage in the development of these ascidians appears to be the result of the failure of
the chordal cells to undergo their typical vacuolation and consequent swelling. An adequate number of chordal cells are present

at the right time in the right location, but they remain inert and no tail grows out. The cells that might have formed the two bands of tail-muscle tissue are also present, but they, too, remain inert at the critical period, which may be for lack of being stretched or, more likely, judging from their appearance, they are as faulty as the chordal cells. No larval sense organs develop; no molgulid tadpole possesses an ocellus, so none would be expected, yet all molgulid tadpoles possess an otolith, but no tailless embryo develops one. The otolithic differentiation fails in spite of the fact that a neural tube is formed, and, moreover, it is that part of the neural tube which normally is responsible for the development of the sensory vesicle. The shortened neural tube, however, proceeds to develop into the neural ganglion, neural gland, and ciliated duct of the permanent organization.

(g) *The developmental origin of the tadpole larva*

We are led accordingly to consideration of two very different topics, the evolution of a tadpole larva as a developmental creation, and the manner in which an ascidian settles and grows without its aid. The latter, however, only becomes significant in the present context when the evolution of the tadpole larva as an ascidian developmental creation has been demonstrated at least as a probability. Meanwhile we are now in a position to consider how a tadpole larva could have evolved as an interpolation in an originally direct type of development and life history. For while the process of perfecting the tadpole stage may have been a protracted one involving many generations, a larval innovation must be a sudden acquisition with immediate value if it is to persist and be improved upon. This is our essential problem.

Even though molgulid adaptation to living embedded in the open sand flats of the sea floor is clearly a late specialization in the evolution of ascidians, and the direct, anural type of development found in many molgulid species is equally clearly a further adaptation to the same form of existence, this anural development gives us some idea of our point of departure. For before a specialized tadpole larva existed, habitat selection of the kind dependent upon the activity and reactions of such a larva also could not exist, and a comparatively non-selective type of larva, developing without much detour more or less directly

to the sessile ascidian state, must have been its precursor. There
is little doubt, however, that eggs were pelagic, somewhat widely
dispersed, and were of a size somewhere between 0·1 and
0·2 mm. diameter.

In view of the preceding discussion, the development of such
an egg is considered to have been more or less as follows: The
egg underwent a sequences of cleavages leading to the formation
of a simple blastula, but without exhibiting the distinctive cell
patterns typical of the present ascidian egg. The blastula invaginated to form a gastrula, although not necessarily as early
as the interval between the sixth and seventh cleavage. The
inner, archenteric, layer evaginated the rudiment of a pericardium, and, possibly by emigrative segregation, gave rise to
some mesenchyme from which muscle, blood, and gonadial
tissue developed; the residual and main part of the archenteron
differentiated into the digestive tract as a whole. The outer,
ectodermal, layer gave rise by invagination to the neural tube,
short though this would be, and later to both stomodael and
peribranchial linings; the neural tube in turn differentiated into
neural ganglion, neural gland, and duct. Somehow, into a developmental course more or less as outlined above, a tadpole
stage must be inserted.

Notochord and Tail Muscle

The key to this insertion appears to be the notochord. The
outgrowth of the tail simply as a protruding structure depends
upon it, while differentiation of lateral muscle tissue seems to be
an associative phenomenon. In any event the notochord is all-
important, and we can get some idea of the course of events by
following the developmental steps backwards in time toward the
start of development. The notochord in its final state is a stiff
rod of closely cohering vacuolated cells. The immediate cause
underlying this condition is the process of vacuolization or
swelling taking place in a group of dorsally situated endodermal
cells. If these cells undergo vacuolation, a tail of a sort inevitably
grows out. If they fail to vacuolate, no tail is formed. The
group of cells vacuolate simultaneously, and therefore effectively,
because they are all cleavage descendants of a common cytoplasmic territory which contained a histogenetic precursor which
eventually causes vacuolation. In order to accomplish such a

distribution of histogenetic effect, the precursor involved would need to be present and spatially localized in the uncleaved egg; at least it is difficult to see any alternative. This, of course, is the actual sequence and situation in the developing ascidian egg as we now find it, yet it is the sequence itself which is the essential thing. If an ooplasmic region acquires a special quality or substance which later leads to cytoplasmic vacuolation of that region, all the cells descending from that region will, at a certain time, vacuolate and swell; and if the original ooplasmic region is so located that the descendant group of cells are in a certain region of the embryo, that region grows out at least with the semblance of a tail. In other words, the localization, in an otherwise and previously unspecialized ovum, of a cytoplasmic agent which evokes vacuolation, would result in some form of tail-like outgrowth at a later stage of development. Such an acquisition on the part of the ovum would necessarily be of a mutant character. It is the kind of differentiation open to any cell, and in this respect the ovum may well be regarded as a single cell, overlarge as it may be. How such a localized vacuolate region could be acquired is a question which is part of the general problem of cell specializations and differentiations, and goes beyond our subject. The point I wish to make, and as forcibly as possible, since so much depends upon it, is that a simple mutant change relating to the regional ooplasmic differentiation of the undivided egg could lead directly to the outgrowth of a tail consisting of at least a central notochordal core and an epidermal sheath constrained to accompany it.

For epidermis does accompany and conform to the thrust, or whatever the growth stimulus may be, of internal growing tissues, as is evident from the appearance of teratological tadpole larvae, and from the manner of growth of tentacles in hydroids (Berrill, 1953) and the outgrowth of the arms of echinoid and ophiuroid echinoderm larvae. The more serious question concerns the lateral muscle bands of the tail, for the tail as a locomotory organ can have no value without them. Would the outgrowing notochord inevitably draw muscle tissue along with it, and would potential muscle cells be available? There is little doubt that if potential muscle tissue is present at the posterior region of the embryo preceding actual notochord extension, it will be involved in the extension of the posterior region as a whole when that begins. And there is considerable evidence, from experiments made upon ascidian embryos and from a comparative developmental histological study of the tail of ascidian tadpoles, that the rate of differentiation of the muscle tissue is dependent upon the rate of extension of the notochord, and is not self-sustaining. This will be taken up in detail later in another connexion. So that we may conclude, with some degree of confidence, that as long as cells are present which lie between the lateral embryonic ectoderm and the central notochordal mass at the time when chordal extension begins, they will be drawn out as part of the tail extension. Whether such cell groups would naturally be present and available is another matter.

Groups of mesenchyme cells tend to differentiate when subject to tension, fail to do so when tension is absent, at least in the development of the chick embryo (Weiss and Amprino, 1940). Several cells in the ascidian embryo, which lie at the anterior ends of the two potential muscle bands, do not participate in tail-muscle formation but at a later stage contribute to a great extent to the mesenchymatous tissue, muscle and other, of the permanent ascidian system. They should be regarded as an integral part of the basic development unrelated to tadpole formation. The two cell groups which become involved in the outgrowth of the tail are essentially posterior extensions of these more anterior groups. It is reasonable, therefore, to assume that potentially mesenchymatous tissue existed in the posterior region of the embryo before even a tadpole larva had been evolved; that with the posterior outgrowth of a tail caused by the noto-chordal extension of the more posterior of these cells became drawn out as passively adhering tissue; and that as a result of the tension so induced, myofibrillae differentiated and con-tractility became precociously acquired. In other words, it is conceivable that, given the initial mutation leading to chordal differentiation and extension, the tail-like outgrowth so formed could have been supplied with lateral contractile tissue from the very beginning. This, admittedly, is not proof that the tail did evolve in this manner, but in terms of embryonic tissue mechanics it could have happened this way, and in my own opinion the possibility is a probability.

There is another aspect of tail outgrowth which is suggestive. The outgrowth as a whole, dependent upon the activity of the chordal cells as pace-makers, may be considered to be a region of local growth. That is, the rapidly differentiating and enlarging chordal cells may be regarded as a mass of cells undergoing rapid growth, although not proliferating. As such, the chordal tissue may well influence adjacent tissues so that the association of tissues has a unified growth rate, the pace being set by the tissue growing the most rapidly. Circumstantial evidence for this interpretation is abundant from the study of local outgrowths in other organisms, both tunicate and coelenterate (Berrill, 1949*a*, 1950*b*). Epidermal and mesenchymal tissues accompany the extending notochordal rod more because they are actually stimulated to a comparably rapid rate of growth than as the result of mechanical stretch or adhesion alone.

Neural Tube

However this may be, the nature of the neural tube in the tail of the tadpole larva calls for close attention. It is above all the obvious homologue of the spinal cord of the vertebrates, for it is undoubtedly neural, it extends throughout the whole length of the tail, it has a central lumen, and it lies in the mid-dorsal position. Yet in spite of all this it is not nervous. Its constituent cells are small, without semblance to neurons or ganglion cells, without trace of nerve fibres. Nor is there any sign either of fibres leaving the nerve cord to supply the muscle bands, or of the muscle bands responding to anything but stimulation at their extreme anterior ends. Each band is functionally and structurally a syncytial unit, and appears to be stimulated from the ganglionic cells mass in the posterior region of the tadpole trunk, not from within the tail at all. That is, the slender neural tube within the tail of the tadpole appears to have no function to perform during the active life of the tadpole, and inasmuch as it is destroyed during the process of metamorphosis, it seems to play no active part whatever. Accordingly, we are faced with two alternative interpretations. Either it is a functionless relic of a once important spinal cord of a more highly evolved chordate ancestor, which is the general interpretation I have rejected, or it is just what it appears to be, a functionless embryonic extension into the tail of the posterior part of a functionally important anterior neural vesicle. In other words, it is the posterior region of the original neural tube of the more primitive embryo, drawn out as part of the tail simply as an inevitable, unnecessary, but harmless inclusion; in a sense it is an embryonic accident of neither advantage nor disadvantage to the tadpole larva. If this be true, then the forerunner of the vertebrate spinal cord was at one time a slender shred of tissue of no importance or activity. The subnotochordal strand of endoderm in the ascidian tadpole is equally without function; its presence simply confirms the above interpretation.

The tail of the tadpole, the essential chordate equipment, accordingly can be fairly well accounted for as an interpolation into a simple developmental cycle produced by a regional histogenetic specialization in the mature but uncleaved egg, and as a structure of immediate functional value. There is neither need nor plausibility for regarding its origin as having been a step by step process involving intermediate non-functional stages, although the tail as first formed and functional would no doubt have quickly been subjected to selective improvement both in its action and in the developmental devices and precision connected with its formation, such as the matching of the chordal ooplasmic zone with one reinforcing the mesodermal-muscle areas.

Sensory Vesicle

A tail, however, is only a locomotory organ and can serve no purpose without direction. In the tadpole as it now exists the tail at first serves to carry the organism toward the light or at least away from the sea floor, and during the last phase of tadpole life turns the organism toward any darker area it happens to be passing.

The first of these reactions is simply dispersive. Before a tadpole existed dispersion must have been effected either by drifting eggs and membrane-confined embryos without any capacity whatever for directed locomotion, which is the present state in the case of anural molgulid species, or by ciliated larvae sentitive to light or gravity or perhaps to both.

However this may be, we are virtually compelled to assume that the precursor of the tadpole larva of ascidians already possessed a directive sense organ of some kind, probably a simple ocellus; an otolith is more likely to have been added as a response to the existence of a propelling tail. The point is that a sensory unit of some sort must have been present before the tail was evolved, since a sudden acquisition of a tail, no matter how clumsy or efficient it may have been, could be of value only in so far as it could serve as a steering and propulsive organ governed by a pre-existing sense organ. And a sense organ could have had significance only in relation to some capacity for directed motion. We seem forced therefore to the conclusion that the pre-tadpole larva was able to move actively through the water, and possessed an ocellus, rather than an otolith, to orientate its movement. Its outer coat was accordingly almost certainly ciliated.

This brings us to the questions of larval sense organs and of developmental timing. The matter of timing is the more readily disposed of, provisionally at least. Assuming an ocellus to have been the larval sense organ in question, the ocellus itself was the result of a process of developmental determination and differentiation, and consequently attained functional maturity at a certain stage in the developmental cycle, necessarily at a time preceding the readiness of the embryo or larva to settle and become attached. Accordingly, the outgrowth of the tail, in order to be effective, would have to have been so timed that it attained its own histological maturity when the ocellus and its associated neurons were sufficiently developed to assume control of its activity. From the beginning, therefore, the rate of development of the new tail outgrowth and the rate of differentiation of the ocellar region must have been closely linked together. This is a fact of ascidian tadpole development as we now know it, but it seems to me to have been an obvious requirement from the start.

Consequently we are forced into a closer study of the organization of the egg and early blastomeres in relation to developmental potencies. In the first place, apart from the absence of either the ocellus or the otolith in the tadpole larvae of certain species of ascidians, and the special circumstance of the botryllid photolith, all tadpole larvae are invariable in having a notochord consisting of approximately forty cells, an ocellus consisting of about a dozen pigmented retinal cells and three lens cells (except in the partly degenerate Styela tadpoles), and a single cell otolith. The cell numbers and quantitative correlations are rigid. A similar fixity in cell constitution of the tail-muscle bands holds only for those tadpoles developing from small pelagic eggs. In other types the developing muscle-tissue exhibits a variability of much significance, though not in the present context.

Ascidian eggs and early cleavage stages have been subjected to a considerable amount of experimental manipulation. The early work of Chabry (1887) and particularly of Conklin (1905–11) in Phallusia and Styela eggs respectively gave a picture of the early development as a rigid mosaic. The left or the right half of the cleaving egg, from the two-cell onward, gives rise to a half gastrula and to a larva not unlike a normal tadpole except that only half the typical number of notochordal and tail-muscle cells are present. Cells derived from the yellow crescent region of the Styela egg, or from the equivalent region of the eggs of other forms, give rise only to muscle or mesenchyme. More recently Conklin (1931) found from the study of the development of centrifuged Styela eggs that the mitochondria responsible for the colour of the yellow crescent of the egg, previously thought to be related to the myogenic functions of the crescent, could be displaced entirely without effecting the development of the crescent region into tail-muscle tissue. At the same time at least three or four visibly different regions of the egg are found to have specific developmental potencies as early as the first cleavage, namely, the posterior crescent (which contains the coloured mitochondria), the anterior grey crescent which gives rise to chordal tissue, the transparent hyaloplasm of the ventral hemisphere destined to become ectoderm and neural tissue, and the yolk-filled dorsal hemisphere. These cannot be displaced without causing serious dislocations of tissues and organs in the larva. Conklin considered the different potencies to be due not to any inclusions but to physical and chemical differences in the cytoplasm or 'ground substance' of these areas. Whatever may be their cytoplasmic basis, however, the locations and types of histogenetic agents are already established prior to the first cleavage of the egg. However, both Dalcq (1932, 1938) and Reverberi (1947) have independently shown that egg fragments obtained before or immediately after fertilization can develop into more or less complete dwarf larvae, though Dalcq concurred that the ascidian egg remains the prototype of those with a cytoplasmic mosaic of germinal localization. Yet the significant fact which emerges is that the setting of the pattern of ooplasmic specializations takes place between the final maturation of the egg, when the egg nucleus ruptures, and the onset of the first cleavage following fertilization. Apparently none of the specialized regions acts as an organizer with respect to others (Von Ubisch, 1939). An apparently normal nervous system develops in spite of the removal of either the chordal cells or the presumptive mesoderm from the pregastrula embryo. In fact a map of presumptive areas of the fertilized but uncleaved egg is more than a projection backwards of prospective fates. It actually represents a distribution or pattern of histogenetic agents, destruction or derangement of which is followed by a corresponding disturbance of the tissue and structure of the tadpole larva. In other words, the organization of the tadpole is essentially portrayed in the ovum, but in such a spatial pattern that the associated parts come together only as the result of the process of gastrulation. This is not to say that the gastrular process is purposive in this respect, but that the mutant changes which brought about the chordal differentiation and either the initiation or reinforcement of the muscle differentiation necessarily had to be localized in the egg in such a way that they became properly located in the right place in the post-gastrulan embryo. Any other arrangement would probably be disastrous, and the morphogenetic relocations during the process of gastrulation were not so much exploited as they were discounted.

Altogether, then, we have a pattern of ooplasmic specializations which appears to be associated with the subcortical layer or transition zone between plasmagel and plasmasol (according to Dalcq) as the actual beginning of the chordate tadpole larva. How such a differentiated intracellular pattern could be produced and perfected goes far into the most basic of all the problems of development, and is beyond the scope of this book and also my own capacity to pursue.

Yet the general linkage between the ooplasmic pattern, the relation to and the timing of gastrulation, and the emergent chordate tadpole larva is a rigid association. It not only is an invariable throughout the ascidians, apart from the breakdown in certain molgulids, but when in a non-ascidian tunicate we do find a difference, it is the whole which is affected and not a constituent part of it. For in larvaceans (Appendicularia), according to Delsman (1912), the whole differentiation process connected with both gastrulation and tadpole has become speeded up relative to the process of cleavage, so that gastrulation occurs between the fifth and sixth cleavage instead of between the sixth and seventh as in ascidians, while chordal and muscle tissues cease cell division and enter their terminal differentiation one cleavage sooner, to form twenty chordal cells in

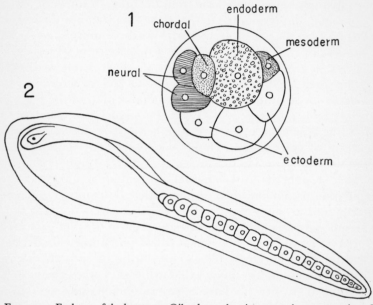

FIG. 12. 1, Embryo of the larvacean Oikopleura showing precocious segregation of presumptive areas, to be compared with figure 7 (5), (after Delsman). 2, Late stage of same to show tadpole with notochord of only twenty cells in place of the ascidian's forty.

place of forty, and muscle bands consisting of ten cells each in place of the eighteen or so in each ascidian band. The whole complex has been changed in a purely quantitative way without any disturbance of the basic determinative pattern.

This analysis and discussion of tadpole development has been long and intricate. I have not proven that the tadpole larva evolved from a type of ascidian egg which originally had no such larval stage, or that the tadpole larva is actually an ascidian creation. Yet I believe that the fact that it has been possible to show on the one hand that the tadpole larva is of vital importance to ascidians in their present way of life, and on the other that its origin can be conceived from the point of view of developmental tissue mechanics as a sudden effective acquisition, goes far to establish the possibility and perhaps the probability that such has been the actual course of events. It is admittedly no more than speculative thinking, but it is speculation tied closely to the known facts of tadpole ecology and tadpole and ascidian development, and to a great extent is self-contained and self-supporting. We leave the tadpole temporarily at this point to consider the organism which in my opinion has produced it.

8

THE NATURE OF AN ASCIDIAN

THE ascidian tadpole, with its notochord, neural tube, sensory vesicle, and lateral tail-muscle bands, is a chordate by all standards. Yet these features by themselves merely define the neurosensory-locomotor system and do not include the sustaining organism. Quite apart from chordate character in this limited sense, ascidians exhibit a certain basic organization which is common to the chordate group as a whole. This is true whether we regard the ascidians as a degenerate offshoot of the vertebrates or as the primitive stock from which they arose.

Since our thesis is that the ascidian tadpole is an ascidian creation which later became paedomorphic, carrying the essential organization of the original sessile ascidian into an adult free-swimming organism, the basic structure of the ascidian type thus emancipated acquires the utmost significance. When the primitive ascidian adult organism and the ascidian tadpole larva are conceived as coexisting in time instead of having the separate temporal existence characteristic of the ascidian life cycle, how much of the whole basic chordate organization is present and what features are missing? Answers to these questions require analysis of ascidian form and function as aspects of a sessile, filter-feeding organism, without reference to the nature or significance of larval stages.

If our thesis is valid and ascidians represent the stock from which the vertebrates and other chordates evolved, the events we are concerned with occurred no later than Cambrian times and in all probability at a much earlier period. Accordingly, the original ascidian stock has had 500 million years or more in which to evolve, differentiate, and increase in size, all the time retaining the ascidian tadpole as a larval form. During such an eternity, which embraces the entire period of vertebrate evolution from the formation of the first free-swimming adult chordate to the present remarkable exhibition of vertebrate behaviour, the ascidians as a group have had ample opportunity to acquire specializations which confuse the picture.

In attempting to determine what the primitive form may have been, we can eliminate certain groups and so clear the field to some extent. The pleurogonid ascidians, for instance, consisting of the three families Styelidae, Pyuridae, and Molgulidae clearly form a derivative order (see Berrill, 1951); from almost all points of view they represent the most advanced and elaborate phase of ascidian evolution. Similarly among the enterogonid ascidians the suborder Aplousobranchia, consisting of the families Polycitoridae, Synoicidae, and Didemindae, has exploited asexual reproduction by budding to such an extent that the individual ascidiozooids in the colonies of all species show evidence of secondary structural simplification as a consequence of dwarfing. And apart from these two somewhat extreme examples there is the complication, as in the course of evolution of many animal groups, of a general tendency toward increase in body size.

There is little doubt that the average size of solitary ascidians is very large compared with the primitive condition, and that many features of present ascidian structure represent adaptations to increase in body size one way or another. One of these adaptations I believe is the thick and sometimes histologically complex outer supporting tunic, which is typically a cellulose matrix together with various cellular and collagenous inclusions. It supersedes the cuticular layer originally secreted by the newly attached post-larval ascidian and, according to Brien (1930), is actually an external supportive and excretory connective tissue which migrates through the epidermis. Its thickness and texture vary with the size of the organism, both comparatively and during growth, and we are reasonably safe in assuming that the histologically and chemically specialized supporting tunic or test now characteristic of ascidians as a whole is a feature that evolved relatively late in the evolution of the class. Other adaptations to absolute body size clearly concern the degree of elaboration of the branchial feeding apparatus, a mechanism whose efficiency depends directly upon its surface-area, but one which has to serve the three-dimensional bulk of the organism as a whole.

On general grounds, which I have discussed elsewhere (Berrill, 1951), I consider the genus Ciona to be as little specialized a solitary ascidian as any, and to represent more closely than any the generalized type; and that among those ascidians which reproduce by budding to form colonial aggregations, Diazona is by far the most primitive and least specialized. These two genera will suffice as a point of departure for our study of the fundamental ascidian organization. Since, however, we are not concerned here to any great extent with ascidian evolution beyond the stage at which the chordate stock may have branched off as an independent 'clandestine' evolutionary venture, it will simplify discussion to start with the youngest stages, commencing with the sessile individual which first attains to a functioning state a day or so following the settling and onset of metamorphosis of the tadpole larva. There is an additional advantage in this approach in so far as we are able to see to some extent how ascidian structure and organization are correlated with the absolute size of the organism. At the same time we inevitably become involved in an appraisal of the general theory of recapitulation.

Once a tadpole larva has become attached by its anterior adhesive organs, metamorphosis follows. The tail is resorbed, the larval sensory structure breaks down, and the trunk region as a whole continues developing the permanent ascidian organization, eventually to become a minute sessile feeding organism. At this stage in Ciona the newly functioning individual is about half a millimetre in length, of which approximately one-half represents a supporting epidermal stalk and the remaining half the body proper with its essential structure and organs. The equivalent stage of Diazona is similar in every way except that the stalk is a little longer and wider, while the same stage of Ascidia and Corella are also almost identical except for their relatively short stalks. These four types represent four of the most important enterogonid ascidian families and, apart from the variability in stalk character, the size and basic organization of all forms is virtually the same, and I believe can be safely regarded as the original and primitive type from which other ascidian post-larval forms have been derived. The trunk or body region of these minute ascidian individuals, of Ciona for instance, is relatively simply organized but it exhibits the general structure with which we are most concerned, and without confusing elaboration.

At the distal end of the more or less barrel-shaped body the branchial siphon or mouth opening, rimmed by eight lobes, communicates internally with a large pharynx or branchial sac which occupies most of the space within the epidermis. The mouth opens into a vestibule containing a circle of slender sensory tentacles which serve to keep out, by evoking a rejection current, any particles too big for the organism to ingest. Behind or proximal to the ring of tentacles is the pharynx proper. Its distal limit is marked by an encircling peripharyngeal band. The endostyle extends in the median plane the length of the body, distally from the peripharyngeal band to the basal limit of the pharynx as a whole. A dorsal membrane or lamina, in subdivided form, also lies in the median plane, although at the opposite side from the endostyle, and extends from the peripharyngeal band to the proximal limit of the pharynx where it passes into the mouth of the oesophagus. The oesophagus narrows and then enters a small ovoid stomach, and from this continues a slender intestine which curves so that it eventually points distally and ends in front of the oesophagus; that is, the post-pharyngeal digestive canal is typically U-shaped. A heart lies below the pharynx in the space between the proximal end of the endostyle and the elbow of the intestine. I have avoided using the terms dorsal, ventral, anterior, posterior, right, and left at this point because these have reference only to the swimming chordate and not to the sessile ascidian which has only a free distal and attached basal or proximal end, combined with a condition of bilateral symmetry. The importance of this distinction will appear later.

In addition to the mouth or branchial siphon, there are, at this stage, a pair of peribranchial siphons. These are present one on each side of the pharynx and each consists of a sac, formed by invagination from the ectoderm of the embryo, which extends inwards from the protruding siphon to lie with its inner wall in close contact with the lining of the pharynx. A pair of large gill slits perforate each lateral wall where the pharyngeal and peribranchial layers come together. Long cilia, borne by the marginal epithelium of the gill slits, extend halfway across a slit so as to bridge the opening completely at a certain moment of their beat. The endostyle is grooved longitudinally, with the trough facing the interior of the pharynx; mucus-secreting cells line the sides of the trough, while exceptionally long cilia extend from the cells at the bottom of the groove. Mucus produced by the endostyle and peripharyngeal band is passed by ciliary activity on to the inner surface of the pharynx, and, by further

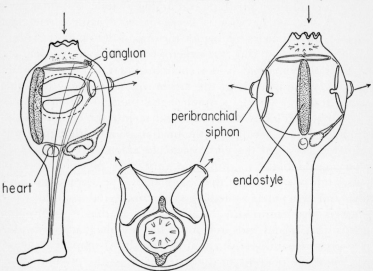

Fig. 13. First post-metamorphic functional stage of Ciona, showing basic and probably original ascidian organization, with primary gill slits and a pair of lateral peribranchial exhalent siphons.

ciliary action, is moved as a sheet toward the serrated median membrane opposite the endostyle. Food particles brought by the incurrent water into contact with the mucus sheet become rolled into a mucus cord at the membrane site, and from there pass downward to the oesophageal opening. The inhalant, food-containing water stream is induced by the activity of the powerful cilia of the gill slits. Water, but not particles, passes through the slits into the peribranchial sacs, and so to the exterior by way of the peribranchial siphons; and in such a direction there is little likelihood of any of the exhaled water being taken in again through the mouth. The intestine opens into the peribranchial sac of one side, and faeces are carried out with the exhalent current of that side.

The heart is an invaginated pericardial sac opening at one

end toward the stomach and at the other into a median vessel passing distally along the outer side of the endostyle and giving off vessels that pass across each side of the pharynx between the gill slits to join a median longitudinal vessel on the opposite side, which in turn continues proximally to break up in the intestinal circulation.

The neural complex consists of a neural ganglion situated about midway along a line extending from the mouth to a point between the peribranchial siphons. Nerves extend from the ganglion toward both the inhalant and exhalant siphons, where they may stimulate constrictor muscle sphincters in order to close them, and to other parts of the body. Longitudinal muscles extend down into the stalk, where they are inserted, and their contraction causes a bending and withdrawal of the whole distal region of the body, an avoidance reaction, in other words. Immediately beneath the neural ganglion, which is the only nerve centre present, lies the neural gland. This is in actual contact with the ganglion, and in fact both take a common origin during development from the residual tissue of the wall of the larval neural vesicle. A ciliated duct extends from the lumen of the gland to open through a ciliated funnel into the pharynx, at a median point of the peripharyngeal band. A cellular, nonfibrous strand extends from the proximal end of the gland as the so-called 'dorsal cord'; the cord passes proximally along the median line and ends within the loop of the intestine where the gonads are destined to develop.

This description of the first functional sessile stage of Ciona, apart from the appearance of the stalk, holds also for the equivalent stage of the other genera mentioned, and in a general but definite way represents a type of fundamental interest. I believe it is the type which has always developed from typically small pelagic ascidian eggs. Where modifications exist, they are either the result, directly or otherwise, of increase in the size or yolk content of the eggs, or of specializations in adult character which are discernible from the beginning. The type itself, as just described, we can look upon from several points of view.

The immediate and natural approach is to regard it simply as a stage in the process of development and growth leading to the mature ascidian, in this case, of Ciona. This has its values since it brings to the fore the correlation of structure with size as growth proceeds; and also enables us to recognize a possible stage in ascidian evolution at which divergence may have occurred, one line taking the path of neotenous free-swimming forms and the other that of sessile ascidian elaboration.

Two phases of growth may be distinguished, although the process itself is a continuous one, with regard to the structural changes which accompany it. The first of these covers growth from the initial functioning stage to a size no more than 1–2 mm. long, still small by any reckoning, but none the less significant. The second phase covers the remainder of growth and results in a sexually mature individual about 10 cm. long.

During the first phase, when the body proper is slowly increasing to dimensions five or six times greater in length and breadth, and the stalk is becoming relatively reduced, several developmental events occur. One feature, which is present to begin with, although in inconspicuous form, consists of a pair of delicate sac-like evaginations from the basal region of the pharyngeal wall, on either side of the median plane. These are the epicardia. One of them descends between the heart and digestive tube, the other on the other side of the heart. As growth proceeds, the one on the outer side remains comparatively small and occupies the space between pericardium and adjacent epidermis, the other enlarges in keeping with the abdomen as a whole and envelops the intestinal loop, the gonad rudiment, and the inner side of the pericardium. The two sacs retain narrow openings into the pharynx throughout life. Histologically, topographically, and functionally the sacs are coelomic, whatever view may be taken of the question of homology.

As the body grows, within this limited range, the branchial wall of the pharynx expands, both in length and in breadth. Additional gill slits appear until six have been formed on each side, each with its long axis perpendicular to the main axis of the body. Yet by the time the fifth gill slit has been formed as the basal one of the series, the first four have constricted at their waist and divided into two. When the sixth has appeared, the fifth has also divided, while the first four are further subdivided. The process in fact continues until the six so-called protostigmata have become six rows of definitive stigmata, each gill slit in a row now having its long axis parallel with the main body axis. Essentially, six primary gill slits are formed, each of which

lengthens and successively subdivides to form a row of secondary
gill slits. The time sequence is somewhat complicated by the
manner in which the branchial wall expands.

Simultaneous with this transformation another change occurs.
The pair of laterally placed peribranchial siphons gradually
converge until finally they fuse together as one in the median

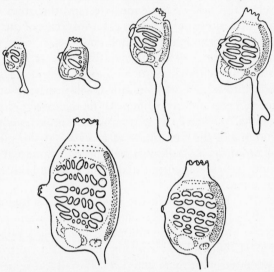

Fig. 14. Stages in the growth of Ciona from the first post-
metamorphic functional stage to the stage of fusion of the
paired peribranchial siphons to form the single median
atrial siphon, during which the primary gill slits subdivide
to form rows of secondary slits.

plane. The process is complete at about the time the six primary
gill slits are more or less fully divided.

The second phase of growth, which is the bulk of it, concerns
us less. Apart from the gradual attainment of sexual maturity,
the structural changes accompanying it consist of continuing
elaboration of the branchial wall, so that additional rows of
secondary gill slits are constantly being formed, and the number
of slits per row likewise increases. The branchial wall as a whole
becomes more complex in other ways, but all of this I think
relates to the attainment of large body size and belongs to that
part of the ascidian evolutionary venture that lies apart from

our theme. The remaining structure that undergoes a marked change with continuing growth is the heart. The originally short pericardial tube, with its myocardial invagination, grows greatly in length between two comparatively fixed points, and this relative growth finds its expression in a looping of the pericardial tube, so that the heart becomes sharply flexed about midway along its length. One end still opens, however, into the wide vessel at the base of the endostyle, and the other towards the stomach and intestine, suggestive, for instance, of the manner of development of the heart in chick embryos.

The above general descriptive outline covers the essential ascidian structure with which we are most concerned. It is necessary to look into it as a self-contained, self-justifying organization related to a certain way of life, without regard to predecessors or descendants. We need also to try and interpret the post-larval transformations of the first phase of growth. At the same time the organization as a whole can be studied as one which may have become basically incorporated in the subsequently evolving vertebrate stock.

Disregarding for a moment the question of absolute size, the young ascidian just described seems to have all of the necessary apparatus for obtaining, selecting, and digesting food; for the distribution of metabolites; and for the general control of re-actions associated with these activities. Equally, it seems to me, there is nothing in the whole organization which can be regarded as superfluous or in any way dispensable. This last is important because it concerns the status of the organism in this form, and indirectly that of the tadpole larva as well.

It is the question of order which is fundamental to this whole discussion. To refer once again to Gregory's two suggested sequences:

$$\text{basic chordate} \rightarrow \text{Amphioxus} \rightarrow \text{Ostracoderm,}$$
$$\downarrow$$
$$\text{Ascidian}$$

or

$$\text{basic chordate} \rightarrow \text{Ostracoderm} \rightarrow \text{Amphioxus} \rightarrow \text{Ascidian,}$$

we have in either case a sessile ascidian derived from a free-swimming chordate ancestor, which appears to be an unavoidable conclusion if the ascidian tadpole is conceived as a relic of such a past. If this interpretation of ascidian existence is a valid one, then the general structure of the sessile ascidian is something made over from one originally employed by a free-swimming chordate to become that of a sessile filter feeder. If so, some indication of secondary adaptation should be evident or at least discernible in the organization of the sessile form. This I believe is not the case. In my opinion the basic ascidian organization as expressed in the young Ciona has all the clarity and purity of original design. The small sessile ascidian is exquisitely fitted to its sessile existence, and has a remarkable degree of efficiency as a filter-feeder. Add a tail to it and propel it through the water, and effort is wasted in locomotion and filter efficiency is lost. That this is so will be evident when we study the pelagic tunicates.

As it stands, the organism is essentially a water filtration system, anchored by one end and opening at the other. Water to be drawn in and filtered must also be passed out. Simple gill slits lined by long cilia do double duty: they create the current and give exit to it. This single device is alone sufficient to make the system work, even in the absence of peribranchial siphons or the common atrial siphon which is formed by their fusion. These siphons simply direct the outgoing currents away from the intake and to a safe distance. They increase efficiency of the current system as a whole. Water drawn into the interior contains particles and solutes of various kinds. The internal structure serves to gather what is suitable and to reject what is not. Particles are trapped in the sheet of mucus propelled by small cilia across the branchial wall. An elongated endostyle secretes and starts it on its way; a serrated longitudinal membrane rolls and directs the end product towards the entrance of the digestive tube. All of it is necessary, nothing merely ornamental, and the whole works in relation to ciliary activity and cilium dimensions. Vestibular tentacles, in connexion with ganglionic reflexes, control the size of entering particles in a mechanical way. Neural gland and ciliated duct control the quality; cilia carry water and particles up the duct into the lumen of the gland, and down again, and the gland, in actual contact with the ganglion, is considered to be the organ of chemical sense, which, mediating through the ganglion, controls the closing and opening of the inhalant siphon, and therefore of what comes in or is kept out.

What is left, apart from organs of reproduction? Only the heart rhythmically reversing the flow of blood through the vessels of the branchial wall and viscera, and the membranous sacs enveloping heart and viscera and bringing the tissues thereof into as close a relationship with the water as the rest of the organism. All this, in brief recapitulation, is the ascidian organism. There can be no actual proof that the design is primitive and not a sessile adaptation from a different kind, but I believe it speaks fairly clearly for itself. The changes that come later in the individual cycle, concerning branchial structure, extension of the heart, and complexity of body wall and tunic, do little more than maintain the system in an efficient state, compensating for increasing size. They are, in other words, only adaptations to growth itself. Absolute size, in fact, is of great significance from first to last.

The key to comprehension lies in our recognizing the extent to which ascidians function by means of ciliary activity, and the dimensional limitations of ciliary structures. Only in the case of certain comparatively large forms, such as Phallusia and Ascidiella (Hoyle, 1952–3) does muscular action appear to play any important part in relation to the water current, and then only as a cleansing process of the atrial cavity and not in connexion with the primary current.

It is quite evident that an ascidian gill slit functions perfectly only as long as the cilia borne by its margin can more or less meet those of the opposite edge when fully extended. Otherwise there is dead water in between. The width of a ciliary gill slit is accordingly limited to twice the length to which cilia can grow, which may be very long in terms of the size of the cell of which they are a part, but is short by any other standard. Likewise, while a gill slit may extend in length more or less indefinitely and still maintain minimal or optimal distance between the two opposing edges, its efficiency falls as a mechanism for moving water in a direction at right angles to the wall through which it opens. The several waves of cilium stroke and recovery which traverse the edge of an over-elongated slit before the circuit is completed comprise a less effective propulsive system than a series of small slits, of equivalent aggregate lengths, of such a size that the phase of beat and recovery of the cilia coincides with the time for a transmission wave to make the circuit. For such is the final state of the ascidian gill slits. There is an optimum size of a ciliary gill slit: no wider than the length of two cilia, and no longer or shorter in circumference than is required for a cilium to complete its action cycle before the wave of beat traverses the gill slit and reaches it once again.

This leads to the conclusion that an ascidian possessing only primary gill slits, or protostigmata, lying transversely across the long axis of the pharyngeal wall, can never have been anything but an exceedingly small organism. The sessile ascidian with six primary gill slits on each side is an organism little more than a millimetre long. Such is the actual size of the juvenile forms exhibiting this structural condition. It is unlikely that the same organizational pattern, with the same histological basis, could ever have been more than two or three times as large. The long ciliated gill slits of an Amphioxus, for instance, have a much more elaborate histological structure; they are an exception which tends to support this conclusion rather than invalidate it.

9

THE POINT OF DEPARTURE

THE transitional stage from the young ascidian with about six primary gill slits to a somewhat larger form with six rows of secondary gill slits is a crucial one. There are three alternative suppositions. The gill slits and their segmental pattern have no phylogenetic connexion at all with those of vertebrates or of Amphioxus; this is a possibility, but it is one that merely puts an end to speculation and discussion. Or the ascidian pattern is descended from the vertebrate type with its simple series of gill slits; which implies that the early ascidian gill slit phase is an ancestral relic and that the secondary modifications are ascidian ventures made after separation from the original stock had taken place, which is part of the point of view I have already rejected. Or, following our own general conception of vertebrate origin from an ascidian stock, the divergence must have occurred before ascidians progressed from the primary to the secondary branchial pattern.

If this argument is sound, and the chordates evolved as mature free-swimming organisms from sessile ascidians before subdivision of the primary gill slits to form rows of secondary slits took place, then it seems to follow that the sessile organism that gave rise to such an emancipated type could hardly have been more than 2 or 3 mm. long.

There is a further consideration. What is the significance of the paired peribranchial siphons and their subsequent fusion to form a single median atrial exhalant siphon? In the most highly evolved and specialized ascidian order, the Pleurogona (or Stolidobranchiata), the atrial siphon develops directly, at the earliest possible stage, as a single median siphon. The young ascidian of this order never passes through the paired siphon stage. In other words it is not, from the point of view of developmental mechanics or morphogenesis, an absolutely necessary stage leading to the final condition. If direct attainment of the final state is possible at the start, at the same stage at which the paired siphons develop in all other ascidians, why is the paired condition developed at all? An answer calls for consideration of the so-called biogenetic law.

The theory of recapitulation or biogenetic law proclaimed that animals during their development as individuals recapitulated in condensed form their particular ancestral or evolutionary past. The original discovery of the ascidian tadpole played a great part in the promulgation of this theory, but since the time Haeckel first presented it the theory has been subjected to ever-increasing criticism. Garstang (1922) in his *Restatement of the Biogenetic Law* brought in the modifying concept that new evolutionary departures or other changes may be associated with any stage in the life cycle; while de Beer (1937 and 1951) in his *Embryos and Ancestors* tends to discredit the theory altogether. Admittedly most of the criticism has been fully justified, yet the apparent historical aspect of the developmental course of many types of animals is something which exists. Without doubt there is an explanation for it in terms of developmental dynamics, but the historical quality, for want of a better term, is there and cannot be argued out of existence. This has been treated at considerable length by Bertalanffy and Woodger (1933).

The frog tadpole is a case in point, perhaps an over-familiar one, although it is one that de Beer does not include in his general discussion of the topic. The frog tadpole is a stage in the process of development of a frog egg into an adult frog, and frog eggs are generally assumed always to have passed through such a stage; no one has suggested that it is an interpolation into the life history, as in the case of the aquatic larvae of certain insects. At the same time, from what we know of the development of organisms in general, it cannot be absolutely necessary for a frog to develop by way of the tadpole organization in its entirety, and in fact some frogs have virtually eliminated the tadpole stage. The reason that frog eggs in general do pass through such a stage may appear too obvious for serious discussion, but it is important to the present analysis. The frog develops in the way it does, passing through a tadpole stage which necessitates a subsequent metamorphosis, because of the nature of its egg. It lays, in fact, an old-fashioned type of egg, of a kind remarkably like that of primitive freshwater fish such as dipnoans and ganoids, and even like the egg of freshwater cyclostomes. Old-fashioned eggs tend to develop in the old-fashioned, i.e. conservative or ancestral, way. Frogs, for instance, became frogs without changing the nature of their eggs, as distinct from the genetic constitution, and the eggs continue to develop as freshwater vertebrates. In other words, the organizational pattern of the fertilized frog egg, while not repeating an ancestral stage as a matter of principle, is itself a replica of an ancestral stage simply because the egg pattern has never been significantly modified from what it was during the early history of vertebrates as a freshwater class. And because the egg has not changed, neither has its developmental outcome; it develops into an aquatic tadpole which, like the egg itself and all intervening stages, repeats the old developmental pattern. It is a recapitulation in a real sense, although I have no wish to revitalize the formal theory.

I believe that the paired condition of the exhalant peribranchial siphons is similarly a consequence of a conservatism in the invisible patterning of the ascidian egg, and represents a condition of great ascidian antiquity—an ancestral condition to all intent and purpose. The question is whether it represents what has always been a juvenile character or whether it may have been a feature of the sexually mature adult. This last possibility has a dual character. Fully grown individuals of Ciona occasionally retain the double siphon and therefore the normal confinement of this condition to the juvenile stages already described may be a consequence of the mutation to the single condition associated with the larger size. Or what is now a small juvenile stage with primary gill slits and paired exhalant siphons may at one time have been an equally small but sexually mature form, producing possibly no more than one or two small eggs. I am inclined to consider that this last condition was the case, as much from general considerations as anything specific to ascidians.

The point may not seem vital to the subject of vertebrate origin or evolution, yet it is relevant in two respects. If the whole chordate flowering stems from an ancient and simplified ascidian stock, then the more ancient evolution of this stock itself becomes a part or an extension of the same sequence. It is as much a part of the evolution of the vertebrates as the evolution of the strictly chordate type itself. The other significance is that it makes a difference whether we attempt to derive the ancestral pre-vertebrate chordate from a type which had a pair of lateral siphons or had a single median one. In any event, as a once-upon-a-time sexually mature adult form or as a juvenile stage at all times, the cionid with primary gill slits and paired exhalant siphons I believe to be a replica of a stage ancestral to the chordate kingdom. It may be small but it is anything but insignificant, and it in turn must have had a past.

10

THE GROUND PLAN

So much of the basic organization of the ascidian, quite apart from that of the tadpole larva, is incorporated in the vertebrate plan that we can only assess its significance by considering, so far as we are able, the original nature of the ascidian itself. At the same time the more outstanding features of both ascidians and vertebrates, such as the nature and location of the central nervous system, of gill slits, heart, and, not least, the coelom need to be brought into close comparison in the two types, as well as related to the earlier evolutionary history. The subject is merely a part of the general one concerning the primary diversification of the animal kingdom, presumably in Precambrian times. This may well have been associated with a relatively sudden discovery of the floor of shallow seas as an alternative to pelagic life, sudden in the sense that extensive opportunity for such discovery may have existed only intermittently. W. K. Brooks in an essay entitled *Salpa in relation to the Evolution of Life*, incorporated in his monograph on Salpa (1893), elaborated a theory along these lines which deserves more attention than it has received, although it is more valuable for the questions it raises than for the answers that he gives. This is not only a plausible conception: it has the additional merit of being, as far as I am aware, the only one in its field. In any case it serves as a starting-point for the present phase of our discussion, and, whether or not the hypothesis is valid for the totality of animal phyla, I believe it holds for at least those groups with which we are most concerned.

If we consider a group of small pelagic animals gliding through the water without the aid of any very elaborate ciliary or muscular locomotory structures such as the gasteropod velum, the medusa swimming-bell, or the specialized epidermal ridges or arms of echinoderm larvae, the average dimensions must have been very small indeed, of the order of a millimetre or so. It is by no means certain but it is at least likely that the littoral was first colonized by such as these, simply as a consequence of increase in weight resulting from a natural tendency to grow beyond the point where the viscosity of the water, surface tension, and the activity of a simple ciliary mechanism combined to keep the organisms suspended. Those that sank to the sea floor would either die or continue to glide more or less in contact with it—perhaps to give rise to those phyla collectively grouped as the spiralia, or else to become attached in some manner to solid material, whether sand grain, stone, or rock ledge. Only those forms that may have become so attached concern us here, but these appear to be several: sponges, coelenterates, echinoderms, brachiopods, ectoproct and endoproct bryozoans, phoronids, pterobranchs, and ascidians.

All of these, in a general way, live according to the same basic plan: they are anchored proximally to the sea floor and they draw water into themselves distally by means of ciliary activity, whether or not ciliary action has been more or less superseded by tentacles as in the case of coelenterates. Leaving sponges and coelenterates aside, however, for they are clearly outside our frame of reference, the remainder all, at least in their more primitive forms, tend to become stalked, with the feeding and digestive apparatus lifted clear of the substratum to various extents. Again in all, whatever the particular ciliary mechanism may be for creating the all-essential water current, the digestive canal is in the form of a loop with the anus opening not far from and more or less at the same level as the mouth. This appears to be so typical of the stalked, sessile, filter-feeders at all stages of their settled existence that one can only consider it to be evoked by and primitive for this kind of existence, no matter what it may have previously been or have led to. Any such small filter-feeder is primarily concerned with the creation and control of the water current, particularly with the stopping of the current when occasion demands, either by closing the mouth opening or inhibiting ciliary activity or both; control of defecation and of the outgoing water current, if there be one, is also in some degree a requirement. Virtually the only other activity of a sessile, stalked organism of this general kind is an avoidance reaction, a contraction either of the whole body wall or of the stalk, or a bending thereof, whereby the distal region of the body especially is drawn towards the base. The control of these comparatively simple reactions is exerted in all forms by a single or centralized ganglionic mass situated in the logical place for the exertion of such control, namely, distally between mouth and anus; the circumoral ring of the stalked echinoderm and of brachiopods is virtually the same arrangement.

Dorsality and Ventrality

Whether or not these organisms exhibit true bilateral symmetry it is not proper to speak of dorsal and ventral surfaces. They have distal and basal (or proximal) ends and a plane of symmetry; but the terms anterior and posterior, dorsal and ventral, and the correlated right and left, relate to an actively moving animal which has one end constantly advancing, and one surface, other than an end, generally orientated toward the floor or the surface of the sea.

The neural ganglion, then, is primitively distal, in as much as the sessile filter-feeding organization is itself a common primitive condition. This is as true of the primitive ascidian and pterobranch as it is of a bryozoan. The contrast between the dorsal nerve cord of a vertebrate and the ventral cords of crawling invertebrates is in fact to a great extent a misleading one. It seems to me most probable that the ventral cords of these forms, whether multiple, fused, or segmented, derive from a gliding or crawling habit that is primitive in the extreme; and that this group, collectively or singly, has evolved from pelagic types that sank but never became attached. This view is of course fairly generally accepted; but I take complete exception to the points of view either that the dorsal chordate nervous system is to be in turn derived from such a type, or that it arose as the result of an Amphioxus-like creature constantly swimming with one side, dorsal by definition, facing the light which penetrates the sea surface, which is an opinion dogmatically upheld by E. W. MacBride. The point of departure for a discussion of the dorsality of the chordate nerve cord is, in my opinion, the distal location of the nerve centre of a sessile filter feeder. The conversion of such a centre into a dorsal nerve cord is an integral part of the evolution of the tadpole larva, even of its development in the individual. This I have already discussed in some detail, although, to reiterate, a larval organism, tailed or not, would tend to migrate toward the light with its light-sensitive or nervous tissue in the lead; an extension of this tissue backwards as an incidental consequence of tail extension as a whole is simply something added. It is meaningless to speak of the cord being dorsal even in connexion with the ascidian tadpole, assuming that this larva is primitive, for the tadpole larvae of all ascidians swim in a corkscrew spiral resulting from torque in the muscle bands and eccentricity in location of the sense organs; such terms as dorsal and ventral applied to the ascidian tadpole are legitimate only by virtue of structural homology. In other words the dorsal and ventral aspects of the fully fledged chordate are qualities resulting from stabilization of motion. All that the tadpole really possesses are anterior and posterior ends, indicative of forward motion. And in the absence of this motion, the sessile ascidian merely possesses distal and basal ends. The long nerve cord of the typical swimming chordate is the result of relative growth of the body between mouth and the anal region, and it has so happened that in the final stabilization of the organism as a swimming type, this side has become uppermost when the individual as a whole is horizontal. 'Dorsal' has no other significance than this, and comparison with the ventral nerve chains of crawling invertebrates, whether annelid, arthropod, or any other, is an irrelevant distraction.

Bilateral Symmetry

There is the residual question of bilateral symmetry. In the different types of sessile filter-feeders mentioned earlier, a plane of symmetry, of varying distinctness, passes through the line joining mouth and anus, with the qualification that in ascidians, for instance, but not in pterobranchs or Phoronis, the gut loop for the most part lies to one side of it, a degree and kind of asymmetry equally characteristic of the vertebrates. Yet it is difficult to see how bilateral symmetry in itself is or can have been necessary or particularly advantageous to an attached filter-feeder, and the suspicion grows that the condition is a general one inherited from even more remote pelagic ancestral forms. Whatever, for instance, the significance of the dipleurula larva of echinoderms may be, there are the facts that the larva is bilaterally symmetrical and that conversion during development to a sessile, stalked form such as a crinoid involves the virtual abandonment or masking of that symmetry. It may well be that in the final analysis bilateral symmetry is no more or less than the possession of a mouth and anus by a polarized organism, one or both of which are situated on a meridian but not actually at the poles. For then only one plane of section can divide the organism equally and at the same time pass through the mouth and anus. Apart from the vague merits of sub-terminal rather than terminal location of one or both of these apertures, no adaptive significance appears to be associated with this form of symmetry. In its origin it seems to be both incidental and yet almost inevitable, but it governs the subsequent de-velopment of form to a very great extent throughout the course of evolution, not only of the vertebrates but of most of the larger invertebrate phyla as well.

The Coelom

The other controversial question concerns the vertebrate coelem, leaving aside for the present the question of its segmenta-tion. The coelom almost more than any other feature has been responsible for the tendency to by-pass ascidians and to link Amphioxus with pterobranchs and echinoderms as the ancestral chordate line. Ignoring the segmental structure of Amphioxus, there is undoubtedly a striking resemblance in the mode of development of the coelom in that animal and in Balanoglossus, echinoderms, and certain other forms.

Two questions emerge at once. From the standpoint of phylo-geny, could a typical body cavity or coelom have evolved on more than one occasion in the course of evolution? The answer of course is affirmative unless we regard all those forms possess-ing such, namely, molluscs, annelids, echinoderms, vertebrates, and various minor phyla, as of monophyletic origin—which is becoming patently absurd. If the coelom of a vertebrate, a chaetognaeth, and a mollusc, for example, has evolved inde-pendently in each group, then there is no particular need to regard the coelom of Amphioxus, Balanoglossus, and an echino-derm as necessarily homologous. The main reason for regarding it as such is based primarily upon the manner of development, rather than on any fundamental identity in the final outcome. It is the difference between the enterocoel and the schizocoel, and while this distinction may reflect a basic division in an ancient pelagic stock from which the marine bottom fauna as a

whole has arisen, it is a problem which involves more an understanding of the development of organisms than it does of their
evolution.

If we allow the balanoglossids to represent the pterobranch-
enteropneust combination, since too little is known concerning
the development of Rhabdopleura and Cephalodiscus, we see
that the coelom originates during development in this type and
in Amphioxus and echinoderms as evaginations of the archenteron, either bilaterally from the start or as a median anterior
evagination which subsequently divides.

Both Willey and MacBride have attempted to homologize
the tripartite division of the balanoglossid coelom with the subdivisions of the coelom of Amphioxus. Ascidians have been
regarded as having only mesenchyme and no true body cavity,
and have played no part in the discussions in this connexion.
Yet once again the crux of the situation seems to lie with the
ascidians. If for instance the ascidians have no true coelom or
homologue thereof, yet are the descendants of coelomate chordates, then the coelom has been lost by them; and this remains
equally true even if the descent has been from any other coelomate group, such as pterobranchs or enteropneusts. If on the
other hand the ascidians represent the ancestral stock from
which the coelomate chordates have arisen, but have no coelomic structure themselves, then the chordate coelom must have
evolved subsequently; and inasmuch as it does not seem possible
to conceive that the pterobranchs and enteropneusts have
evolved from an ascidian stock of any kind, the coelom of this
group would on this reckoning have had to have been of independent origin.

The alternative approach, which I have suggested earlier, is
that a true coelom does exist in the ascidians, but it is one that
goes by other names and is not generally recognized for what
it is. It is known as the perivisceral sacs in Ciona and as the
epicardium in all other ascidians that still possess its equivalent
in a recognizable form. General agreement concerning its nature
and significance has been lacking among ascidiologists. Because
the epicardium plays a dominant role in the histogenesis and
morphogenesis of buds in many ascidians, Garstang has considered it to be primarily a budding organ, and that any other
function it may have is secondary, in spite of the fact that the

epicardium plays no part in the actual making of a bud but only in its development once segregation has taken place. Because Ciona is a comparatively large, non-budding form with an elaborate branchial sac, Van Name considers it to be a specialized type and that accordingly its perivisceral or pericardial

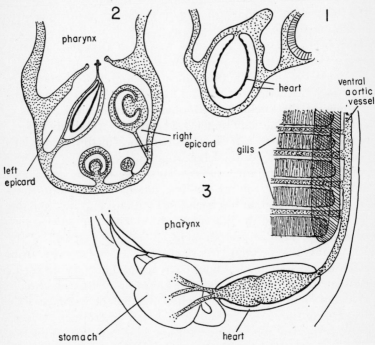

FIG. 15. 1, section through heart (and pericardium) of first functional stage of Ciona (after Kuhn) showing descent of pharyngeal (epicardial or coelomic sacs) on either side. 2, similar section through later stage (corresponding oldest stage in figure 14), showing the coelomic or epicardial sacs on either side of heart and enveloping also the intestine and gonad. The openings to the pharynx are permanent. 3, lateral view of part of young Ciona showing the heart within its pericardium, opening by several vessels in the region of the stomach and at the other end by way of the ventral aortic or subendostylar vessel to give rise to vessels traversing the pharynx between the gills.

sacs cannot be properly regarded as being in a primitive condition; yet branchial structure is related to size, and in any case organisms may possess elaborate structures of one kind and at the same time retain another in a relatively primitive form. I am convinced, as I have stated at greater length elsewhere

(Berrill, 1935, 1951), that budding organs as such do not exist, but only local epidermal growths which may enclose various other tissues; and accordingly epicardial tissue, being histologically unspecialized, plays a very active role whenever it is included; while on the other hand branchial structure varies according to size and independently of other features.

The epicardium can be considered entirely on its own merits as a feature of the intact ascidian of which it is a part. A good case can be made for Ciona as probably the least specialized of ascidians, although the discussion would necessarily be an extended one. Yet it is important, for if my own views are correct, we can see in it the chordate coelom in its original state. Much of this is a matter of opinion, but I hold strongly to the view that ascidians were primitively (a) small, solitary forms in which the viscera did not descend into the stalk of fixation, (b) that those in which the viscera (i.e. gut loop, heart and epicardium, and gonads) occupy the stalk represent a more specialized, derivative type, and (c) that the reproduction by budding has been acquired among ascidians on several occasions and is not a primitive feature, and that such reproductive activity effectively reduces the individual size of the ascidiozooids with resultant but secondary simplification of branchial structure. In other words, the relatively elaborate nature of the Ciona branchial basket does not mitigate against the view that the genus is primitive in general character. It is the only genus (and family) in which the viscera continue to occupy the position they held from the beginning. In all other families the viscera either descends into the stalk during the course of development or is dislocated forward along one side of the branchial region of the body.

The epicardium varies accordingly in these several types. In Ciona it exists as a pair of perivisceral sacs opening into the basal end of the pharynx at either side of a ridge denoting the median plane. Each sac is spacious and is lined with simple, unspecialized epithelium. That of the right side envelops the right side of the pericardium and also lines the inner surface of the right side of the body wall. The sac on the left is the larger of the two, and it lines not only the left inner surface of the body wall but also the left side of the pericardium; while it envelops as an investing epithelium the whole of the digestive tube and the gonads as well. The unspecialized nature of the epithelium is shown by its capacity to regenerate virtually all thoracic structure, both branchial and neural, when necessary; yet the amputation that removes the precise extent of the body necessary to invoke response at the epicardial level, without destroying the whole, is not at all likely to occur naturally. In other words, the regenerative potency of the epithelium merely indicates its unspecialized character and is not indicative of its normal function. On the other hand, there is little doubt that it serves for excretion, enabling waste metabolites of gut, heart, and body wall to diffuse freely into water-filled cavities in open communication with branchial sac and its circulating water currents.

This conclusion might be surmised from a study of Ciona alone, but in other ascidians the excretory function is unmistakable. In the Ascidiidae, Styelidae, and Molgulidae, a perivisceral sac develops in the young individual shortly after it has become attached and is fully functional, much as in Ciona except that it becomes separated from the pharyngeal floor where it originally evaginated.

In all of these a small opaque concretion is secreted by the lining of the sac so formed. In the Ascidiidae (and Corellidae) proliferative growth of this primary vesicle gives rise to multitudes of similar ones, each secreting a typical concentrically-formed concretion within, the numbers of vesicles increasing throughout the life of the individual. In the Molgulidae the sac retains its original unity and grows in size with the body as a whole, and remains closely apposed to one side of the pericardium; a single large concretion is secreted within continuously. In both the single and dispersed types, the concretions are for the most part urates. The excretory function is certain. Yet morphologically these are simply specialized forms of the epicardium, and it is reasonable to assume that the Cionid condition is the more primitive, for the original developmental state persists and excretion is accomplished by diffusion. All ascidian morphology confirms this. Similarly, in those families of ascidians in which there is a typical abdomen, i.e. with viscera descended into the stalk, the two epicardial sacs are also extended in their proper relationship to the adjacent organs and tissues, but the developmental connexions with the base of the pharynx are subsequently lost. This also appears to

be a condition derived from one similar to that of Ciona. Without carrying this argument further, and in detail it can be
elaborated almost indefinitely, I believe that the evidence shows
that, first, the Cionid condition of the epicardial sacs is by far
the most primitive among ascidians and, secondly, that they
serve primarily as a coelom, with particular reference to its
excretory function; and they function as such from their first
appearance and do so progressively thereafter as the body grows.
There is no doubt at all, in my opinion, that if a homologue of
the vertebrate coelom exists at all among ascidians, the so-called
epicardia, and in particular their presence as perivisceral sacs
in Ciona, represent it. In other words, if the chordates have
evolved paedomorphically from the ascidian tadpole, carrying
basic ascidian structure along, then the coelom is well accounted
for as a pair of perivisceral sacs of the primitive sessile form, sacs
which serve mainly as an excretory device for heart and intestine.
Moreover they function as such from the very beginning of the
active life of the ascidiozooid.

The epithelium of the Cionid ascidian coelom, to give it the
name it deserves, invests the heart, all of the post-pharyngeal
intestine, and the gonads. These structures in turn are of
interest in so far as they set the stage for vertebrate evolution.

Heart and Blood-vessels

The heart is significant both in itself, that is, in its structure
and development, and in its spatial relationship to blood-vessels.
In the young ascidian, when the heart first begins to beat, it
consists of a vesicle about twice as long as it is wide lying in the
median plane at the base of the pharynx. One side of the vesicle,
lying along the long axis of the inward side, is invaginated. Its
outer wall is the pericardium, the invaginated inner fold is the
myocardium, while a closed pericardial cavity lies between. The
long lips formed by the invagination lie apposed to one another
so that functionally the myocardium is closed, although not
actually fused, and the myocardial cavity remains open only at
the two ends of the elongated vesicle. This is the original condition in all ascidians. The dislocations and extensions associated with large individual size or with descent of the viscera
into the stalk lie outside our present frame of reference. They
have been described at length elsewhere (Berrill, 1936, 1951).

The cardiac vesicle in its first appearance develops from mesenchyme; but only in the absence of an endothelial lining is it significantly different from the newly functioning heart of vertebrate embryos. It is of the same general type, and moreover it forms in the same relative place. It lies at the base of the pharynx and one end opens into a large vessel which runs forward in the median plane immediately external to the endostyle; in relation to the heart and pharynx the vessel corresponds to the ventral aorta of a vertebrate, and it gives off lateral vessels on each side which pass between adjacent primary gill slits or between rows of secondary ones. On the opposite side of the pharynx, or branchial region, the lateral vessels reunite as a median vessel corresponding in position to that of the dorsal aorta, which passes basally to break up into vessels supplying the viscera. These in turn re-collect to open into the other end of the heart. The whole circulating pattern therefore is essentially that of the vertebrate. The outstanding ascidian peculiarity is the regular reversal in the direction of heart beat, of myogenic origin possibly based on alternating fatigue of two initiation centres situated at opposite ends of the heart; the circulation reverses in consequence, since no valves exist to impede movement of the blood.

Postbranchial Intestine

The post-branchial gut is relatively simple and in all forms consists of three distinct regions: a narrow oesophagus; an enlarged region, of variable character, which may be called the stomach and into which a glandular extension secretes proteases, lipase, and amylase; and a long, recurved absorptive intestine. The mucus food cord is moved along the tube by ciliary action. The three divisions appear to foreshadow the vertebrate system, and there is little doubt either of the function or location of the digestive gland as equivalent to a pancreas (Yonge, 1925; Berrill, 1929).

Gonads

In all but the most specialized of ascidian families the gonad is a single hermaphrodite gland, lying more or less within the loop of the intestine, with oviduct and sperm duct typically following the course of the ascending limb of the intestine to

end near the anus close to the cloacal funnel. Apart from the
general significance of the hermaphrodite condition and of the
topography, the most striking feature is the physiological and
histological connexions between the gonad and the neural
ganglion–subneural gland complex, which is discussed below
under this heading.

Neural Ganglion, Neural Gland, and Reproduction

The neural ganglion and neural gland are so closely associated in development and in position that they are generally
regarded as a single complex. In the fully developed condition
the complex consists of the neural ganglion or brain, the neural
gland closely apposed to the under surface of the ganglion, a
duct which runs forward from the gland to open by a ciliated
funnel or tubercle into the prebranchial region of the pharynx,
and a so-called dorsal cord which extends along the median line
to the region of the gonad. The homology of the neural gland
with the pituitary gland of vertebrates was first suggested by
Julin (1881) and has been the subject of controversy ever since.

Development is essentially similar in ascidians taken from the
three ascidian suborders (Willey, 1893; Garstang and Garstang,
1928; Elwyn, 1937). After closure of the neuropore the anterior
region of the neural tube separates into right and left components, the details of which vary with the genus. The right
enlarges to form the sensory vesicle of the larva, the left to form
the hypophysial duct of the adult, the anterior end of which
extends forward to open into the pharynx. Behind the sensory
vesicle the neural tube differentiates into the visceral or larval
ganglion (which controls the tail-muscle action, &c.) and the
apparently non-functional caudal nerve cord. The walls of the
hypophysial tube later proliferate both the adult ganglion and
the entire neural gland. The dorsal cord, according to Brien
(1927) is non-ganglionated and non-fibrillar, and consists of
histologically undifferentiated cells; it is derived from the neural
tube like the other components of the complex and is a non-
nervous basal (or posterior) extension of it. Of these components
the sensory vesicle, visceral ganglion, and caudal nerve cord
degenerate at the time of metamorphosis of the tadpole larva.

Ascidians are highly efficient filter-feeders; a medium-sized
individual of Ascidia nigra (Hecht, 1918), for instance, filters

173 litres in twenty-four hours, and there is no reason to suppose the filtration system is less efficient at any smaller size. It is clearly important that exhaled water with its possible content

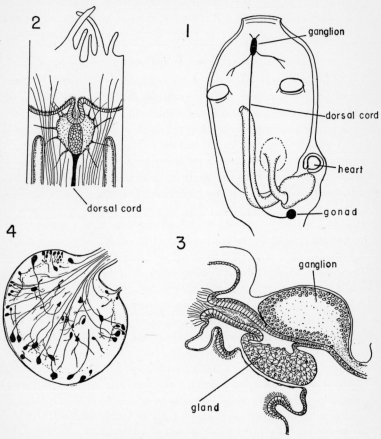

FIG. 16. 1, dorsal side of first functional sessile stage of Corella (after Hŭus), showing paired peribranchial siphons as in Ciona, and dorsal cord connecting posterior region of neura mass with the gonad. 2, neural complex of Leptoclinum (after Lahille), showing ciliated opening of hypophysial duct, the subneural gland, neural ganglion, and dorsal cord. 3, sagittal section of neural complex of Fragaroides (after Maurice), showing same structures as in (2). 4, cerebral or neural ganglion of Phallusia (after Hilton), showing cortical neurons.

of faeces and gametes be not inhaled again, and also that all particles and organisms larger than a certain critical size, which varies according to the size of the ascidian, be kept from entering. Consequently most of the activity of the neural ganglion lying between the inhalent and exhalent siphons is concerned with the closure and opening of the siphons and also of a general contraction of the body equivalent to an avoidance reaction. One method of ensuring the immediate safety of gametes in process of liberation is to cease feeding for the duration.

The neural gland is of primary interest in this connexion. We have to consider not only the possible homology of the gland and its associated structures with the pituitary gland of vertebrates, but also, and in any case, the problem concerning the function performed by the gland in its ascidian context. Carlisle (1951) has given the most recent account of this matter, together with new investigations. Concerning homology he points out that release of gametes in vertebrates is always immediately followed by the discharge of secretion by the anterior pituitary, and that also in the ascidians, Ciona and Phallusia, the neural gland discharges its secretion immediately after the release of gametes; and corpora lutea appear in the ovaries of Ciona after ovulation. The physiological effects produced by neural gland extracts are an oxytocic activity (Butcher, 1930, and Bacq and Florkin, 1935), a vasopressor activity (Bacq and Florkin, 1935) and a chromatophoric activity (Bacq and Florkin, 1935, Abramowitz, 1937). Carlisle sums up the situation as follows:

The endocrinological evidence, then, suggests that the neural gland is the homologue of the pituitary of vertebrates and confirms the anatomical evidence. Until the discovery of Hogg (1937) of the gonadotropic activity of the neural complex it was believed that this homology was restricted to the posterior lobe only of the pituitary and that the anterior lobe was not represented in the ascidians (vide Húus, 1937). Hogg's discovery however suggested that this was not the case. His view that the neural gland represents the whole pituitary can be supported by several slight pieces of evidence.

(1) The method of secretion of the neural gland is comparable only with that of the anterior lobe of selachians and is nowhere found in the posterior lobe (vide Butcher, 1930).

(2) The discharge of secretion by the neural gland after ovulation is strictly comparable with that by the anterior pituitary of vertebrates under like conditions.

(3) A mammalian gonadotrophin will stimulate ascidians to ovulate and discharge sperm.

(4) An extract of the neural gland will stimulate an ascidian to discharge gametes.

(5) The chromotophoric principle of the vertebrate pituitary is believed to derive from the intermediate lobe and therefore to be of hypophysial origin, not infundibular (vide Landgrebe and Waring, 1950). This is likely also to apply to the chromotophoric principle of ascidians.

(6) Van Beneden and Julin (1884) showed that a stomodaeal element entered into the formation of the neural gland which thus has a dual origin, stomodaeal as well as neural. This was confirmed by Metcalf (1895).

The weight of evidence would seem to suggest that the neural gland (including ciliated pit) of Ascidians represents the entire pituitary of Vertebrates, adenohypophysis as well as neurohypophysis.

So much for the relationship with the vertebrate pituitary. An equally chronic concern has been the function of the neural-gland complex within the ascidian. Hŭus (1937) concluded that the neural gland and ciliated pit of ascidians serves as a sense organ to detect the presence of gametes of the animal's own species in the imbibed water, so that all animals in one neighbourhood can discharge their gametes simultaneously and thus ensure a great measure of cross-fertilization. Carlisle found that if chorionic gonadotropin is injected, the positive response is prevented by section of the nerves from the ganglion to the gonad region but not by destruction of the heart and removal of the blood; the stimulus must act upon the neural region. Moreover for gametes to act as the stimulator the neural gland must be intact, which is not necessary in the case of gonado-tropin injections. Accordingly the stimulus must pass to the neural gland by way of the ciliated pit and duct, from there to the ganglion, and then from the ganglion to the gonads by nervous rather than humoral pathways.

The food stream of ascidians and other tunicates carries particles to the mouth of the ciliated pit (Van Weel, 1940; Carlisle, 1950), and Carlisle has postulated that the organ is the sense organ controlling (via the central nervous system) the rate and mode of feeding. Gametes are merely a sample of the ingested food, and it seems likely that the function as a general sense organ is primary and that the control of ovulation and sperm release is a superimposed exploitation of it. In the latter connexion Carlisle visualizes the path of communication as follows:

Stimulus:	Chemical (?) from ingested gametes
Receptor:	Neural gland
Afferent pathway:	Hormonal—gonadotropin
	Central Nervous System
Efferent pathway:	Neural
Effector:	Gonads
Response:	Release of gametes

To this I would add one suggestion, namely, that the dorsal cord rather than nerves as such may be the efferent pathway to the gonad, and in spite of its cellular and non-fibrillar nature that either neuroid or hormonal transmission may take place along its plasmal surface. If so, loss of the cord during later evolutionary phases would leave the pituitary homologue with the circulating blood as the alternative means of transportation; or, of course, true humoral transmission may have taken the place of cordal transmission and so led to the disappearance of the cord.

It seems to me therefore that if we accept both the homology of the neural gland complex with the vertebrate pituitary, and the sensory transmission function relating to ingestion as being the primary function in ascidians and tunicates generally, that we have a definite relationship between the two types and that this relationship is one that could have evolved in one direction only, namely, from ascidians to vertebrates.

PARENTHESIS

11

IN THE BEGINNING

THE basic organization of ascidians is clearly related to that of vertebrates. Does it also relate to that of pterobranchs and balanoglossids? I have already expressed my opinion that these forms do not represent the ancestral stock either of ascidians or of the chordates independently of ascidian connexions. They have, however, entered so greatly into discussions of chordate origins that they cannot be dismissed lightly. At the same time the following consideration departs from the positive thesis we have been developing, in so far as it is primarily an exclusion.

A full and recent account of this group has been given by Dawydoff (1948), to which the reader is referred for detail. In the present context I wish to discuss the structure of these forms mainly in its relation to the ascidian, although the intrinsic interest is great. The following features common to the three types, Rhabdopleura, Cephalodiscus, and the balanoglossids, which are obviously relevant in this connexion are the general body plan, the position of mouth and anus, the nature and location of the nervous system, the heart, and the tripartite coelom. These are considered first.

All forms have a plane of bilateral symmetry, a distal or anterior and a basal or posterior end, and a mouth which is subterminal. These are such general features that they cannot be taken by themselves as indicative of relationship with other forms. The body in all cases, however, can be divided into a pre-oral region, a collar region, and an abdomen. This links them together but tends to set them aside from the ascidians; neither does there seem to be anything in the ascidian organization that can be compared with the collar region. Even if pterobranch and ascidian stocks have had a common origin, the distal region concerned with the process of feeding seems to me to have evolved along very different lines, and I find it difficult to see how either type could have evolved from the other, at least in the form in which they now exist.

Rhabdopleura and Cephalodiscus may be taken together. Both have a disk-shaped pre-oral lobe which is employed as a sucker in moving either within or outside the sheltering tubes of the colony, and each has bilaterally disposed lophoral feeding tentacles which cause water to converge toward the mouth. The nervous system is generally referred to as a dorsally located ganglion, suggesting affinity with chordates, a description that is of doubtful validity. The nervous system is in reality a ring surrounding the mouth. Nerves pass from the ring towards the posterior end of the body along what would be the ventral side if we could legitimately call any side ventral; while the ring itself is enlarged on the opposite side to form a ganglion lying effectively between mouth and anus and giving off nerves to the tentacles and disk. The objections I have already raised to the terms dorsal and ventral in the case of ascidians apply equally here, but if for expediency we now employ them, then the pterobranchs have a nervous system which is essentially a circum-oral ring which has become hypertrophied on the dorsal side in relation to the pre-oral feeding and locomotory structures, and extended ventrally and posteriorly to supply the abdomen. Nothing of a circum-oral nervous organization exists in ascidians, and I believe we have instead indications here of a significantly close relationship of these hemichordates to a crinoid echinoderm stock, particularly if we regard the radial symmetry of echinoderms as a secondary condition imposed upon a basic bilateral symmetry.

The balanoglossid nervous system is not essentially different. Commissural nerves encircle the body at the junction of the collar and trunk regions, with so-called dorsal and ventral nerve cords extending anteriorly and posteriorly respectively. Balanoglossids in fact may be looked upon as pterobranchs that have abandoned the tubicolous habit and the associated exploitation of asexual budding processes, to become free-living burrowing forms, with consequent lengthening of the body and straightening of the gut. The tendency of the pterobranchs to wander about within or without their tubes suggests how such a change may have started. Or a simple, small wandering form may have given rise to the two extremes by divergent evolution.

In both the pterobranchs and balanoglossids the heart is in itself very much like that of an ascidian and consists of a pericardial vesicle invaginated on one side to form a myocardium. It is a simple device and could have evolved from any vesicular structure possessing muscle cells with a tendency to contract regularly in a polarized manner. The significant point in the

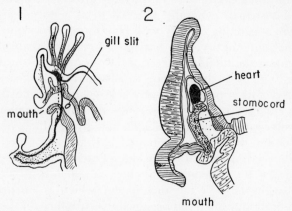

FIG. 17. Cephalodiscus (after Schepotieff). 1, nervous system (in black) and single gill slit. 2, section through proboscis to location of heart and position of stomocord.

present connexion concerns the location of the heart rather than its construction. In all ascidians it lies far behind the mouth at the base of the endostyle, at a place corresponding to the junction of collar and abdomen of pterobranchs and balanoglossids. In these forms, however, the heart lies in front of the mouth, distal to the neural ganglion, and projecting into the cavity of the pre-oral lobe. No amount of anatomical distortion or of relative growth can bring the location of the heart of the one into the position of the other. A disruptive dislocation is necessary to get the pterobranch-balanoglossid heart into the ascidian position, or vice versa. It seems impossible to regard the heart in the two groups as homologous.

The coelom of pterobranchs and balanoglossids is tripartite, and Dawydoff among others regards the condition as equivalent to a three-segment organization. The manner of development of the coelom varies considerably even among balanoglossids, yet in all cases it is formed during the embryonic period of development and appears as a process of evagination from the archenteron. In a general way the coelom develops in a manner and form remarkably like that of echinoderms. The question is to what extent we can compare the pterobranch-balanoglossid coelom with the perivisceral coelom of a Ciona, either ontogenetically or phylogenetically.

The embryos and larvae of echinoderms, balanoglossids, and Amphioxus have been frequently grouped together as phylogenetically related types because they share certain outstanding developmental features. In each case cleavage is comparatively indeterminate, a blastula with a large blastocoel forms, gastrulation is strikingly invaginative, and the mesoderm with its coelomic cavity evaginates from the archenteron to form, either directly or indirectly, a subdivided coelom on either side of the median plane.

Ascidians do not readily fit into a grouping of this kind and it is because of this as much as any other reason that the ascidians in general have been more or less allowed to wilt by the wayside, while a line running from larval echinoderms through larval balanoglossids to a larval amphioxid type has received more attention. The assembly and the exclusion, however, rests upon developmental qualities which have little if any phylogenetic significance.

Generally speaking, invaginations, evaginations, and other foldings of epithelial layers are the simplest forms of morphogenetic movements. Gastrulation is strongly invaginative whenever adequate cell numbers and internal space for manœuvring permit. Similarly, mesoderm evaginates from the archenteron when the latter consists of a relatively thin epithelial tissue consisting of very many cells. Granted that balanoglossids and Amphioxus have a fairly spacious coelom and eggs of relatively indeterminate type, the manner and similarities of development are to be expected. Absence of specialization in the egg and the presence of a coelom in the adult account for the resemblances in development. I see no other significance. Whether or not coelomic cavities are to be regarded as homologous throughout the animal kingdom must be decided on grounds other than the manner of development.

Accordingly I believe that the manner of development of the perivisceral or epicardial coelom of ascidians also is not relevant to the question of homology. In ascidian development, gastrulation occurs and an archenteron is formed relatively precociously, when the number of cells at each stage is barely more than the minimum required to permit the necessary invagination. There are neither cells enough nor blastocoelic space enough to allow mesoderm and coelom formation to occur by evaginative pouching of the archenteron; mesoderm formation is essentially segregative, while coelom formation is mechanically impossible at the developmental stage equivalent to that at which the process occurs in the other type. In other words a coelom cannot develop at the stage and in the manner typical of Amphioxus and the other forms simply because in the ascidian egg the determinative process is accelerated relative to the process of cleavage.

Inhibition of a developmental process resulting from numerical insufficiency of cells at a critical time and place is a common developmental phenomenon, which I have discussed elsewhere (Berrill, 1940). Whenever a structure or an organ which usually forms during the embryonic developmental period is suppressed for this reason, it develops at a later period when embryonic development has ended and post-embryonic growth of a functioning organism is in process. This is true for both developing eggs and buds, and applies to all manner of tissues. Consequently the perivisceral coelom of ascidians develops as it does because the conditions for its development at an earlier time are not fulfilled at the critical embryonic stage, and because the opportunity, of a somewhat different kind, reoccurs at the close of egg development proper.

We therefore reach the conclusion that the difference in the manner of development in Amphioxus and ascidians is as much without phylogenetic significance as is the similarity of developmental method among Amphioxus, balanoglossids, and echinoderms. These differences and resemblances, however, are of profound interest developmentally, although as such they lie outside our present frame of reference.

If, in view of this argument, we admit the ascidian with its belatedly developed perivisceral coelom to the company of coelomate forms represented by Amphioxus, echinoderms, and others, we are faced by the general question of coelom homology. Even if we exclude the Spiralia-type phyla as a group that has evolved perhaps independently from the rest almost from the beginning, we are still left with such forms as brachiopods, bryozoa, Phoronis, and chaetognathes, in addition to the echinoderms, pterobranchs, balanoglossids, Amphioxus, and now ascidians, as a coelomate assembly. We in consequence have the choice of regarding the coelom as homologous throughout this group or else as having evolved on more than one occasion within it. If the former then the coelom of any of these forms has been inherited from a past which preceded the diversification into the existing phyla and in all probability goes back to a semi-microscopic phase of pelagic evolution, so far in fact that it hardly profits us to pursue the question further. On the other hand if the coelom has had a polyphyletic origin within this group of phyla, then we are at liberty to assume that the ascidian coelom may have been an ascidian innovation, leading to the coelom of chordates as a whole, but that the coelom of balanoglossids and pterobranchs, let alone that of echinoderms, may not be homologous with it. In fact the coelomoducts opening to the exterior, and, in balanoglossids at least, the presence of a hydrocoel, link pterobranchs and balanoglossids with echinoderms; by the same token they separate them from ascidians and other chordates; if the ascidian coelom is to be homologized with that of the pterobranch and balanoglossid, it is with the abdominal division alone.

I have avoided using the term hemichordate for pterobranchs and enteropneusts together because of its implication that a halfway-evolved notochord is present in these forms. Great efforts have been made at various times to recognize the homologue of the notochord in the stomocord of pterobranchs and enteropneusts, with the wishful thought of bringing these animals within the chordate fold. In spite of such good will this interpretation has steadily lost what support it may once have had. I can myself see no basis for so regarding it, and I think it more profitable merely to regard the structure for what it is, namely, a turgid supporting tissue which affords a degree of mechanical stability to the pre-oral lobe. Pseudo-cartilaginous tissue supports the tentacle bases of sabellid worms; pseudo-chordal tissue, that is, consisting of turgid vacuolated cells, supports the

lophophoral and proboscis base of pterobranchs and enteropneusts respectively; turgid chordal cells extend and support the
tail of an ascidian larva. These are three independent solutions
of a common problem, evolved in different ways and places in
three different kinds of organism.

The remaining feature of importance is the most difficult to
appraise, namely, the presence of a series of gill slits in balanoglossids, of a single pair in Cephalodiscus, and their absence in
Rhabdopleura. Of the several basic characters generally considered to denote chordate status, the notochord can safely be
said to be absent, the coelom is at the best of a non-committal
nature, the so-called dorsal nervous system is no more than a
distal ganglion inevitably situated where it is found, and only
the gill slits seem to be unmistakably the same in hemichordate
and chordate alike. Yet the gill slit is a simple device serving
primarily to permit superfluous water, entering the mouth as
an extension of the lophophoral feeding current, to escape without having to be passed through the intestine. The slits have
very obvious value and it is as remarkable that Phoronis and
bryozoans have not evolved them as it is that hemichordates and
chordates both possess them. We have no assurance therefore
that gill slits may not have evolved independently in the two
groups, and yet my own feeling is against such a conclusion,
although it has no rational basis.

Altogether then, we reach a somewhat unsatisfactory state of
indecision. A case can be made for the complete exclusion of
the pterobranchs and balanoglossids together with the echinoderms, from the chordate scheme; or we can assume that such
features as are shared in common have not been separately
evolved but do indicate a common heritage at some point in the
past. If so the point becomes much more remote than has
generally been considered.

Echinoderm, pterobranch, balanoglossid, and ascidian larvae
all develop a pre-oral lobe by which they become temporarily
or permanently attached. The lobe develops from the apical or
anterior region of the larva, and Willey (1893-4) made out a
good case for regarding the structures as homologous in the
several types. This may or may not be so, for all small organisms
originally settling on the sea floor would tend to settle by one
end, and that end in all probability would be the apical sensory

region. In other words the pre-oral lobe would have been an almost necessary response of the growing organism to the need for settling and might well have evolved during each and every successful venture of this kind.

If, however, we do regard the group as a whole as having a common origin, the pterobranchs and balanoglossids seem to be set apart from ascidians by the location of the heart, that is, the heart evolved independently in the two after they had become sessile organisms; while the tripartite coelom plus hydrocoel unites balanoglossid and echinoderm and suggests that any union with an ascidian ancestral stock preceded such an elaboration of the coelom, and that divergence probably occurred during a pelagic evolutionary phase. If then the gill slits represent a common inheritance, we have to look to pelagic existence to account for their presence; that is, the settling organisms that became pterobranchs on the one hand and ascidians on the other were equipped with at least one pair of gill slits before this change in habitat took place. If so, the organisms that settled to give rise to ascidians, and thereby in my opinion to the rest of the chordates, must have been bilaterally symmetrical with a subterminal mouth and a sensory apical region, feeding by means of a ciliary mechanism involving the use of internally situated gill slits for the escape of the water current. Ascidians elaborated the internal gill-slit components, pterobranchs the external ciliary field into the form of a lophophore, although Rhabdopleura, presumably because of extreme reduction in size (to 0·3 mm. total length) and consequent ineffectiveness of correspondingly small slits, lost the pair of gill slits it may have started with.

In any case Cephalodiscus, Rhabdopleura, and balanoglossids seem never to have become completely sessile forms. They all retain the pre-oral lobe either as a disk-shaped sucker for locomotion within or without a system of tubes or for progression in sand. It is easy to conceive the original bottom-living form as a small non-budding organism creeping about by means of its pre-oral disk; those that secreted a protective tube evolved into budding forms, which in turn limited or reduced individual body size to dimensions where gill slits became of doubtful value—to be lost in Rhabdopleura and restricted to one pair in Cephalodiscus; while others evolved larger body size as a condition for burrowing, and gill slits multiplied accordingly. I find it difficult, if not impossible, to bring the primitive ascidian into such a setting as this, and were it not for the gill slits I would say that the two groups are unrelated. As it is, this inquiry must be left in an inconclusive state.

12

EMANCIPATION

WHEN we combine the organization of the primitive ascidian with that of the tadpole larva, what do we find? Enough, I think, to show the chordate organism well on its way. If we go a little further and orientate the organism according to its homologies with the vertebrates, assigning it dorsal and ventral, right and left, anterior and posterior aspects, we have a free-swimming and somewhat stream-lined form with most of the essential features.

In brief these are as follows:

(*a*) A nervous system consisting of the following points: an antero-dorsal brain with a central cavity the wall of which contains an otolith and ocellus; a hollow tubular neural tube extending dorsally throughout the tail; and a ganglionic mass innervating mouth, pharyngeal, and visceral regions, which lies at the junction of sensory vesicle and the neural tube. In other words, there are neural divisions corresponding to the spinal cord, medullary region, and the anterior distance-receptor region of the vertebrate central nervous system; and to this we can add a hypophysial gland connected with the central, ventral region of the system. All the basic components appear to be present.

(*b*) A digestive system consisting of an anterior terminal mouth which leads through a sensory vestibule into a capacious pharynx perforated on each side by a series of gill slits, and supplied with an endostyle and dorsal membrane; together with a postpharyngeal gut divisible into oesophageal, pancreatic, and absorptive regions. The system as a whole, apart from its reflex curvature, is remarkably similar to that of a lamprey larva.

(*c*) A heart and vascular system which in position and fundamental pattern are essentially the same as those of the more primitive aquatic vertebrates.

(*d*) A coelom consisting of a pair of contiguous epithelial sacs lining the posterior body wall and also investing the viscera and the gonads.

(*e*) Hermaphrodite gonads, which appears also to be the primitive condition of vertebrates, with sperm duct and oviduct opening close to the end of the intestine.

(*f*) Control of reproduction by the neural or hypophysial gland.

(*g*) A locomotory tail consisting of a central axial supporting notochord, lateral bands of striated muscle, and a dorsal neural tube, enclosed within an epidermal sheath carrying dorsal, ventral, and tail fins of a cuticular nature.

Altogether the basic chordate appears to be present and all that seems to be necessary is to combine the two temporal phases of the ascidian cycle into one. Accordingly, without carrying the structural and functional continuities of ascidians and vertebrates any further at this place, the nature and possibilities of paedomorphic evolution call for attention.

Two distinct approaches can be made to this question. Ascidian tadpoles and the nature of their metamorphosis can be studied to see to what extent neotenic or paedomorphic development may be possible; and we can examine tunicates as a whole for evidence that such a major evolutionary event may actually have occurred. Only the first of these is considered in the present chapter.

The ascidian egg develops as a dual system. It develops to form a tadpole, and it develops to form a small sessile ascidian. The organization of the egg preceding or following fertilization, in so far as it is discernible, relates almost entirely to the development of a tadpole larva at a comparatively early stage in the developmental course. So far we have considered only the least modified type, namely eggs of minimal size and yolk content, which are shed oviparously, to be fertilized and develop free in the water. Even in these the essential duality is evident, for the processes which culminate in the formation of a tadpole occur more rapidly than those leading to the permanent organism, and the precociously differentiated tissues suffer disintegration shortly after they have matured; in other words, metamorphosis takes place.

Comparative and experimental studies show that two possibilities exist. One is that the nature of the egg may be so modified that the developmental pace of the two emerging patterns may become more or less equalized, so that, while metamorphosis still occurs, there is at least a momentary period when both tadpole and ascidiozooid structures coexist. The other is increase in stability of the precociously differentiated tadpole tissues so that to a great extent, at least, the tadpole organization persists until both patterns are present together.

The first of the possibilities is of widespread occurrence and is to be associated with the development of all ascidian eggs, whatever their size, in which there is a relative increase in the amount of yolk. These types have been described and analysed in much detail elsewhere (Berrill, 1935 *a*, *b*) and need only be reviewed here briefly. It appears that when there is an increase in amount of yolk relative to the cytoplasm of the egg, the additional yolk finds its way mainly into two presumptive tissues, the endoderm and notochord. The significant factor is that the presumptive chordal tissue partakes of the additional yolk and while this extra yolk content apparently has little effect on the stability or fate of the chordal cells, for they are still more or less fully laden with yolk granules at the time of their metamorphic disintegration, the presence of the yolk in effect slows down the rate of histological maturation. In other words, while the pattern and number of cleavages and final cell number of the notochord remain unaffected, the rate of cleavage and differentiation is retarded, and the notochord may attain functional activity much later than is characteristic of the forms previously discussed. There is no doubt that the rate of differentiation of the notochord acts as the pace maker for the development of tadpole structure and the general result when the maturation of the chordal cells is slowed down by internal yolk is a prolonging of tadpole culmination and activity virtually to the stage at which the sessile ascidian structure is also complete. The following are a few examples, one from each of the three ascidian suborders: Ecteinascidia turbinata, Distaplia rosea, and Botrylloides leachi. The development of these may be compared with that of various species of Ascidia, of Ciona intestinalis, of Diazona violacea, and Styela partita respectively, although to all intent these may be treated as a single type. The contrast is both in timing and in structure, for increase in yolk content has

other effects in addition to modification of relative developmental rates. This topic has been treated at length elsewhere
(Berrill, 1935, 1940, 1951). Primarily, the effect of increase in
egg size or in relative amount of yolk, or both, is seen to be
structurally expressed in the branchial structure at the time the
gill slits first begin to function. Rows of secondary gill slits may
develop and function directly, as in Ecteinascidia, or they may
pass through the primary gill slit condition while yet embryonic,
so that the first functional stage is again the secondary form, as
in Distaplia; or primary gill slits may develop and remain as
such, although the number may be exceptionally large, as in
Botrylloides. This developmental variation has its particular
interest, but it is not relevant in the present context. What is of
importance is the dominant role played by the notochord as a
pace-maker, the indications of adaptation in the tail musculature, and the relative independence of the developmental larval
and permanent features.

In the case of the standard type represented by Ascidia, Ciona,
Diazona, and Styela, in which the eggs are about 0·15 mm.
diameter and have little yolk, the tadpole (at 16° C.) becomes
active about 30 hours after fertilization, while the sessile ascidian
stage first functions later than 130 hours after fertilization. In
Botrylloides leachi, with a very yolky egg of 0·26 mm. diameter,
the tadpole functions at about 220 hours after fertilization, while
the completely metamorphosed functioning ascidian stage is
attained about 40 hours later. Eggs of Distaplia rosea (0·42 mm.
diameter and heavily yolked) develop to the tadpole stage in
about 370 hours, but have completed metamorphosis and become functional ascidians only a few hours later. The larger but
somewhat less yolky egg of Ecteinascidia turbinata (0·72 mm.
diameter) develops in much the same way, to produce a tadpole in which the ascidiozooid structure has almost completed
its development; in which, like that of Distaplia, the heart is
already beating. In all of these the notochord remains a rod
formed by about forty cells; its rate of histomaturation depends
upon the size and yolk content of the constituent cells, and the
time of tadpole functioning depends upon completion of this
process. No doubt exists that the rate of notochord development
and differentiation is the pace-maker for the development of the
tadpole organization as a whole; it is just as certain that the

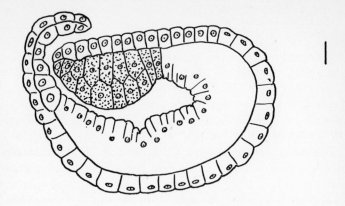

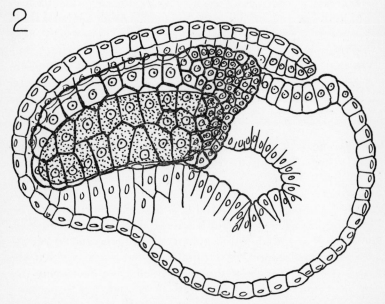

Fig. 18. Sagittal views of early and late neurulae of Clavelina (after Van Beneden and Julin). 1, early stage with both neuropore and neurenteric canal, showing chordal cells in final position before extension. 2, later stage showing grading of tail mesoderm into trunk mesoderm. Trunk mesoderm is proliferating at maximal rate, tail mesoderm has completed its divisions, although it has progressed one division beyond the standard number.

rate of development of the permanent ascidian tissues is entirely
independent of it. The variable gearing of the two is very
great.

The other significant feature is that while the pace-setting
notochord remains histologically restricted to its forty cells
throughout the ascidians, and while the histodifferentiation of
the muscle bands of the tail proceeds at a corresponding rate so
that the functional state coincides with the final stiffening of
the notochord, the number of cells in the muscle bands does
not remain constant and restricted to the 36 or 38 characteristic
of the standard type. Additional cell divisions take place, as
many as six in the case of Ecteinascidia turbinata, so that in this
case approximately 1,400 cells comprise the two muscle bands.
Such an emancipation from the usual constraint is suggestive.

Increase in egg size alone, however, does not bring about a
shift in the gearing of the development of tadpole and permanent
structures; increase in relative yolk content is necessary. The
important points are that the gearing is potentially changeable,
and that secondary histological changes may follow changes in
developmental rate. I do not suggest in any way that increases
in size or in relative yolk content of the eggs has at any time
led to the kind of paedomorphic development we are looking
for. The essential requirement is not the prolongation of tadpole
development so that the larval and permanent patterns culminate together, but the inhibition of metamorphosis so that
the tadpole tissues and organization continue to exist into the
adult organism.

The examples just given indicate that metamorphosis occurs
not after any given time but when the larval tissues of the tadpole have acquired full histological maturity and a certain
degree of senescence. It is significant, for instance, that the
free-swimming period of tadpoles which have developed at a
retarded rate is comparatively very short, and may be no more
than a few minutes.

We come therefore to the third important step in the making
of a vertebrate. The first was when the settling organism, the
primitive sessile ascidian, made and set the pattern of most of
the chordate organization not concerned with locomotion. The
creation of a tadpole larva within the original ascidian developmental cycle supplied the model for the locomotor carrier, and

constituted the second step. The third is the combination of the two as co-existing patterns in a swimming organism, and the primary need is the avoidance or suppression of the histological breakdown of the tadpole tissues which comprises the essential aspect of metamorphosis. The axial chordate structures exist in the tadpole larva, but they are built out of precociously differentiated and precociously ageing tissues consisting of relatively small numbers of large cells. Any comprehension of how such tissues, and the structures and functions dependent on them, may have become stabilized, and the tendency to settle and transform into a sessile ascidian overcome, calls for an analysis of the metamorphic phenomena, both histologically and experimentally.

The extensive experiments of Grave and Nicol (1939) on larvae of Ascidia nigra and Polyandrocarpa tincta yielded results of two kinds. Extracts both of adult and larval tissues, even when dialysed through collodion membranes, accelerated metamorphosis, while so did otherwise non-toxic concentrations of copper, iron and aluminium salts, and iodine. Since these last are substances which are notorious for their 'oligodynamic action' on living cells and organisms generally, their effect indicates probably little more than a relative general susceptibility of certain tissues to any metabolic disturbance. Grave (1935) had previously concluded that normal metamorphosis is conditioned by two factors, one that appears with an 'ageing' of the larva after its liberation, and another dependent more upon the swimming activity. His final conclusion, based on studies of the tadpoles of Styela partita (1944), was that the larvae produce a substance which greatly accelerates metamorphosis and that the effect increases as its concentration increases, until a lethal concentration may actually be obtained. Glaser and Anslow (1949) attempted to assign the controlling role to copper released within the tadpole tissues, but I do not find the facts particularly convincing with regard to this conclusion. In many ways the histology of tail destruction is more illuminating (Berrill, 1947).

Phagocytosis does not occur. During tail resorption both notochord and muscle cells appear to play a passive role; the active agent in forcing the whole structure progressively towards the base of the trunk is the shrinkage of the epidermis, which becomes nutritionally exhausted, progressively from the tip to the base. This is very clearly seen in the case of Stolonica socialis tadpoles, which are possibly the largest ascidian tadpoles existing. The epidermal cells nearest the tip of the tail are the most extended and the most remote from any possible sustaining influence of the body as a whole; they are also the most susceptible to toxic metabolites or to traces of heavy metals. This utilization and final exhaustion of the intracellular reserve of the tail epidermis is undoubtedly the ageing factor noticed by Grave, while the activity factor appears to be the accumulation within the distal part of the tail of toxic metabolites, including CO_2, resulting from contractions of the tail-muscle tissue.

There is a general problem here as well as a specific one. An ascidian tadpole consists of two sets of tissues which are distinct from one another in a sense quite apart from their structural significance. The purely larval tissues, irrespective of cell number and size, consist of fully matured, differentiated cells. The residual tissues which will form the sessile ascidian are all at this time still in process of development and cell proliferation, and are far from being histologically mature. When such a mixture of undifferentiated and fully differentiated cells is subject to adverse conditions of almost any sort, the mature cells become casualties while the immature cells survive and may even proliferate more rapidly as nutrient substances become more available. Thus heat tolerance in the hydroid Tubularia is much less for the differentiated cells of the hydranth than for the unspecialized cells of the stem (Berrill, 1948). In closed stolonic systems of hydroids in which one end is proliferating and the other consists of older, non-dividing cells (Berrill, 1949b), and in which no nourishment can be obtained from external sources, the recently divided cells survive and the older cells die; in other words, when nutriment is restricted below a certain threshhold, cells or tissues that are growing or proliferating take what they need, while older cells and tissues break down. When marked differentiation is added to age itself, the contrast becomes even more striking. In campanularian hydroids placed in water a few degrees above their normal tolerance, all developing units, whether destined to be hydranths or gonophores, continue with their development until they become functionally active individuals, in spite of adverse conditions;

but as soon as their development is complete and they cease to consist of juvenile growing cells, disintegration takes place at once. Such examples can be supplied indefinitely. We see the same phenomenon in the formation of restitution buds in certain ascidians, such as Perophora and Clavelina (Huxley, 1921,

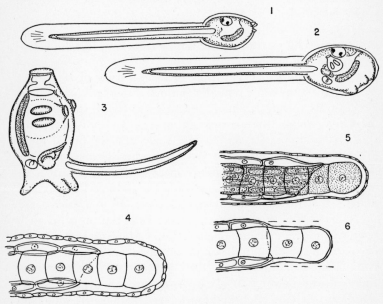

FIG. 19. Metamorphic phenomena. 1, normal tadpole of Ascidia (or Phallusia); 2, tadpole with delayed metamorphosis in high alkaline sea-water; 3, functional sessile ascidian in sea-water of high alkalinity, with trunk fully developed but with twitching tail attached to base. 4, 5, 6, three stages in onset of resorption of tail in Distomus, showing progressive inanition and shrinkage of the epidermal sheath as the resorbing agent.

1926; Ries, 1937). Old differentiated tissues disintegrate and cytolyse; simple, unspecialized tissues grow and proliferate within the mass. (In Obelia stolons bearing hydranths and well supplied with food, the proximal stolon cells survive for a much longer time than when chronically starved.)

I believe this to be the essence of all metamorphic phenomenon—the dissolution of histologically differentiated or mature tissues, together with structure dependent upon them, under the impact of conditions adverse to their survival, although such conditions may be and usually are encouraging to less specialized cells and tissues; the initiating circumstances may be critical temperature (Tubularia), critical metabolic levels (amphibians and insects), relative tissue starvation (hydroid and ascidian colonies), or partly controlled breakdown of larval tissues by metabolites or Cu liberated in system or derived from immediate environment (ascidian tadpoles, mussel and oyster larvae, &c.).

From this standpoint the ascidian tadpole is precariously organized. The essential structure consists of cells which have matured at an astonishingly fast pace and are of exceptionally large size, two factors that leave them in a particularly vulnerable state. At the same time this mature, structurally completed system rests within or among residual tissues still in full course of development; the permanent organs are not functional, there is no circulation or beating heart, and the larval tissues are self-contained amidst a potentially hostile tissue environment. The chordal cells in many species fail even to utilize the yolk reserves that they possess when the tadpole first becomes active—they do not lack internal reserves; and to a lesser degree the same is true of the muscle-tissue. Inanition appears to be primarily an epidermal phenomenon. Altogether the factors involved in the dissolution of the tail tissues are numerous and complex and it is difficult to distinguish cause from effect, but there is little doubt that it can be counteracted, at least to a significant extent. High alkalinity (sea-water of pH 9·0) tends to inhibit metamorphosis in the simple type of tadpole as, for instance, that of Ascidia or Ciona, so that the tadpole remains more or less active for many days, during which time the ascidian structure continues to develop, finally yielding a swimming organism with beating heart and active gill slits. It is not uncommon for the ascidiozooid to form and become fully active as a sessile organism with the tail still intact and still twitching at the base.

The problem remains. Yet enough has been said, I think, to show that, theoretically at least, dissolution of the tadpole tissue might well be counteracted completely if we understood a little more of the interacting processes involved. It may be possible to bring about the paedomorphic condition experimentally, or we may merely see more clearly how it might have been attained. The possibility exists.

13

TRANSITION

Neotenous or paedomorphic evolution of ascidians, by which the essential organization of the sessile filter-feeder is combined with a permanently motile tadpole, is more than a hypothetical possibility. If it were only this, then the step from the marine ascidian to the primitive freshwater vertebrate would be uncomfortably long for contemplation, although the ascidian-plus-tadpole organism would still, I believe, be the most likely candidate for this promotion. At the same time I think it is just as improbable that the primitive vertebrates could have evolved from a stock such as the ascidians without leaving relics along the way as it is unlikely that vertebrates could have evolved from any but a group that has been successful in other ways. Ascidians, which have colonized almost every conceivable part of the marine world, have been an enterprising and highly successful group, and only their lack of economic value has drawn our attention from their numbers and variety. And among the most abundant of all marine organisms are their immediate descendants, the thaliacean and larvacean tunicates. This statement I realize contains the conclusion that the pelagic tunicates have evolved from the sessile tunicates, and not the other way round as Garstang (1928) and others have at times supposed; but I propose to show that this has been the probable sequence and that the four basic types of pelagic tunicates are those relics of transition that were mentioned above.

It stands to reason that if ancient ascidian tadpole larvae became neotenous forms, abandoning the sessile existence and becoming sexually mature pelagic filter-feeders propelled by the tadpole tail, the change was made for immediate benefits and had no reference to any possible vertebrate outcome. In fact, in this attempt to trace the vertebrate stock to its earliest beginnings, it is just as necessary to show that an abundant free-swimming chordate stock existed in the early seas as it has been to show how such a chordate stock itself could have evolved from a sessile ascidian. Only from such a group is it at all likely that the further step of penetrating river systems could have been made. Yet since the time of this occurrence the vertebrates as such have come into being and have progressed to the state of writing about their origins; during the same extended period of time the marine stock from which they arose has had equal opportunity, in the temporal sense, of changing from its original state, and this applies as much to the pelagic group as it does to the sessile. Sessile ascidians have become large, complex, and specialized in various ways; pelagic tunicates have become exquisitely adapted to oceanic life; and in neither case is the primitive form evident in the fully evolved forms that now exist.

If the creation of minute filter-feeders attached to the sea floor was the first phase of our ascent, and the making of a tadpole larva was the second, then the exploitation of the oceanic surface pastures was the third. This is our present topic.

The pelagic tunicates are at the present time represented by Pyrosoma, Doliolum, Salpa, and the Larvacea. Fundamentally, each type exhibits the same basic organization that we find in the ascidians; all are filter-feeders, in spite of their free, non-attached, existence. And in each we see not an oceanic migrant but a pelagic form in which locomotory activity is restricted to maintenance of location with respect to sea surface, and more importantly to filtration of adjacent water. Apart from the need, shared with all planktonic organisms, to remain within certain limits of depth, effort is directed almost entirely to the creation of a feeding current, and locomotion as such is little more than a by-product of this activity. None of the four existing types represents an entirely primitive condition and it is only by an analysis of each, together with subsequent comparison and summation, that we get a picture of what the original state of the pelagic tunicate may have been. Of the four Doliolum appears to afford the best point of departure.

Doliolum

In brief, the organization and life cycle of Doliolum is as follows. The sexually mature adult, the gonozooid, is a small, delicate, barrel-shaped organism, with the mouth or inhalant siphon at one end, and the atrial or exhalant siphon at the other. Eight bands of muscle completely encircle the body, equally spaced from one another, and their regular contractions force water through the interior, at the same time causing the individual to move forward through the water by what is virtually jet propulsion. The pharyngeal chamber, complete with endostyle, peripharyngeal bands, ciliated funnel, and gill slits, occupies the anterior two-thirds of the body. The atrial or cloacal chamber occupies most of the posterior third, and its lining more or less envelops the viscera (i.e. digestive loop, gonads, and heart). The branchial wall is little more than a thin membrane perforated by gill slits, slung across the passage between the anterior and posterior siphons. Each side of the branchial wall of the gonozooid may have sixty or more elongate gill slits, which are generally and probably correctly regarded as primary gill slits. In the oozooid, which is the alternate generation, only four primary gill slits are present on each side. According to Garstang and Platt (1928) the endostyle, while structurally a long open groove as in ascidians, transforms itself functionally into a closed tube opening only in front, so that the mucus destined to form the food trap is driven forward to be released by way of the peripharyngeal bands.

The neural ganglion is like that of an adult ascidian, lying more or less midway between the inhalant and exhalant siphons and sending fibres to both siphons and to the lateral walls of the body. An ocellus is not present, although a statocyst occurs on each side of the body where one of the lateral nerve branches terminates; they occur only in the oozooid generation and not in the gonozooid. The outer tunic is made up of cuticle alone, secreted by the epidermis, and, unlike ascidians in general, does not contain cellulose or tunicin. A budding stolon forms in the median plane posterior to the endostyle and consists of an epidermal envelope containing tissue outgrowths from the floor of the pharynx (which may be regarded as epicardial outgrowths), from the pericardial wall, and from the cloacal or atrial lining.

The individual as a whole, whether of oozooid or gonozooid generation, is clearly and exquisitely well adapted as a pelagic filter-feeder, with a set of circular muscles serving as the main source of power with regard both to passage of water internally and to movement of the organism through the water. The relative posterior location of the gill slits and the effective anterior release of the mucus sheet, taken together with the muscle ring

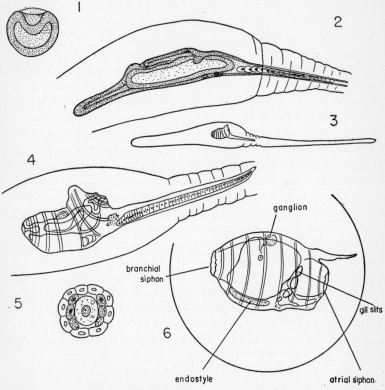

FIG. 20. The development of Doliolum. 1, gastrula (after Uljanin); 2, 3, 4, 5, 6, stages in development with gelatinous tunic which serves as float; the tail with its full complement of notochord cells seen in (4) is resorbed before liberation; 5, cross section of tail to show central notochord and lateral muscle bands. (2–6 after Neumann.)

system, indicate a marked degree of subordination of the ciliated gill slits as creators of the internal water current and filtration equipment. The terminal anterior and posterior positions of the siphons is obviously related to effective movement of and movement in water.

Reproduction occurs both by budding and by the production

of eggs and sperm. Bud formation is by successive constriction
from the distal end of the bud stolon, and occurs only in the
individual which develops from the egg, i.e. the oozooid. The
buds, or probuds, migrate along the surface of the parent and
wander out in three lines along a dorsal spur, giving rise
by subdivision to the definitive buds. Some of these become
merely nutritive individuals permanently attached to the parent,
others become gonozooids which detach and become sexually
mature. The gonozooid develops gonads but lacks a budding
stolon. The oozooid has a budding stolon but does not develop
gonads. The details of these events are of extreme interest from
the standpoint of developmental studies, but in the present context the important features are the position of the stolon, the
alternate character of gonozooid and oozooid, and the migratory nature of the original buds.

Doliolids unfortunately are small transparent oceanic forms
that shed their eggs at the time of fertilization. What is known
of the development is very fragmentary, mostly observations
of Uljanin (1884), and highly significant. The egg is very small
and transparent; the exact dimensions are not recorded but
are apparently of the same order as those of most oviparous
ascidians. Cleavage is total and rapid, and according to
Uljanin within five hours of fertilization a gastrula has formed
by invagination and has proceeded to the stage of being a
tailed embryo. In later stages the larva acquires the appearance shown in figure 20 (2); it is cigar-shaped, and consists
of an anterior rostral extension, a trunk region which represents
the future entire individual, a large median vesicular region, and
a posterior tail. The whole is enclosed within a large perivitelline
space bounded by the original vitelline membrane. Both the
balloon-like perivitelline envelope and the vesicular region of
the larva are devices serving to keep the embryonic doliolid
sufficiently buoyant during the course of development. The
rostral outgrowth, which is transient, may possibly represent
the similar outgrowth which appears in the development of
many ascidians (e.g. Ciona, Diazona, and Clavelina) and becomes the stalk.

The tail, while virtually of a non-functional character, is of
great interest and importance. Shortly after gastrulation it is
seen to contain about forty chordal cells and this number appears

to be the final one. Fibrillated muscle-cells form a band along each side of the notochord, and their number, as far as an incomplete drawing of Neumann's (1906, 1935) indicates, is of the same order. The organization and actual cell numbers of the notochord and muscle bands are unmistakably the same as those of the ascidian tadpole. The tail of the tadpole larvae is retained, although without connexion with the anterior region where the neural tissue develops, and without any association with any kind of sense organ. When we also consider that the larva or embryo is more or less effectively enveloped by a perivitelline membrane and that the tail has little opportunity for functional activity, it becomes fairly evident that the tail is in a residual rather than a primitive condition, indicating a past relationship with ascidians rather than any antecedent condition. The evidence, in other words, suggests that Doliolum is a paedomorphic form in which the ascidian larval tail develops but does not persist far beyond the stage which it is characteristic of in the ascidian life cycle. The distinction in fact is that while cleavage, gastrulation, and tail formation appear to proceed in a typical ascidian manner, the larval sense organs of the ascidian tadpole do not develop and no settling or attachment takes place. Metamorphosis is more or less inhibited; although since the tail is resorbed, it cannot be said to be entirely omitted. It seems to me that the clue here is the absence, probably suppression, of the development of larval tadpole sense organs, and what may well be a consequent failure of the tailed larva to settle on the sea floor and find a suitable site for attachment. I see no reason why the stalk-like rostrum of the young Doliolum, which is also a transient structure, should not be regarded as the developing pre-oral stalk homologous with that of Ciona and other ascidians.

That region which lies between the transient tail and the transient stalk is the main body of the tunicate in a relatively early stage of its development, comparable to the stage of development of the trunk region of most ascidians at the time of tadpole activity. If we take the Doliolum stage when the tail is functionally differentiated even though ineffective, the resemblance to a typical ascidian tadpole larva is striking, except that the sense organs are absent and so are adhesive organs for attachment. These, however, are features which are developmentally associated in the sense that experimental injury or dislocation readily suppresses both structures, and their elimination from doliolid development may have been fairly simply accomplished (Rose, 1939; Tung, 1937).

I think it is reasonable therefore to interpret Doliolum as an ascidian that has lost larval sense organs and adhesive organs but has retained the larval tail, and has converted the bands of muscle normally associated with the closing and opening of the ascidian siphons into contractile locomotor bands for the creation of the internal water current. Loss of the sensory structure may well have inhibited settling, while retention of the tail would keep the organism motile. Conversion or evolution of the trunk-muscle bands conferred locomotor and current-creating power upon the ascidian body, making the tail subsequently unnecessary, while at present the tail is partly or wholly superseded as a motile agent even in juvenile stages by the acquisition of buoyancy through perivitelline and other devices.

A few questions remain to be answered. If Doliolum is to be regarded as an ascidian secondarily adapted to pelagic life, the fact that its gill slits are undoubtedly protostigmata suggests that the divergence occurred before ascidians as such had evolved rows of secondary gill slits in place of the single primaries, a change almost certainly associated with the progressively increasing body size of the attached stock. At the same time Doliolum possesses a single atrial siphon, like that of the later growth stages of the ascidian, rather than the lateral paired siphons of the primary stage correlated with the presence of primary gill slits. Accordingly, either the siphonic fusion evolved earlier than I have previously suggested, or it is an independently acquired condition in Doliolum. The latter is a reasonable hypothesis inasmuch as the general development of the siphons as the effective and greater part of the active body would almost inevitably bring about such a fusion of lateral siphons into a single terminal one. Whatever the initial condition, the final state would almost certainly be what we see.

The remaining point concerns the coelom. The reduction of the visceral region to relatively small dimensions and the correspondingly great enlargement of the cloacal or atrial involution effectively eliminates the need of a coelom as an excretory envelope—the atrial lining serves the same purpose, just as it does in all polystyelid ascidians. An epicardial outgrowth still forms from the basal part of the pharynx, from exactly the same region from which arise the perivisceral sacs of Ciona or the epicardium or renal vesicle of those ascidians that possess such structures. I believe the doliolid outgrowth to be homologous, but without surviving coelomic or excretory function. The fact that it plays perhaps the leading role in stolon formation and in the morphogenesis and histogenesis of the buds merely adds support to this contention; for the epicardial lining in ascidians is by far the most general and potent source of new tissue and structure during regenerative and budding processes.

Larvacea (or Appendicularia)

Larvaceans, or Appendicularians, have been in the forefront of discussions of chordate origins for a long time, the older point of view being that they represent the primitive form of tunicates from which ascidians and other tunicates have evolved, and in turn have descended perhaps from a more advanced free-swimming chordate type. This view has been tacitly abandoned and I do not propose to set it forth in detail here simply in order to put it down again. Garstang (1928), however, has made a strong case for interpreting the Larvacea as paedomorphic doliolids, and it is this that calls for consideration at this time, together with the general relationship the Larvacea may have with the ascidian tadpole larva. The development of the larvacean Oikopleura is now fairly well known as the result of Delsman's (1912) investigations, and, taken together with the extensive studies of Lohmann (1933) and others on the nature of various adult forms, a reasonably clear picture appears. The following outline presents the essentials.

The oikopleuran egg is small (about 0·085 mm. diam.) and is fertilized and develops free in the water. The first two cleavages are similar to those occurring in the ascidian egg, but the third, horizontal, cleavage is unequal; no segmentation cavity is formed. The presumptive territories, however, are identical with those of ascidian embryos of this stage with respect to plan of symmetry and location of the axes, but are represented by fewer cells. One can recognize ventral ectoblast, neuroblasts bordering the outer blastoporal lip and subjacent to presumptive chordal cells. The archenteric cavity is occupied entirely by a single large endoblastic cell. Mesoblasts border the posterior margin of the blastopore. The stage illustrated is actually the equivalent of the ascidian embryo in mid-gastrulation. The territories are present in complete form and in exactly the same mutual relationship as in the ascidian, but whereas the ascidian embryo begins and completes the process of gastrulation between the sixth and seventh cleavages, it is evident that here the process is accomplished between the fifth and sixth. This, taken together with the difference observable at the third cleavage, already mentioned, indicates that while the basic pattern of development of the ascidian and oikopleuran egg is remarkably similar, the general process of differentiation, leading both to the histogenesis of the primary tissues and to gastrulation, is relatively accelerated in Oikopleura, so that the several events occur one cleavage sooner in the course of development. The validity of this interpretation is shown by the fact that in later development the presumptive chordal region yields 20 notochord cells in place of the ascidian's 40, and 18 tail-muscle cells in place of the standard 36. In other words, in so far as the tail is concerned, the larvacean tail develops exactly as the tail of the ascidian larva except for a degree of accelerated differentiation, a difference that is more quantitative than qualitative. And, although further developmental details are rather meagerly known, a sensory vesicle develops and a typical neural tube extends into the tail as in the ascidian tadpole. In fact, apart from the matter of acceleration of differentiation relative to cleavage, the general development of the ascidian tadpole larva and of the oikopleuran is virtually the same up to a comparatively late stage. The morphological differences, however, while small, are significant. The ocellus and otolith of the ascidian larva are absent in Oikopleura, and so are even traces of anterior adhesive organs. At the same time a multicellular statocyst develops in relation to the neural ganglion, consisting of a hollow vesicle of cells bearing sensory hairs, with a statolith in the cavity. I can see no way in which this organ can have evolved from the unicellular otolith of an ascidian larva and can only conclude that it has been independently acquired. The significance of this will be discussed a little later.

Meanwhile the larvacean tail is of further interest in itself. In the first place it becomes twisted at its base so that it lies in the horizontal rather than vertical plane. This is also characteristic of the tadpole larvae of most compound ascidians and in these is clearly an 'impressed' character associated with the coiling of the tail around a relatively large, yolky trunk region. The condition in the Larvacea, which Garstang suggests is derived from a compound ascidian type exhibiting this character, may imply that the present small size of the egg is secondary and that the egg has at one time been comparatively large; or it may be merely an adaptation in connexion with the peculiar function of the larvacean tail.

In other ways the larvacean tail is more differentiated than that of the ascidian tadpole. In place of the purely cuticular tail fin of the ascidian tadpole, the morphologically similar fins of the Larvacea consist of epidermal keels. Perhaps the most striking difference, however, is that in the Larvacea the neural tube contains a series of ganglionic cell groups, each of which has dorsal motor nerves and sensory ventral ones, both associated with the muscle bands. Some investigators (Langerhans, Van Beneden and Julin, and Dumas) have seen in this a vestigial metamerism. At the same time, however, it seems to me that there is nothing in the construction of the larvacean tail that cannot be readily interpreted as a moderate degree of further differentiation of the tail of the ascidian tadpole larva. In the larvae of many simple ascidians, e.g. Ascidia, Phallusia, &c., the notochordal cells fuse together to form a continuous turgid cylinder; in the Larvacea a similar fusion occurs, but the core substance sets to an almost cartilaginous consistency. In both the tail of the tadpole larva and of the Larvacea the muscle cells fuse to form a syncytium in which myofibrillae run continuously from one end to the other. And in both the neural tissue is a slender, posterior, tubular extension of an anterior neural vesicle, although the larvacean cord acquires histological neural differentiation while the other does not.

Most Larvacea are minute, with a body rarely exceeding 1 mm. and a tail usually not more than three times that length, although some species, e.g. Oikopleura vanhöffeni, have a body as long as 8 mm. and a tail correspondingly large.

The body or trunk region presents problems independently of the significance of the tail. A short endostyle is usually present, and a single pair of branchial openings (primary gill slits) lead from the floor of the pharynx to the exterior. There are no peribranchial cavities as such, nor is there a cloacal or atrial siphon. A simple heart lies in the usual position on the ventral side posterior to the endostyle, except in one genus (Kowalevskaia) which has neither endostyle nor heart. The gonads are relatively large, occupy the posterior region of the body, and open directly to the exterior.

The feeding mechanism is of particular interest. It is a complex and specialized arrangement involving the pharynx, the tail, and a cuticular house secreted by the so-called oikoplastic epithelium covering the anterior part of the trunk. All three components are essential. Within the pharynx the mucus secreted by the endostyle is directed forwards and dorsally along the peripharyngeal bands, and the micro-organisms brought in by the current induced by the cilia of the gill slits are caught up not in lateral sheets of mucus moving up along the sides of the pharynx as in ascidians but in a twisting cord passing freely back like a vortex from the peripharyngeal bands. It is a peculiarly specialized system which Garstang (1928) has discussed at considerable length and which he interprets, correctly in my opinion, as a type derived from that of Doliolum and not in any way directly related to that of ascidians.

This internal system, however, is only a part of the total mechanism, and Garstang's interpretation of the Larvacea as paedomorphic doliolids becomes even more convincing when other aspects of their structure and activity are studied. In all tunicates other than the Larvacea, the entire surface of the epidermis is active in secreting the superficial tunic. In the Larvacea the epidermis is sharply divided into an antero-dorsal oikoplastic zone and an extensive postero-ventral region incapable of tunic secretion. The boundary between the two zones is sharp, and it is in the posterior zone that the gill slits, rectum, and gonads open. Garstang regards this non-secretory region as equivalent to a shallow atrio-cloacal chamber, homologous with that of Doliolum, the cavity of which has been suppressed and the epithelial lining everted. This is plausible, and so far no other explanation of the peculiar state of the larvacean epidermis has been put forward.

The oikoplastic epithelium secretes a tunic or house at first as a continuous sheet of cuticular substance (cf. Lohmann,

1933). The ventro-lateral wall is almost uniformly gelatinous, but the dorso-lateral wall is from the start differentiated into alternating zones of gelatinous material and membranous laminations. It is at first a continuous mosaic of cuticular products resting on a continuous matrix of diversified secretory epithelium. By subsequent foldings and readjustments of one part to another as the whole becomes lifted off from its epithelial base, a 'house' is formed of varying degrees of complexity among the different species of Larvacea. The 'house' serves as an efficient food trap and is cast off and replaced from time to time. Garstang's discussion of this subject is intensive and should be consulted for further detail. His conclusion is as follows:

From this examination it results that in all probability the primitive type of Appendicularian 'Haus', from which all others have been derived either by elaboration or reduction, consists of a hollow, oval or spherical capsule with two apertures at opposite extremities, one oral, and the other formed round the boundary zone of the oikoplastic epithelium, which in primitive cases is limited by the base of a dorsal hood or veil. Assuming this to mark the limits of a former atrio-cloacal cavity, the primitive house must have been a cast-off test, with opposite oral and cloacal apertures. Such a test could only be formed by a pelagic Tunicate of the Doliolid type; and since Doliolum, at least D. mülleri, is known to possess the power of total ecdysis (Uljanin, 1, c.p. 14), there is no need to say more than that the case is complete. There can be no question of the fact or of the correspondence in essential details. Uljanin observed the process under the microscope under conditions which enabled him to describe it as 'eine vollkommen normal Erscheinung', and to assert 'dass unter der abgeworfenen beschmutzen Cuticula eine sehr dünne neue immer schon angeschieden wird'. He points out, moreover, that in Doliolum the test throughout life remains hyaline and structureless, like that of the youngest larval stages of ordinary Ascidians, and contains no cellulose, and that, as in the Larvacea (Appendicularians) alone among the Tunicata, there is no involution of test-substance within the oral aperture (or within the cloacal aperture). These are precisely the conditions required for the beginnings of the evolution of the Larvacean house.

The modifications introduced into the house for purposes of food collection form a story which does not concern us here. Garstang goes on to say:

Thus, after a fairly exhaustive survey of Appendicularia peculiarities, there can be no doubt that their simplicity is more apparent than real. When the structure and working of their pharynx and endostyle are examined closely and comparatively, these organs alone yield conclusive proof of a derivation from the more normal Tunicate type. Moreover, in every respect—position and number of gill slits, structure and function of endostyle, form of intestinal loop, position of the anus, and torsion of nerve-cord—Doliolum has been shown to provide the key to their phylogeny. Finally, the architecture of the house, and its relations to the oikoplastic epithelium, have confirmed our view that the absence of a cloaca and of peribranchial cavities is a secondary phenomenon, and that the ancestor of the Appendicularians was essentially a Doliolum with a barrel-shaped test subject to periodic exuviation. . . . The remarkable thing about these features of resemblance to Doliolum is that they are all essentially adult, as distinct from larval characteristics, and may be thought to give a final refutation of the neotenic theory I began by defending, since only the tail is left as a relic of larval conditions. As was remarked however, at an earlier stage, Ascidian larvae do not feed, and have no visceral organization of their own distinct from that of the adult phase which, in varying degrees, they seek precociously to develop. The same conditions must have prevailed among primitive Doliolids before the larva was finally boxed up in an inflated egg-capsule serving as a float.

The appendicularian or larvacean tail acquired function, not only for the creation of currents through the 'Haus' (or into the vesicle, as the case may be) by a mode of undulation recognizably different from that used in free locomotion, but also of manipulative powers, by which the tail assists in extending the house-rudiment over the body and in enlarging and shaping its internal spaces. Clearly a tail which has acquired a motility and versatility of this order cannot be expected to have retained the primitive features of its origin. Its free articulation with the body, its width, length, and flexibility, its smooth surface, sensitive tip, and specialized neuro-muscular apparatus, must all be the result, more or less, of specialized modification.

The tail, in other words, while like that of the ascidian tadpole larva in its basic cellular constitution, serves primarily as a more elaborately differentiated organ for the creation of a feeding current and placement of the food trap, rather than as a simple organ of locomotion.

There is, however, one further feature of the larvacean organisms which Garstang did not consider, and it is one I believe that confirms his conclusion concerning their neotenic nature. Not only is the number of cells which constitute the several components of the tail firmly fixed but those of the body appear to be so as well, and in some genera to a remarkable degree. In Fritillaria, for instance, the endostyle is invariably 4 cells in cross section, the stomach consists of about 20 large cells, and the heart of 2 cells only, all of comparatively large size. This is a common characteristic of neotenous forms, which tends to show that the permanence of the larval pattern is obtained perhaps by a 'freezing' of the constituent cells both in number and quality. We will, however, have to reconsider the significance of the larvacean characteristics in relation to the general setting of the pelagic tunicates at the end of the present chapter. Meanwhile some consideration needs to be given to the thaliaceans Salpa and Pyrosoma before appraising the situation as a whole.

Salpa and Pyrosoma

Salpa, Pyrosoma, and Doliolum clearly constitute a related group of organisms. Salpa and Doliolum swim and feed in much the same way and have much the same structure. Each is essentially a barrel open at both ends, through which water is pumped by the action of more or less complete encircling muscle bands. The individuals of the several species of Doliolum and Dolioletta are relatively small, ranging from about 3 to 12 mm. in length in the case of gonozooids; while 8 or 9 mm. is typical. The maximum size of doliolids, however, is roughly the minimum size of salps, and the latter for the most part grow to lengths from 25 to 150 mm. This difference in order of size is significant, for whereas doliolids possess a small number of large gill slits in the posterior region of the branchial sac, salps have none, unless the single extensive passage on either side of the gill ridge may be interpreted as a hypertrophied gill slit. However this may be, I think we can reasonably look upon salps as equivalent in a general way to enlarged doliolids in which a typically fenestrated posterior branchial wall would offer too great a resistance to the volume and force of water being driven through the body barrel by the powerful muscles. The delicate structure of the relatively small doliolid gill sheets would rupture in a larger form. Salps, I believe, have become more vigorously adapted to pelagic life than the doliolids. And in spite of the general similarity of salps and doliolids as motile, feeding organisms, the salps show no trace of developmental affinities with ascidian tadpole larvae. The egg, while small, develops directly into the final form. At the same time this directness of development is anything but primitive, and the actual mode of development of the Salpa egg is fantastically specialized, and takes place in relation to architectural structures formed at first by purely maternal tissues (Brien, 1928; Berrill, 1950). The egg is to be regarded as secondarily simplified, with complete elimination of all determinative processes which may at one time have led to distinctive cleavage patterns, gastrulation, and the formation of a tailed larva.

In this last respect Pyrosoma is somewhat similar. The egg is comparatively large and yolky, and while its blastomeres do not derive nourishment directly from maternal tissues as in the case of salps, all trace of those features so distinctive of the development of the ascidian egg, and clearly recognizable in the development of the egg of doliolids and Larvacea, is absent. The pyrosomid eggs develop more or less *in situ* and, in their own way, are as clearly secondarily modified by yolk and viviparity.

The individual zooid of a Pyrosoma colony is constructed along much the same plan as the salp and doliolid. Mouth and cloacal apertures lie at opposite ends of a long axis. At the same time there is a much closer resemblance to the sessile ascidian type than is the case in the other two forms. Numerous primary gill slits are present, arranged serially along the whole length of the branchial sac or pharynx. The water current is created by the ciliary action of the gill slits, not by the muscles of the body wall, and it is the conjoined outflow of the currents produced by all the members of the colony that causes the colonial organism as a whole to glide through the water. The individual zooids are small, 8–10 mm. long, of which about half is represented by an elongated atrial siphon. In order of size, therefore, the pyrosomid individual tends to be even smaller than the doliolid, and it is because of this, in my opinion, that primary gill slits are retained as the effective agents for creation of the feeding current, while the co-operative effort of the numerous individuals composing a colony effectively transports the collective whole, and obviates such effort as is put forth by muscle bands in salps and doliolids.

Asexual Reproduction in the Thaliacea

To complete this brief picture of the thaliacean types we need to look at the process of budding and asexual reproduction in general.

The processes of asexual reproduction in salps, doliolids, and in Pyrosoma may be regarded as various elaborations of a single basic kind. In all three groups a budding stolon grows out from the midventral region of the body wall immediately posterior to the endostyle. In all three the stolon consists of an outer epidermal envelope and an inner tubular extension from the posterior wall of the pharynx. Apart from a strand of mesenchyme which differentiates as gonadial tissue, these two layers in the case of Pyrosoma and salps give rise to all the tissues of the individuals subsequently budded off. In Doliolum additional components grow into the stolon from peribranchial and pericardial epithelia, but, in contrast to Garstang's opinion on this point, I consider these to be secondary involvements of interest from the point of view of tissue growth, but not relevant to the present discussion. In my opinion the two outstanding points of interest are as follows: the basic similarity of the primary budding process in the three groups is so great that it can only indicate the origin of the three from a common stock, and also indicates the possible, and to me plausible, interpretation of the pharyngeal outgrowth as the homologue of the epicardium and therefore of the Cionid perivisceral coelom. With the great expansion of the cloaca and atrial lining, the coelomic function of the epicardium would in any case have been superseded, even if the epicardium had not already assumed a character typical of those ascidians with abdominal and post-abdominal regions.

If we accept Garstang's interpretation of the larvaceans as neotenic doliolids, then the pelagic tunicates as a whole can be regarded as a single group of organisms that has evolved in diverse ways from a common stock. The nature of this ancestral stock and the reasons for departure from it are what concerns us most at this stage of our argument.

14

THE ORIGIN AND EVOLUTION OF
PELAGIC TUNICATES

Assuming that the pelagic tunicates are derived from a sessile ascidian stock, an assumption generally made by students of the group, pelagic existence is acquired most simply by suppression of metamorphosis and continued activity of the tadpole locomotor equipment. At the close of embryonic and larval development, when the sequence of cell divisions initiated at fertilization of the egg has come to an end both in tadpole tissues as such and also in tissues normally destined to form the permanent ascidian, we would have a free-swimming form equipped with the typical tadpole tail and a trunk similar to that of Ciona at the onset of feeding, that is, with a terminal mouth, a pair of lateral peribranchial siphons, and two or three primary gill slits on each side. At the time such an emancipation took place, growth of the trunk region beyond this stage and size may or may not have been considerable. Undoubtedly there would have been growth to some extent, but the fact that only primary gill slits occur in pelagic tunicates suggests rather forcibly that growth of the trunk remained within the limits compatible with the presence of a series of simple, ciliated primary gill slits. The zooids of Pyrosoma colonies are indicative of the probable maximum size that could be attained. Fusion of the paired peribranchial siphons to form a single posterior cloacal siphon may be an inheritance from the ascidian or it may well have been independently acquired, for the same reasons of mechanical efficiency in water-current production, and the consequence of a similar process of enlargement. The single cloacal siphon of thaliacean tunicates in fact is not in any way informative concerning the early pelagic condition. The lateral gill openings in the Larvacea in the same way may indicate that the originally inherited condition was lateral and paired, or it may be a consequence of neoteny. I can see no

other way in which a transformation from a sessile to a permanently pelagic existence could have taken place.

At this point we need to consider again the significance of
asexual reproduction by budding as it occurs in the three
thaliacean types; the Larvacea can be left aside for the time
being. In spite of the diverse ways that this method of reproduction has been exploited in these forms, the basic similarity of the
process is profound and in its essentials the process must have
been present in the ancestral form common to them all. It has
been customary to attempt to derive the primitive thaliacean
from this or that family of ascidians according to resemblances
in budding processes, or conversely to derive various ascidian
processes from thaliacean types as Garstang has done. But my
own acquaintance with methods of budding in the Tunicata
(cf. Berrill, 1952) inclines me to the opinion that budding has
been acquired on several occasions within the class, and that
the basic kind typical of the Thaliacea is unrelated to those of
any ascidians. In other words, since the type of budding in
Thaliacea appears to be distinct and since there seems to be no
particular reason to assume that the comparatively small and
simple ascidian stock from which the thaliaceans probably arose
had acquired such a process, the simplest procedure is to assume
that the process was acquired some time after emancipation
from an attached existence. Budding in ascidians is primarily a
means of extending the living, reproducing ascidian entity in two
rather than three dimensions, in relation to the exploitation of
flat surfaces on which uniform three-dimensional growth leads
to increasing insecurity of foothold. As a form of reproduction
in the narrower sense of propagation it hardly ranks at all.

Budding in thaliaceans is primarily a means of propagation
rather than colony building, at least in doliolids and salps, if not
in Pyrosoma. It is comparable I think to the asexual reproduction of certain medusae, e.g. species of Rathkea and Bougain-
villia, where reproduction by budding is employed to build up
enormous populations in oceanic regions which are particularly
suitable. Reproduction by budding in medusae and thaliacean
alike is an effective adaptation to a pelagic oceanic existence.
This may have been the motive from the beginning, as far as
the thaliaceans are concerned, in which case the process was
converted to colony formation to give us Pyrosoma, at a rela-

tively early stage, but has become elaborated in various ways as a strikingly effective method for rapid population building in forms that have evolved as doliolids and salps.

Apart from the acquisition of asexual reproduction, involving what I consider to be a superannuated coelom or epicardium, thaliacean evolution as a whole has been one of continuing adaptation to pelagic oceanic life. In all three forms the tadpole tail has been structurally or functionally discarded.

As long as the larval tail retains its original cellular constitution, it can grow no larger than those limited cell numbers permit. The tail may be effective in propelling a comparably small trunk through the water, but not anything of another order of size. Doliolum, more clearly than the others, appears to show what has occurred. Increase in body size, as distinct from tail, made the tail progressively ineffective, and trunk muscles became specialized as rhythmically contractile bands capable of propelling the whole organism through the water, and also water through the organism. The tendency was to reduce the need for a series of small gill slits, and to supersede the tail as an organ of locomotion. And at the present time we accordingly find Doliolum producing an ascidian-type egg which develops into an abortive tadpole retaining the tail with its limited cellular constitution, but in a confined and non-functional form; continuing to grow in the trunk region and becoming adult as an ascidian modified for pelagic life. The tadpole was a means to an end, so to speak, but not a permanent one in itself.

Salps may be considered as having gone further in the same general direction: whether independently or not is another matter. But final body sizes are larger, asexual reproduction is more effectively exploited, judging from population densities, and the original character of the egg and any dependent larval development has been completely eliminated. The same holds true for the egg and early development of Pyrosoma, although in this form the individual zooid has not departed so far from a typical ascidian condition, since motility has been acquired by co-operative effort of the constituent zooids of the colony, and the elaboration of contractile muscle bands as in Doliolum and Salpa has not been necessary.

The main point in all of this is that the tadpole larva tail was necessary to launch ascidians upon a pelagic career, but it rapidly became unnecessary and even ineffective as a means of propelling them through the water. In fact, once pelagic existence is attained, directed locomotion of the whole organism has little significance or value. The important activity is the passing of a food-bearing water current through the body, and locomotion through the water is virtually a secondary by-product of this.

The Larvacea support the various contentions put forward above. Body size is adjusted to the restrictions of the cellular constitution of the tail, by what appears to be an inhibition of growth beyond what can be accomplished by increase in cell sizes as distinct from cell numbers. Moreover, in spite of the fact that the larval tail persists as a permanent organ, it serves primarily for the creation of a feeding water current passing through a specialized cuticular house or food trap, and only incidentally for causing the organism itself to move through the water.

There is one final matter I believe to be highly significant. The Larvacea possess a statocyst, in association with the cerebral ganglion, but it is almost certainly not homologous with the otolith of the ascidian tadpole. Doliolids, at least in the gonozooid generations, possess a statocyst situated in the left body wall, which is obviously an independent acquisition, and they retain no trace either in adult or larvae of an otolith of the ascidian tadpole type. Neither Larvacea nor doliolids have any trace of an ocellus. Salps possess no statocyst at all, but they all possess, in all types of individuals, an eye in close association with the central ganglion: but as Metcalf has shown conclusively, this eye is not a derivative of the eye or ocellus of an ascidian tadpole and must be regarded as an independent development.

It is clear therefore that in the first place the sensory equipment of the ascidian tadpole has not been carried over into the pelagic types, and in the second that the pelagic types, with the exception of Pyrosoma, have felt the need for organs that orientate in respect to either gravity or light, just as do medusae and most other pelagic forms.

The probable answer I think is suggestive. If the ascidian tadpole larva has been the vehicle of emancipation, as I have argued, and the tail employed as the locomotion organ, the sense organs would also have been employed and even elaborated had they served the same end. Yet we know that first of all these sense organs serve primarily for bringing the tadpole larvae of ascidians into shaded secure locations near or on the sea floor, and secondly that they have not survived with the tail as part of the pelagic equipment. It means, I think, that as long as they persisted, metamorphosis occurred and the organisms became sessile as before—and that suppression of the larval sense organs may well have been a condition for the suppression of metamorphosis as a whole, including the typical premetamorphic reactions. The tail was retained at first purely as a propelling mechanism without directive sense organs, and any directive sense organs possessed by pelagic forms have been new acquisitions.

Accordingly the pelagic tunicates should be regarded as the successful but highly specialized pelagic descendants of an originally relatively simple free-swimming form consisting of an ascidian tadpole tail propelling a small ascidian body devoid of statolith or ocellus and having a general organization not far removed from that of a Ciona at a stage close to that associated with the onset of feeding. This stock must have been at one time a successful and vigorous one to have evolved the four types of pelagic tunicates that now constitute such dominant components of oceanic life—and it is to such a stock as this I believe we must look for the ancestral form that may have given rise to primitive vertebrates.

MIGRATION

15

THE PROBLEM

RECAPITULATING briefly the theme so far: we start with simple, more or less microscopic, pelagic organisms settling or colonizing the shallow sea floor and becoming, among other kinds, small sessile ascidians no more than a few millimetres in height, equipped with one or more primary ciliated gill slits on each side, and a pair of lateral exhalant siphons. Such ascidians in turn evolved non-feeding tadpole larvae, not for dispersion—which was well effected by drifting developing eggs—but for retreat from pelagic drift and for the selection of sheltered, shaded sites upon which to settle. Pelagic tunicates evolved from primitive ascidians before they had grown in size to the point that the primary gill slits were no longer adequate, and by the device of suppressing metamorphosis, possibly as a result of elimination of the larval sense organs otherwise employed in the settling procedures. The existing four types of pelagic tunicates represent various adaptations relating to more efficient pelagic existence or to increase in body size or both. The tadpole larva, in so far as it is to be seen in the structure of the Larvacea and in the larva of Doliolum, is typically ascidian inasmuch as the tail tissue shows at least the same degree of restriction of cell numbers. If this is the stage of divergence, from which not only the pelagic tunicates evolved but the vertebrates as well, certain very definite changes and related problems have to be considered.

Whether a single stock of this sort gave rise both to pelagic tunicates and to vertebrates, or whether such a stock evolved on more than one occasion and in one case gave rise to pelagic tunicates and in the other to vertebrates, makes very little difference to our discussion, or to the nature of the free-swimming organism we have to consider. In the absence of any evidence to the contrary, it is simpler to assume that the abandonment of a sessile existence occurred but once and the two free-swimming groups evolved diversely from the common stock.

In any case, whatever the actual sequence, we are faced with a relatively great gap with no surviving organisms to give supporting substance to imagination. Amphioxus is not forgotten, but comes into the story later.

If our contention is a valid one, then we need to see how a small marine pelagic tunicate, probably no more than a few millimetres long, could have become a primitive but relatively large vertebrate feeding and breeding in fresh water, that is, widely distributed among the lakes and river systems of Ordovician and of probably much earlier times.

The problems are many and difficult, but at least they can be recognized and examined. They fall into two distinct categories. What were the environmental pressures or attractions which caused free-swimming marine organisms to enter the river systems, and in what ways would successful entrants have had to differ from the marine ancestral form we have just postulated? A simple answer can be given provisionally to each of these. River systems were colonized primarily as feeding territories because their lower regions were relatively rich in the detritus and such unicellular organisms that small filter-feeders thrive upon. And the primitive marine chordates could enter such rivers only in so far as they had the motive power to progress against a current, which necessarily involved a great increase in size. The question of increase in size and speed will be considered first, for at least we have a starting-point.

The neotenous ascidian tadpoles, with typical tadpole larva tail and relatively simple ascidian trunk structure, probably of the order of size of 2 or 3 mm. in length, could not have migrated from the sea into freshwater rivers. With the equipment so far envisaged and at this size, they could neither have sensed the presence and direction of a current entering the sea nor have made any progress against it had they done so, no matter how flat the land surfaces may have been and how slowly the water in extensive river systems meandered towards the oceans. Present day conditions are a poor guide to what may have prevailed during the times in question.

Quite apart from speculations such as these, we can take our more or less hypothetical primitive marine pelagic tunicate and in a sense calculate what must have happened to it by analysing how such an organism could grow and transform into one more closely resembling a primitive vertebrate both in size and in tissue and organ structure.

The small size of the ascidian tadpole larva determines its low speed as a swimming organism. Some idea of the relationship of size to speed can be gained by comparing the swimming tadpole larvae of various ascidians. This is done in the accompanying table, which shows that as size increases, with general body and tail proportions and contours remaining more or less unchanged, the speed increases while stroke (number of tail strokes per minute) decreases.

TABLE I

Species	Length of tadpole larva in mm.	Speed at 16° C. mm. per second	Stroke per second
Ascidiella scabra .	0·6	4	25–30
Aplidium proliferum .	1·5	10	15–20
Botrylloides leachii .	1·8	15	12–18
Distomus variolosus .	2·6	20–25	11–14
Stolonica socialis .	3·0	25–30	8–12

There is no doubt that the larger tadpoles are by far the most effective swimmers, or that their motion is effected at a slower rate of muscle beat. Tadpole larvae such as these, however, merely suggest what may have occurred; they themselves are specialized and are comparatively recent developments of the more specialized modern ascidian families. Their speed is still too low to be particularly effective in swimming against a current, although not hopelessly so as is the case of the smaller kinds. Apart, however, from the demonstration of the relationship of speed and size in this type of swimming organism, a relationship which must have operated as a gear ratio all along, the larger ascidian tadpole larvae, which develop from eggs both larger and yolkier than the primitive kind, show certain significant histological changes.

The penetration of estuaries and rivers where there was any significant current flowing towards the sea required increase in size beyond that attained by any recent ascidian tadpole larva

or, with one or two exceptions, by the Larvacea. The Larvacea
in fact live their individual oceanic lives with a tail made up of
only half the number of cells that even the tail of the ascidian
tadpole possesses, and have made a kind of compromise: they
have grown tails as large as possible by simple enlargement of the
cells initially present, and may be said to have reduced the size
of the trunk to that which the tail can operate. The notochord
of the larvacean with the largest tail, Oikopleura vanhöffeni,
5–10 mm. long, still consists of merely 20 cells, with no more than
9 or 10 correspondingly large muscle cells on either side of it.

Tissue limitations of this kind obviously would have been
incompatible with increase in overall size beyond certain rather
definite and relatively small limits. Accordingly, if the provertebrate stock evolved from emancipated ascidian tadpole
larvae, a profound change must have taken place in the nature
of the tail tissues. The capacity for proliferative tissue growth,
in contrast to growth resulting from cell enlargement exclusively,
is necessary for increase in size to the extent required. The
Larvacea represent an exploitation within the terms of increased
histological rigidity. The pro-vertebrates, if they came from the
source we have suggested, represent a loosening of embryonic
shackles, rather than a tightening. Obviously it did occur,
unless our reasoning is invalid throughout. Some insight into
the matter is afforded by a comparative histological study of
existing ascidian tadpole larvae, although these particular forms
are not to be regarded as anything more than illustrating possibilities—they cannot be considered as representing ancestral
conditions themselves but only as indications of the general
nature of developmental tissue relationships which could on
another occasion have led to the type of growth required.

We find, to start with, that the histological constitution of the
tail of all those tadpole larvae of ascidians developing from eggs
less than 0·2 mm. diameter, which includes all oviparous
examples and some that are viviparous, is remarkably uniform
and gives every indication of rigid determination. The notochord consists of forty cells, the lateral muscle bands of twenty
cells each; in each case the cells are relatively very large. The
cells constituting the larval sense organs are equally constant
and few in number and are large, apart from degenerative
changes or actual loss. The neural tube and epidermis consist

of very much smaller cells which are correspondingly more numerous.

Several comparative series are available. These are given in Table II, each series representing a group of related species arranged serially in order of increasing egg size, and showing the number of cells constituting the notochord and muscle bands of the tail.

TABLE II

Species	Diameter of egg in mm.	Number of cells at gastrulation	Number of cells in notochord	Number of cells in tail muscle
Ciona intestinalis . .	0·16	64–128	40–42	36–38
Styela partita . . .	0·13	64–128	40–42	36–38
Styelopsis grossularia .	0·48	64–128	40–42	76
Distomus variolosus . .	0·59	64–128	40–42	76
Stolonica socialis . .	0·72	64–128	40–42	378
Perophora listeri . .	0·25	64–128	40–42	76
Ecteinascidia conklini .	0·58	64–128	40–42	756
Ecteinascidia turbinata .	0·72	64–128	40–42	1134
Clavelina lepadifornis .	0·26	64–128	40–42	126
Clavelina picta . .	0·48	64–128	40–42	128

It is evident at once that in the first place the notochord remains rigidly determined in all cases. The number of cells which constitute it remains virtually constant at about forty. I have shown elsewhere (Berrill, 1935) that this tissue is the pacemaker for the development of larval structure, and that concentration of yolk in presumptive notochordal cells greatly retards the rate of differentiation not only of the notochord as such but of larval tissues in general. Functional differentiation of the muscle tissue of the tail occurs approximately as the tail acquires its maximum length, i.e. when the notochord cells have individually and collectively enlarged and extended as far as possible.

In contrast to the notochordal cell constancy, the muscle tissue is evidently in a different category. Muscle-tissue is determined at the onset of development in the sense that certain ooplasmic territories are thereafter destined to become tail-muscle tissue and no other kind. There is not, however, the same restriction with regard to cell numbers. As eggs become

larger and/or more yolkier, the presumptive muscle-tissue becomes correspondingly larger and differentiates more slowly,
and above a certain rather critical egg size (0·20 mm. diam.)
the lateral muscle bands consist of increasingly large numbers of
cells. This is the kind of histogenic emancipation required.

16

THE PENETRATION OF
FRESHWATER SYSTEMS

PRIMARILY we are concerned with the time, the circumstances and the means of penetration into freshwater systems by a primitively marine stock of small free-swimming filter-feeders. On the one hand those forms that succeeded in so doing must have been more powerful swimmers and have been better equipped with orientating sense organs than the neotenous ascidian tadpoles we have reconstructed; on the other hand, the general character of the freshwater region that they entered, and particularly the transitional regions between completely fresh water and undiluted sea-water, must have been notably different from the general conditions prevailing today.

The conclusions I have reached concerning this last question I have subsequently found to have been expressed in essentially the same form in a paper by T. C. Chamberlin (1900) on the *Habit of Early Vertebrates*. Similar conclusions independently arrived at, particularly when reached from different starting-points, gain a certain degree of validity from this very fact.

Chamberlin observed that the oldest fossil fish and eurypterids were from freshwater deposits, and that marine fossils of these forms were of creatures washed down to the mouths of estuaries; and that of the three dominant groups of freshwater animals, the crustacea and molluscs held station in a current by clinging with legs or foot, and the fish alone did so by swimming. He noted that current flow impresses a rhythmical undulation on a passive column.

In the movement of a rope of vegetation in a pulsating current it is the pressure of the pulses of water against the sides of the rope that gives the incurvations. The two phenomena are natural reciprocals in the active and passive voices. The development in the fish of a rhythmical system of motor response to the rhythm impressed upon it by its persistent environment and duly adjusted to it in pulse and

and force, is a natural mode of neutralizing the current force and securing stability of position or motion against the current, as desired.

He derived the notochord itself from this situation, having started with the assumption that some primitive animal aggregate invaded the freshwater regions far back in pre-Cambrian times. For he concluded that the Cambrian sandstones are typical disintegration products, and the voluminous carbonaceous Huronian deposits suggest at least that lowland vegetation was abundant. He pictured the linking up of river systems by piracy and by common junction with terminal lagoons; that river flow increased generally and intensified the struggle to hold position, bringing about improvement of the provertebrate type and causing those that could not hold station to be swept out to sea, and from such as these last the ascidians and Balanoglossus are descended. This was his conclusion.

Now, half a century later, it is possible to see the past a little more clearly, and while the general concept which follows is my own, its basic resemblance to Chamberlin's is unmistakable.

At the present time the earth is in a phase following a period of intense mountain building and also one in which great amounts of water have been segregated in the ice caps, even now only partly returned to the sea. The continental masses are virtually dry. Rivers run swiftly to the sea, some less swiftly than others but still with very few 'meandering with a mazy motion'. These are not conditions which encourage marine animals to migrate from the sea to rivers. Only comparatively powerful swimmers among vertebrates are able to do so, and even the crustacea and molluscs, among invertebrates, which could undoubtedly crawl along river bottoms from the sea, are for the most part unable to face the suddenness of the chemical transition, if not the physical. The topography of land and water at present, it seems to me, is about as poorly suited to invasion from the sea as it can ever have been.

Our primitive chordate I am sure needed all the help it could get in order to make that original migration, and required conditions as far from the present extreme as possible. In simple form these are readily imagined. Lands should be low-lying almost everywhere, without interior ranges to precipitate and accelerate too much water flowing to the seas; while the seas receiving the quiet, slow-moving streams should be shallow

inland seas rather than the open oceans with their turbulent
margins. Conditions such as these have prevailed through much
of the earth's history, at different times, in varying pattern, and
over enormous periods. The earliest period of this sort that is
known to us is the Cambrian, which will serve as a model,
although I believe that the period of invasion of the fresh waters
we are dealing with should be pushed back probably well into
pre-Cambrian times.

Throughout most of the Cambrian period, without too much
change, the sea level was relatively high and lands were low;
and great inland seas of shallow depth flooded the North
American and Asiatic continents. Europe lay under water, beneath a shallow sea extending from the continental shelf east as
far as the present Urals and south to Africa. Narrow land masses
lay where the Urals and Himalayan ranges now are, and more
extensive land existed in the regions of Mongolia and eastern
Siberia.

The interior of the North American continent also lay beneath shallow seas, except for a very large and low-lying central
emerging plain, so that in relation to present ranges Cambrian
seas extended the length of the continent, one immediately west
of the Appalachians and the other east of the Cordilleras, the
latter at times being discontinuous in mid-continental latitude.
These seas apparently were warm, shallow, and abundantly
rich in most forms of littoral marine life. They were, moreover,
of such size, volume, and shape that they may well have been
without tidal rhythm other than currents induced from outside
the seas themselves. The margins of these seas were in all probability quiet waters merging with the low-lying land mass
through salt and brackish water lagoons; while streams and rivers
entered either lagoons or an inland sea itself with perhaps an
almost imperceptible flow, without a significant gradient from
sea-floor to river beds. Sea-water of high salinity would extend
far up from the mouths of rivers, and fresh water would flow
gently over it towards the sea. We could expect to find salinity
stratifications at the mouths of estuaries and inlets comparable
to those prevailing off the west coast of Sweden today, and
farther in toward the upper ends of embayments the water may
well have been brackish to the extent we now find in the upper
Baltic, where the oceanic jellyfish Aurelia swims comfortably

in water supporting the growth of freshwater flowering plants. It is in fact possible to see in the Baltic Sea and its marginal waters just such conditions that might well encourage interchange of fauna between salt- and fresh water, and there is little doubt that similar situations have at times been commonplace, without the present restrictions of winter cold, and that we might well expect this to have been the case along the margins of the continental Cambrian seas. This is shown perhaps by the one really clear glimpse we get of mid-Cambrian life.

High on the side of Mt. Stephen (Mt. Wapta) in eastern British Columbia is an exposure of some layers of Burgess Shale a little more than 100 feet across, discovered by Walcott in 1910. It is slaty black shale of Middle Cambrian date, in which fossils are preserved as delicate carbon films on planes where bedding and cleavage coincide. Each lustrous film is the residue of a soft body pressed to an immeasurable thinness, but preserving in amazing detail the form of delicate external appendages and even the presence of viscera. Walcott described 130 species of seventy genera, including sponges, jellyfish, annelids, trilobites, branchiopods, and, of all things, a peripatus-like onychophoran. The deposit was once a mud so fine of grain and so rich in decaying organic matter that it must have formed a soft oozy sea floor, deficient in oxygen and pervaded by H_2S, for the texture of the shale is extremely fine and the organisms contained in it are almost unbelievably well preserved, with no recognizable evidence of decay even of soft tissues. Carl Dunbar (1949) suggests that the locality represents a depression somewhat deeper than the surrounding sea floor, and that when dying organisms settled into the poisoned water below the wave base, they sank into the ooze and were never again disturbed by either scavengers or bacteria. According to Walcott the area was an embayment of some sort opening into the mid-Cambrian continental sea of the Cordilleran geosyncline, that is, opening eastward into the shallow sea rather than west into the Pacific Ocean.

The fossils constitute an amazing and puzzling collection. Hutchinson (1930) re-examined them and confirmed the identification of the various branchiopods and cladocera and also that the peripatus-like creature is truly an onychophoran with typical hook-bearing appendages. Hutchinson assumes, as did Walcott, that all the fossilized forms were marine.

Another interpretation, however, is possible. I believe we have in this deposit, with its contained fossils, evidence of just those conditions I have been discussing. This remnant of the inland sea represents not a blind marginal embayment but a junction of fresh water and salt inlet of some kind, where fresh water drifted quietly over the deeper salt, and the muddy sea floor, perhaps of a lagoon, remained normally undisturbed at the bottom.

Polychaetous annelids lived abundantly in the surface layers of the soft mud; trilobites and other forms searched for food on or a little above the muddy bottom; medusae swam through the water above; all in salt water, unless there was a gradual gradient, in which case the medusae may have extended upwards into brackish layers. I suggest, however, that the various and abundant branchiopods were not marine, but swam in fresh water overlying the salt, and when something occurred to disturb the soft bottom mud and released H_2S, the bottom forms were engulfed, as Dunbar suggested, together with the branchiopods likewise killed by the rising gas. The presence of the peripatoid more or less confirms this, and I think the picture is a composite, consisting of a marine bottom with marine inhabitants, overlain by fresh water already swarming with branchiopods, although these may have drifted from upstream; while the peripatoid may well have been a casualty from a community already feeding more or less out of water on the marginal vegetation of inland fresh waters.

The interest of the Burgess Shale deposit and fauna in the present context is first of all the glimpse it gives us of the richness and comparative modernity of the mid-Cambrian marine fauna, and in the second place the strong indication of an advanced freshwater fauna already in existence in waters communicating with the sea in gentle manner. Annelids, arthropods, molluscs, brachiopods, echinoderms, and others were in fact so well evolved and differentiated at this time that I can see no reason to suppose that chordates should have been laggards. The free-swimming neotenic tunicate which I have postulated would, according to our earlier discussion, have evolved from an ascidian stock of a stage comparable to much earlier evolutionary stages of the just-cited invertebrate types than those of Cambrian times. I believe therefore that the chordate invasion of fresh waters probably occurred not later than the late pre-Cambrian and in any case under circumstances similar to those prevailing along the margins of the shallow Cambrian continental seas. The ratio of carbon isotopes in pre-Cambrian schists of Finland definitely indicates that these deposits are of organic origin and represent an abundant life of some kind.

The motive for invasion, no matter when the event occurred, is implicit in the foregoing. The fresh waters, particularly during those periods when land was low and the seaward flow reduced to a minimum, would have been relatively rich in phosphates and have supported an abundant unicellular flora, not to mention the rich organic detritus that would have resulted from it. And this abundant source of food, so well suited to motile filter-feeders, must have been carried into the marginal seas. A gradient in decreasing concentration would be established as fresh water mixed with or spread out over the salt. There are several possibilities. Long tongues of sea-water extended far up the channels of river beds, underlying placidly flowing streams of fresh water, and received a veritable rain of manna as dying or decaying microflora sank to the bottom; living microflora, as well as its disintegration products, flowed seaward over a widening body of sea-water as the stream left its narrow constrictions; salt and fresh graded one into the other both vertically and horizontally under various conditions. In all of these cases the fresh water would offer comparatively rich nourishment to marine creatures and in such a way that those that could cross the sharp or gradual osmotic barriers would obtain the greatest supply.

All this is of course sheer speculation, but so is this story as a whole, and all that is claimed for it is a reasonable plausibility. Whether or not it can be proven it is important to comprehend why an event such as this supposed migration of chordates from sea to rivers might have occurred and how it could have been accomplished. So, in short, I see the invasion bait in the form of a gradient of particulate nutriment passing from the sea margins in the delta- and lagoon-mouthed rivers of the shallow inland seas, with little current and perhaps a gentle gradient in salinity reducing obstacles to invasion to a minimum.

We left our neotenic tunicate at the fork of the road, one branch of which led to the present pelagic tunicates equipped with sense organs suitable merely for control of location in the vertical plane of the sea, and with a tail either embryonic or with a secondary, non-locomotor, function. At the stage of divergence the tail presumably was a swimming organ, but orientating sense organs were lacking. Exploitation of the special feeding opportunities offered by the circumstances I have outlined demand not merely an increase in the locomotor power of the tail, obtainable by increase in size, but navigational sense organs to direct movement against a current, however slow-moving it may be, or at least to maintain station within it relative to fixed landmarks.

Aquatic animals whose movements are mainly concerned either with maintaining position in a particular horizontal stratum or with vertical migration to or from the surface appear to find a single median ocellus or eye at least as effective as a pair of lateral organs, for example, as exhibited by ascidian tadpole larvae, the larvae of many other groups, salps, and perhaps above all the Cladocera in which the median eye is clearly a secondary fusion from an originally paired condition. Paired organs, unless they are an inevitable consequence of bilateral neuro-muscular organization, as may well be the case in annelids, are primarily organs associated with movement directed in the horizontal plane. And, since I cannot see any indications that the typical vertebrate paired sense organs have evolved from those of any protochordate stock, or that the conditions of pelagic life of marine filter-feeders, such as those of the pelagic tunicates, would in any way encourage such development, I conclude that this characteristic sensory equipment is itself a general evolutionary response to the new circumstances of river life.

In all likelihood the nasal organs evolved first. At least, a pair of anterior chemical receptors placed sufficiently far apart to permit a regularly alternating sensing of a difference in concentration of significant chemical substances, could by itself have served the primary need of the organism. This need as I see it was, and in most primitively aquatic vertebrates still is, the ability to sense the direction in which the greater concentration lies. Such organs could have functioned effectively from the beginning, no matter how simple. A single patch of sensory cells at the dorso-anterior end of the swimming organism would function more or less adequately as long as the nerve connexions to the cerebral ganglion were paired, and separation into a pair of more laterally placed patches would be a natural consequence. Invagination of such sensory areas is the obvious continuation for increase in efficiency. There is no stage or step at which function is interfered with, and the only initial requirement is the presence of sensory cells at the distal end and some trace of nervous connexion with the central nervous system. In simple or in more or less elaborate form this initial condition already exists in ascidian tadpole larvae in connexion with the tissues and reactions involved in the act of settling by attachment of the distal end. It is easy to conceive the neotenic or paedo-morphic tadpole, through selection, becoming progressively sensitive at its distal end to chemical differences in the water and orientating in relation to this so that it tended to swim in line with the gradient axis. Under these circumstances the significant gradient might have been one of salinity or one of more specific chemical qualities associated with the water flowing from the land. Orientating to head into or swim against the fresh or brackish water flowing into the sea must have been the all-important reaction that differentiated or selected between those that remained marine and became progressively specialized to become the pelagic tunicates and those that proceeded to evolve in relation to freshwater currents.

The evolution of the vertebrate eyes, median and lateral, presents much greater problems, and I am inclined to limit consideration of these at the present to a possible stage for departure. Once we have launched our chordate on its journey into the rivers, facing upstream by virtue of paired nasal organs, any sensitivity to light that it might initially possess would probably be exploited either to direct it toward the upper layers of the water where algal organisms would be most abundant, or toward the bottom where detritus, bacteria, and other forms of parti-culate food could be easily obtained. Such photosensory orienta-tion, in either case, would have been chiefly in the vertical plane, and a median, general sensitivity of the neural cells lining the roof and sides of the cerebral vesicle could have been effective in controlling such reactions. The salpas are a case in point, for in these tunicates the eye has almost certainly evolved from the roof of the cerebral mass as a particular adaptation to a pelagic life involving vertical migrations; the salpa eye, as already mentioned, is not homologous with the tadpole larva ocellus and has evolved apart. It is no less likely that the stock which gave rise to salpa on the one hand, and, as I have argued, to vertebrates on the other, should have elaborated in some degree a comparable photosensory region in connexion with the homologous nervous tissue of the provertebrate. Such a tissue quality, which hardly merits organ-designation such as is implied in the terms eye or ocellus, could have functioned from the beginning, just as the primitive nasal epithelium, and may well have foreshadowed the later evolution of elaborate median and paired eyes. For the time being this is all we need to assume. The beginnings are there and, as described, are in keeping with the general simplicity so far envisaged for the organism as a whole.

Apart from the question of differences in the salt content of sea-, brackish, and fresh water, penetration of the river systems depended upon both orientation in the right direction and power to proceed in that direction. Of these orientation is at first the more important (or significant). For as long as our primitive marine chordate employed its tail and its newly acquired sensory apparatus to head into a seaward-drifting flow of fresh water and its contained micro-organisms or detritus, the advantages of this source of food would be realized. Even if the swimming power were so relatively weak that the small chordates either were at times carried back to varying distances from the land or were unable to enter river mouths at all, orientation alone, together with the initial locomotor capacity, would enable them more or less to hold a station and move relatively through the food-containing stream, even if they were actually stationary with regard to the sea floor. In such a situation natural selection would certainly operate to favour the survival of those who held their position best and that could progress the farthest into the out-flowing water before the flow and the locomotor propulsion became equalized and a station obtained.

For opportunity of this sort to have existed on a scale large enough and for a long enough period for the forces of natural selection to have made themselves felt, rather specific circumstances must have prevailed. If we once again picture North America as a possible scene of this action, we get essentially the same general topography for both Cambrian and the Beltian system of the late pre-Cambrian. If we assume that the Appalachian and Cordilleran sea-filled troughs of the Cambrian period

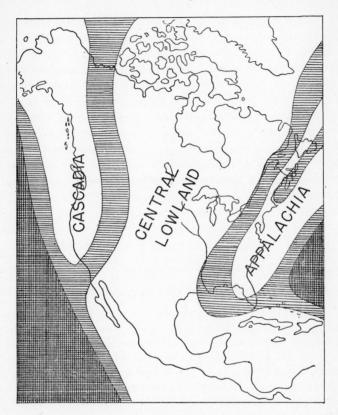

FIG. 21. North American continent in early Cambrian time, with coastal mountain ranges and low central tableland, with shallow seas occupying the Cordilleran and Appalachian geosynclines (after Dunbar).

were more or less persistent descendants of those of the Beltian period, we have time enough. From late pre-Cambrian through the Cambrian into the Ordovician the two shallow seas extended more or less north and south for 2,000 miles, serving on the one hand as regions of intense competition among the shallow sea fauna, and on the other as drainage troughs for the great central

lowlands and the somewhat higher coastal land belts. Innumerable streams and medium-size rivers entered the troughs more
or less at right angles to their axes, carrying down silt and micro-
organisms at rates varying with rainfall and height of land,
forming deltas at times probably along the whole length of the
sea margins.

Other continents may have offered comparable systems and
opportunities over the same extended period; although it is
sufficient to cite the one we know most about. Under the conditions I have just outlined the invitations to freshwater invasion
would have existed over periods vast enough to permit almost
any magnitude of evolutionary adventure, and chances to enter
a freshwater outlet might well have existed around almost every
bend of the shore; moreover, the two seas were so narrow for so
much of their existence that only a comparatively restricted
region running along their middle and deepest part could have
been significantly beyond the influence of the marginal streams.
It seems to me that this arrangement of land and water was
ideal for the general transition we are concerned with. Inland
seaways totalling in aggregate length perhaps 10,000 miles, in
width no more than 200 to 400 miles, persisted in one form or
another for the order of more than 150 million years, if we
include the period between the Beltian and mid-Ordovician.
During this period, to quote Dunbar,

The borderlands were from time to time worn low, but were
repeatedly uplifted; they were the mobile areas—the land's Paleozoic
mountains—while the interior of the continent remained relatively
low until the end of the era. The geosynclines trapped most of the
debris eroded from adjacent lands and would soon have been filled
if they had not continued to sink. In them we find the most complete
record of Paleozoic times in strata that reach an aggregate thickness
of 30,000 to almost 50,000 feet along the axes of the troughs. During
much of the era they were occupied by shallow seas, but at times
they were drained by uplift or filled somewhat above sea level with
fluvial sediments.

I believe that we have need of all three components of the
continental scene (it does not matter much whether other continents reflect these conditions; one continental scene is adequate,
although a wider stage might be even better). The long, narrow,
shallow seas form the home territories in which the pelagic

paedomorphic stock swarms. The quiet, innumerable streams and rivers of the central table, and for much of the time the border land belts as well, form the ever-enticing feeding-grounds encouraging feeding migrations to whatever extent is possible, although the seas are returned to for breeding. The repeated uplifting of the border lands introduces great fluctuations in stream flow and response thereto. This last we will return to a little later. Meanwhile it is desirable to move our foraging chordates farther upstream from the river mouths and adjacent waters. For before there could have existed vertebrates worthy of the name, there must have been chordates capable of swimming far into the fresh waters in search of food, while yet returning to the seas in order to breed. Amphioxus I believe is a relic of this phase of chordate evolution.

AMPHIOXUS

17

AMPHIOXUS AND THE
SEGMENTATION PROBLEM

I HAVE pictured the environmental setting for the evolving chordate or proto-vertebrate as shallow, extensive, but narrow seas communicating with innumerable streams and rivers of gentle flow. The seas are the common pool to which all return for the purpose of breeding, and there they shed eggs of a more or less old-fashioned kind in the old-fashioned way. The eggs develop, the small chordate larvae hatch and have to grow considerably before they are powerful enough to begin to work their ways into the brackish regions of the freshwater inflows. During this time they feed in the same way as the larvae of those neotenic ascidians that took the evolutionary road to oceanic exploitation: they feed on the smallest available organisms of the plankton, such as those obtained at present by the smaller Larvacea and by the larvae of Amphioxus at the time they commence to feed.

As greater growth and differentiation increase the swimming powers, the larvae migrate into the river mouths and upstream, to feed in the rich inland waters until full size is attained. During this sojourn in fresh water, the problem of salt homeostasis is undoubtedly present and some means of adjustment exists. When sexually mature, the return migration to the sea is made, and the next generation is spawned.

A general scheme such as this I think was essential. No single river or river-system, however extensive, could have been great enough or have persisted long enough for the conversion of a marine chordate into a freshwater vertebrate to have taken place. The collective freshwater systems of one or more continents, persisting through many million years, seem to me to be necessary for the kind of evolutionary change we are contemplating, and such a theatre could function as a whole only as long as free communication existed between one part and another. And the only common ante-room was the sea; the narrow continental seas, although they themselves communicated with the oceans, would have afforded perfect conditions for intercommunication of a sort. Each generation of larvae in a sense struck out for itself, with selection pressures maintained through uncountable generations to produce more efficient swimmers at all stages and mature adults of progressively larger size.

Where does Amphioxus come into this? I believe that in the world of today Amphioxus is out of time and out of place; and that it epitomizes this phase in the evolution of vertebrates.

There must have been a criticial phase when lands were uplifting and rate of flow of rivers increased to a point where the invading chordates were, in a sense, faced with the choice of get on or get out, or better perhaps a choice of stay in or stay out. As long as currents were gentle, the chordates returned to the sea to breed and depended upon the small fry of the next generation to repopulate the freshwater feeding-grounds. As long as they spawned small pelagic eggs, of the order of 0·1 mm. diameter, which developed into larvae correspondingly small, the ascent of the rivers was accomplished none too easily even under the best circumstances. Somewhere in this prolonged phase a stock must have arisen which laid a larger egg in the upper reaches of the freshwater systems, an egg large and heavy enough to be laid without drifting, or else anchored in some way while it developed, and large enough to develop into a larva powerful enough on hatching to maintain position in the flowing water. Then land uplifted, the rate of flow of the freshwaters increased, particularly towards the lower, seaward ends, of the main rivers. Those that laid eggs in the upper reaches now became truly landlocked, in fact as well as by habit. Those that laid small pelagic eggs in the sea, as was their ancestral custom, became equally cut off from the freshwater paradise, and either became extinct or else made the best they could of the changed circumstances. Amphioxus I believe alone survives to the present as a representative of this last forlorn community, the original Adam put outside the gates of Eden. And in consequence of being thus exiled, Amphioxus lost its head, a statement that is much more than a figure of speech. On the assumption that on the whole this interpretation of the nature of Amphioxus is more or less correct, our interest concerns two contrasting questions: what Amphioxus is and what Amphioxus is not.

I propose therefore to employ what is known of Amphioxus, using the name to denote all amphioxids, as illustration of what I think has been the course of evolution of vertebrates from a paedomorphic tunicate poised at the mouths of Cambrian or pre-Cambrian rivers, and also of what I believe to have been the peculiar history of Amphioxus itself, from the time at which its evolutionary history diverged from that of the vertebrates. Many topics are involved which would be better for simultaneous inspection, but the limitations of language restrict discussion to one at a time.

Segmentation

In the first place, if our paedomorphic tunicate tadpoles ascended the rivers to give rise to vertebrates, they needed to be much more powerful swimmers than they were to begin with, as I have already emphasized. Increase in power requires increase in size, which in turn imposes changes in the character of tissue growth; and increased efficiency, apart from the power-size relationship, is associated with segmentation of the muscular system. In other words, ascent of the rivers in which flow was at all appreciable became possible only to relatively large and segmented chordates. Both the increase in size of the swimming tail and segmentation of the muscle are responses to the necessity of maintaining or improving position in spite of currents, and were invoked during the early phases of freshwater invasion. I am unable to see any indication that either of these changes occurred or could have been advantageous during purely marine life.

Segmentation of tail and trunk musculature was almost certainly superimposed upon an organism the tail of which was already growing beyond the cell limits and histological restrictions typical of tunicates. Yet there are certain general aspects of segmentation which are more conveniently discussed in advance of any specific comparison of tunicate and amphioxid.

The problem of segmentation perhaps more than any other single feature has been a stumbling block in speculations concerning the origin of vertebrates, and the selection of segmented invertebrates as ancestral types has in part been an attempt to avoid this particular issue. On the other hand, as a carry-over of Lamarckian thought, both Garstang and MacBride have implied that segmentation was acquired slowly by efforts at propulsive undulation or wriggling as a habit eventually expressed in the form of structural segmentation. Segmentation, however, is primarily a phenomenon of development and growth and requires analysis in terms of growth activity before we can consider how it may have arisen during the course of evolution.

Two distinct phenomena are frequently included under the single heading of segmentation, namely, strobilation and metameric segmentation. I have already discussed these briefly in connexion with budding in worms and tunicates (Berrill, 1952 and 1951), and will present a more detailed analysis shortly in relation to certain theories of development. Meanwhile a short analysis must suffice here.

Strobilation consists of those regularly repeated constrictions of the epidermis of an organism, or of a part thereof, which eventually cut completely through all contained tissues and result in the separation into distinct units each of which sooner or later acquires the character of the whole. We see it in the strobila of schyphozoan medusae, in the bud chains of flatworms and annelids, in the stolons of thaliacean tunicates, and in a somewhat abortive form in the strobilation of tapeworms. In all of these the epidermis alone is the active segmenting agent, the units thus formed are more or less complete and independent of one another, and the process as a whole is in sharp contrast to that which leads to true metamerism.

As a process of development and differentiation, segment formation is essentially the same in annelids, arthropods, and vertebrates, and in annelids this holds whether the process concerns the development of the egg or the regeneration of a tail.

In this last case, for instance, segments are produced successively forwards from a zone of growth of a band of mesodermal tissue lying on either side of the posterior end of the intestine. As it grows, each band develops a transverse constriction which separates an anterior part, which is a presumptive segment, from a posterior part which remains as the zone of growth. This posterior part repeats the process, so that as long as axial growth

continues presumptive segments are successively segregated
anteriorly from the growing region proper. Segment formation,
by successive formations of transverse grooves in the mesoderm,
is associated with a falling off of the growth rate from the
maximum rate in the zone of growth (Berrill, 1951). There is in
fact a rhythm or pulse in the mesodermal growth along the
longitudinal axis, the frequency of which progressively decreases,

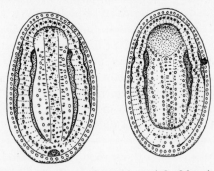

FIG. 22. Embryos of Amphioxus (16–18 hour)
showing waves of mitosis in notochordal and
endodermal tissue, and rhythm in formation
of presumptive mesodermal pouches (after
Conklin).

which results in the segregation of successive semi-independent
tissue blocks. These independently in turn proceed with their
individual differentiation and influence adjacent tissues in varying degree. The formation of segments in arthropods such as
Artemia (Weisz, 1947) is as exclusively mesodermal and proceeds
in much the same way; while in vertebrates the time-structure
studies of lamprey (Damas, 1944), fish, and chick embryos, show
the pulsing character of the mesodermal growth. This I believe
to be a general property of growth, although it is highly exploited
and exaggerated in these forms. I have discussed the phenomenon already (Berrill, 1948) in relation to hydroid growth,
and will present an extended treatment of the subject elsewhere.
Meanwhile I wish to emphasize here, with no more substantia-
tion than I have just given, that segmentation is primarily a
growth phenomenon of the mesoderm, consisting of the innovation or an exaggeration of a latent pulsative quality of growth
which results in the characteristic partial subdivision of the body.

Such a pulsative quality is clearly one which can be gained suddenly, or, if already present in unrecognizable form, can be suddenly exaggerated to the point of yielding a visible segmentation. In either case a certain timing is necessary to allow one block to initiate its own unit differentiation before the next one is added to the series—otherwise structural continuity would be the outcome. In other words a critical threshhold relating to frequency is involved, and I believe the pulse-rate either permits segmental development or it does not. Segmentation of the mesoderm is not something that can be gradually attained—it evolved suddenly as the result of a critical modification of a developmental process and could well have appeared as a single mutant type. Neither as a developmental innovation nor as a mutant change initiating such an innovation do I see any particular reason why it could not have occurred as suddenly, as decisively, and as readily as almost any other kind of innovation or mutation. The magnitude of the structural, functional, and evolutionary consequences is somewhat beside the point.

Admittedly it would be a form of macro-evolution, but as the developmental outcome of just as small an initial change as most others. So, with this digression on the nature of segmentation in mind, we return to the theme of our discussion and attempt to relate Amphioxus to the sequence of events as I conceive them to have been.

Development of Amphioxus and Tunicates

If the interpretation of Amphioxus as an animal with a tunicate past is valid, it should be possible to analyse much of the structural differences between Amphioxus and tunicates in terms of developmental processes, and these in turn in terms of differences in the nature of the eggs of the two groups. Conklin's early work on the embryology of ascidians, and his later comparable analysis of the development of Amphioxus (1932–3), make this possible.

Except for certain significant features, the egg and the early development of the ascidian and of Amphioxus are remarkably alike. According to Conklin, in the unsegmented but fertilized egg:

in all of these movements of the substance of the peripheral layer Amphioxus is precisely like ascidians. Since the character, movements, and final location of the substance of this peripheral layer is so remarkably like that of the peripheral layer in ascidians, it is very probable that it has a similar destination in development, and studies of later stages show that this substance goes into the mesoderm; therefore, the crescent around the posterior side of the egg, parallel to the first cleavage amphiaster in Amphioxus, may be called the mesodermal crescent, as in the case of ascidians.

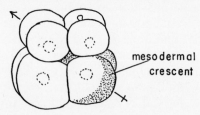

FIG. 23. Eight-cell stage of Amphioxus showing embryonic axis and position of mesodermal crescent (after Conklin).

These and other observations establish a general identity of pattern of ooplasmic regions of Amphioxus and ascidian eggs at the onset of development. With regard to cleavage patterns Conklin writes:

Comparison of the cleavage of the egg of Amphioxus with that of ascidians shows that there is a notable general resemblance between the two in the distribution of the different ooplasmic substances to the blastomeres, in the generally bilateral type of cleavage and the order of division, but in all these respects the ascidian egg is more precise and more precocious in differentiation than that of Amphioxus.

Concerning the gastrula he says, 'in all of these respects the early gastrula of Amphioxus closely resembles that of ascidians, the chief difference being in the smaller number of cells and the smaller size of the blastocoel in the ascidian embryo'. And,

Even in the method of closure of the blastopore, namely, the tilting up of the ventral lip together with the middle of the mesodermal crescent so that the arms of the crescent come to lie nearly at right angles to their earlier position, there is close resemblance between Amphioxus and ascidians. In the latter I was long puzzled to know how this change in the direction of the rows of large muscle cells came about (see Conklin, 1905 a, figs. 48 to 50), but it is plainly due to this dorsal growth of the ventral lip as in the case of Amphioxus.

He sums up his description, which is not only the most recent but by far the most meticulous and authoritative account of early amphioxid development, as follows:

the general result of this study of the normal embryology of Amphioxus is to show that the localization pattern in the egg and embryo is essentially the same in Amphioxus as in ascidians, (1) that in both these groups the mesoderm arises from a crescent rich in granular material and poor in yolk which surrounds the posterior side of the egg, blastula, and early gastrula; (2) that in both groups the chorda and neural plate develop from a crescentic area lying around the anterior side of the egg opposite the mesodermal crescent; (3) that in both these groups the endoderm comes from the yolk-laden area on the vegetative side of the egg, which is surrounded by two crescents, while the ectoderm comes from that portion lying on the animal-pole side of these crescents.

The general picture thus obtained of the Amphioxus egg as one remarkably similar to the ascidian egg, but less rigidly organized, is born out by Conklin's experiments on the development of isolated blastomeres. In the case of ascidians Conklin (1905, 1906, 1911) demonstrated that either one of the first two blastomeres would develop into an apparently normal larva which was actually no more than the right or left half of a bilateral larva; but neither anterior nor posterior 2/4 blastomeres nor any 1/4 blastomere would give rise to a normal larva. 'Indeed, each isolated blastomere of the ascidian egg gave rise only to those organs or parts of organs which it would have produced if it had remained part of a normal egg. The development was therefore a "mosaic work".' The more recent work of Dalcq (1932, 1938) and Reverberi (1937) confirms this conclusion, although they show that the state of more or less rigid determination present at the time of the first cleavage has not been attained immediately before and after fertilization; egg fragments obtained at these times develop into more or less complete larvae.

In contrast to the restricted developmental capacity of the ascidian blastomeres the blastomeres of the Amphioxus egg,

---

separated at either of the two-cell or four-cell stages, segment as if they were entire eggs. Bilateral cleavage is restored and leads to typical gastrulation, except for size. Right or left 1/2 or 2/4 blastomeres give rise to typical embryos and larvae. Incomplete separation of the first two blastomeres gives rise to twins. 1/4 blastomeres or anterior or posterior 2/4 blastomeres, while able to gastrulate, form only partial larvae.

The right–left axis is established before the first cleavage, but any blastomere of the 2- or 4-cell stage that is entirely separated from its bilateral mate undergoes regulation by the flowing of its peripheral cytoplasm over the original median side and by the bilateral distribution of formative substances already present in the blastomere; in its further development it gives rise to all the symmetrical and asymmetrical organs that belong typically to the right and left sides.

In other words the pattern of determination is the same in the ascidian and amphioxus egg, but the rate of determination relative to the rate of cleavage is slower in the egg of Amphioxus.

We can now make a profitable comparison of the development of an ascidian, a larvacean, and Amphioxus in a quantitative manner. The pattern of development is essentially the same for all three, but quantitative and temporal differences are highly significant. I have earlier indicated that the larvacean egg develops as though it were an ascidian egg with an increased histo-determination rate relative to cleavage rate, and we have just seen that in the development of the Amphioxus egg the determination rate is comparatively retarded relative to the cleavage rate.

Now, without prejudice to the question of the primary significance of gastrulation as a stage and process of development, the cleavage stage at which gastrulation commences appears to be regulated by whatever determinative processes are associated with cleavage patterns and ooplasmic segregations. Thus histogenesis of notochord and muscle in the larvacean embryo is completed one cell division earlier than in ascidians, so that these two tissues consist of only half the number of cells, which are compensatingly large; gastrulation correspondingly occurs one division earlier. A unified complex appears to be associated with gastrulation and precocious histogenesis which may be altered in a quantitative manner, but only as a whole. Compared with the ascidian egg and its development the system in the larvacean has, so to speak, been screwed as tight as it will turn. It is mechanically inconceivable that a process representing gastrulation could take place at a stage even one cleavage sooner, when only sixteen cells would be present. On the other hand, to employ the same analogy, the system can be turned the other way or loosened, within reason, to an almost unlimited extent, which appears to be what has occurred in the egg of Amphioxus. Accordingly, we can take the cleavage stages associated with the process of gastrulation in these three types as an index of determination-cleavage ratio and analyse the development as a whole from this standpoint. In the Larvacea gastrulation occurs immediately following the fifth cleavage, in ascidians following the sixth cleavage, and in Amphioxus not until after the ninth. That is, the gastrula of the ascidian consists of twice as many cells as the gastrula of the Larvacea, while the gastrula of Amphioxus consists of about eight times as many cells as that of the ascidian. Therefore, according to this reckoning, the notochord and muscle-tissue of the Amphioxus larva at the close of egg development, and before growth resulting from feeding has started, should consist of about eight times as many cells as the corresponding tissues of the ascidian tadpole, namely, about 320 and 300 for notochord and muscle. Actual estimations, based upon Conklin's illustrations, amount to about 330 and 400 respectively, indicating a close correspondence in the case of the notochord and a tendency for muscle tissue to show a degree of freedom as in the case of the tail muscle developing in over-large ascidian eggs. These numerical relationships are shown in the following table.

TABLE III

Animal	Gastrulation		Notochord		Tail muscle		Diameter of egg
	Cleavage number	Approx. cell number	Divisions of pre-sumptive material	Approx. cell number	Divisions of pre-sumptive material	Approx. cell number	
Oikopleura	5–6	38	4–5	20	4–5	20	0·09
Styela	6–7	76	5–6	40	5–6	36	0·13
Amphioxus	9–10	780	8–9	330	8–9	400	0·12
Petromyzon	11	2,200	9	500	..	..	1·00
Trituris	14	16,000	11–12	1,200	..	..	2·60

If we take the cleavage number at which gastrulation commences as the index of determination rate, and take the ascidian state as the standard, we can say that the larvacean has undergone a 20 per cent. acceleration and Amphioxus a 50 per cent. retardation. These relative changes are reflected in histogenesis and various other aspects of development as a whole, and I suggest that the basic differences are differences in the relative concentration of the package of determinative agents released into or activated in the cytoplasm at the time of rupture of the germinal vesicle and subsequently set into operation at fertilization. Whether of course we are dealing with variation in concentration of a whole complex of determiner agents or simply of a single pacemaker is impossible to decide, and in the present context is unimportant. What is important is that the whole complex is apparently variable as a unit and can be geared in varying ratio with cleavage rate.

The basic change, therefore, in passing from the ascidian stage, neotenic or otherwise, to one represented by Amphioxus is one which appears to be an intensity change in a certain key component of the agents liberated or activated at or before fertilization. A simple mutation might well cause such an effect as this, and if it did do this and nothing more, the developmental consequences could be startling.

In retrospect such consequences may be conveniently summed up here, to afford a basis for further analysis of the amphioxid type. Essentially it is the above discussion in reverse. I have shown elsewhere and at length (Berrill, 1932, 1935, &c.) that there is an incompatibility between precocious histogenesis and continued cleavage. Histological specialization, at least in a structural sense, as a general rule is postponed until cell proliferation has come to a provisional end; this is as true of the development of buds as it is of eggs. When, however, histogenesis is initiated precociously, as it is in ascidian and larvacean eggs, not to mention those of numerous invertebrates, and tissue maturation is rapid, cell division in the regions concerned becomes inhibited. This is as true for the prototroch tissue of the annelidan trochophore as it is of the ascidian notochord. In the larvacean and the typical ascidian tadpole the histogenetic determiners in the crescentic zones act so intensively or so rapidly that the chordal and muscle territories divide no more than four or five times. By then the maturation process is so far advanced that further cell division is inhibited. Other tissues not so affected continue to undergo cell division at least for a considerable period. In the ascidian tadpole the precociously differentiated tissues, which thereby are relatively aged, undergo resorption at the time of metamorphosis. In the larvacean the even more precociously differentiated tissues survive with persistent cell integrity, but the growth of the rest of the organism is held in check as far as possible, to reduce the size to conform with that of the non-growing tail.

What happens when the crescentic patterns of the egg cytoplasm are retained but the action of the histogenetic determiners is weakened (whether by a lessened concentration of the whole or by a reduction in some metabolic pacemaker activity does not matter)? Can tissues be determined histogenetically as before, without necessarily losing permanently their capacity for proliferation? A case in point in the development of the pyurid ascidian Boltenia echinata (Berrill, 1929) suggests that this last is possible. In this form the crescentic area destined to become tail muscle is coloured a deep orange by mitochondrial inclusions. The mitochondria are not considered to be the actual histogenetic determiners but they are definitely topographically associated. The tail muscle of the tadpole larva of this species consists of the usual 36–38 cells, and the intense orange pigment becomes confined to the muscle bands. In the early embryo, however, the anterior horns of the orange crescent contribute to the formation of cells which are a much paler orange than the rest. These, which contain a weaker concentration of the orange lipoids and by inference a weaker concentration of the myogenic determiner, give rise to the mesenchyme of the trunk region and subsequently to muscle-tissue which is that of the young growing metamorphosed ascidian. That is to say, the diluted agent still retains its histogenic character but does not apparently inhibit the capacity for cell division and the dependent capacity for continued growth and proliferation.

In the Amphioxus egg we appear to have just such a dilution effect. The histogenic pattern is there but it is not so intense. The results flowing from its weaker or slower action are the greater lability of the blastomeres of the first division, a slower attainment of the critical condition initiating gastrular

invagination, and a slower maturation of the presumptive
notochordal and muscle territories, permitting much greater
numbers of cells to be produced before the specific differentiations call a halt. The retarded approach to gastrulation results
in the formation of a thin-walled blastula, with a large segmentation cavity, before invaginative procedures begin.

The general effect, with reference to time, is to slow down
the rate of differentiation of just those tissues which correspond
to the purely larval tissues of ascidians, so that instead of maturing very much sooner than the remaining tissues they are hardly
precocious at all. The separation in the time of maturation of
larval and post-larval tissues, which is so extreme in the case of
ascidians, is here so small there is no certainty that it actually
exists. Chordal and muscle tissues, while forming from or under
the influence of the crescents, no longer appear to be in a
developmental strait jacket, and a renewal of growth occurs
in these tissues after the end of cleavage of the egg, when the
young organism begins to feed, just as in the case of tissues that
were not subjected to histogenetic coercion. This may well be
the main consequence of dilution, and perhaps the most important are those following a weakening of the ascidian crescental
agents. What were originally larval tissues, neotenic or otherwise, take on the character of permanent tissues, and both larval
and non-larval tissues and organs are enabled to continue growing side by side as a temporal unity. In other words, the tadpole
was able to grow to much larger dimensions, not by cell enlargement as in the Larvacea, but by typical growth in all tissues.

The remaining problems involved in this phase of analysis
concern the development of the coelom and of segmentation.

In an earlier chapter I compared the perivisceral or epicardial
sacs of Ciona with the vertebrate coelom and concluded that they
are homologous. Apart from any question of comparative morphology the difference in time or stage of development at which
the structure appears needs to be accounted for. This I have
already attempted, though a brief restatement may be helpful.

In Ciona, as is the case in other ascidians in which the epicardial sacs exist only in modified form, the sacs develop as
posterior outgrowths from the pharyngeal endoderm only after
the young ascidian is attached, fully metamorphosed, and completely functional, at about the time the individual commences

to feed. In Amphioxus, in contrast, the coelomic or mesodermal pouches develop at a relatively much earlier period. The developmental picture is also complicated by the combination of coelomic development with that of muscle tissue, and by the imposition of segmentation upon the whole. These are features that I think are best examined separately, even though their development is that of a unified system. The question of time accordingly may be considered by itself.

Whether or not a structure can invaginate or evaginate from a layer of embryonic tissue is a matter of tissue mechanics. It depends to some extent upon the size of the cells, which determines the thickness of the layer, and to a greater extent upon the number of cells present in the presumptive area of invagination or evagination. An area including no more than three or four cells cannot evaginate from the layer of which it is a part; an area including thirty or forty or more can do so readily. In the case of ascidians there are simply insufficient cells present in the endoderm during embryonic stages to permit coelomic evaginations of any kind. Under such circumstances a structural unit fails to develop in spite of expectations, but develops later, not only when sufficient cells are present, but always only after the egg has completed its development and the individual has become a functional feeding organism. The formation of perivisceral or coelomic structure only in the post-larval stages of ascidians can be accounted for along these lines, as I have previously indicated. In the case of Amphioxus the converse holds. The embryonic state is in a manner of speaking dragged out; endodermal cells are relatively numerous at a comparatively early morphological stage and evagination is mechanically feasible during embryonic development. This phenomenon of shift and of alternate developmental temporal possibilities is commonly seen in developing organisms and is of profound significance, but it relates more to fundamental problems of development as such and a full discussion here would be too great a digression. It must suffice to state that, supposing the ascidian perivisceral sacs and the coelom of Amphioxus to be homologous, the marked difference in the time of their appearance during the course of development is accountable in terms of developmental physiology and has no fundamental phylogenetic significance by itself.

We are left with the problem of segmentation in so far as it applies to the development of Amphioxus. In oviparous ascidians the embryo (at about 18° C.) begins to gastrulate about 5 hours after fertilization, and completes the process an hour or so later. The chordal and muscle cells attain their final number, and the neural plate completes its neural invagination, about 10 hours after fertilization. The tail is fully extended, i.e. the noto-chord fully differentiated, and sensory pigment becomes visible after about 15 hours, and the tadpole hatches at about 20 hours. The tadpole attaches, the tail resorbs, and finally the mouth opens, gills function, and feeding starts about 180 hours from fertilization.

In comparison with this sequence Amphioxus development is extended in every way. Gastrulation commences after about 8 hours but is not completed until 13 hours. The neural plate starts to close at 15 hours and completes the process by 23 hours. Notochord cells become distinguishable as such only after 16 hours, when about 40 constitute the chordal rod; but final embryonic number (about 330) and maturity is not reached until more than 100 hours have elapsed. Each embryonic event begins later and lasts much longer than the equivalent event in ascidian development. In the ascidian the chordal tissue, for instance, completes its cell divisions virtually before the cleavage rate as a whole has significantly slowed down. In Amphioxus on the other hand the situation is very different. According to Conklin's figures the first five intercleavage intervals average about 25 minutes each, which is similar to those of ascidian eggs. The inter-cleavage intervals 6 to 8 inclusive average 35 minutes, 9 to 10 average 65 minutes, the 11th is about 160, the 12th about 240 minutes, the 13th and last very much longer. The retarda-tion curve as a matter of fact is much the same in the two forms. The great difference lies in the correlation of morphogenetic events with the various cleavage stages. So that, for example, the early neurula of Amphioxus and the actively swimming and fully differentiated tadpole of the ascidian are correlated with approximately the same cleavage stage and are of much the same actual age.

The significant features, however, are that in the development of the ascidian tadpole the notochord and muscle-tissue com-plete their cell divisions while the division rate is still near its maximum, and histogenetic differentiation then sets in almost at once. In Amphioxus the final three divisions of the presumptive notochord and muscle-tissue are associated in time with the closing phases of egg development as a whole, corresponding to the late tadpole and post-tadpole phase of the ascidian cycle; they are in fact geared down to correspond with the rate of proliferation of the endoderm. This relative slowing down I believe to be of the utmost importance. Conklin's figures of sixteen- and eighteen-hour Amphioxus embryos (of between eleventh and twelfth cleavage) show clearly that waves of mitosis pass slowly along the length of the notochord, presumably from anterior to posterior end, and that similar waves pass along both the endoderm and neural plate. An axial gradient of proliferation undoubtedly is present, with differentiation in general more advanced anteriorly and growth most active posteriorly. This seems to foreshadow the axial growth and differentiation gradient of vertebrate embryos generally. It is, however, discernible only because the rate of cell division and differentiation is greatly retarded at this phase of the whole cleavage curve. The same gradient transposed to that part of the cleavage curve where muscle and chordal differentiation occur in the ascidian would be so condensed and accelerated throughout that axial differences would be undetectable. Under the latter circumstances I believe tissue segmentation of any kind is inconceivable, and that it can only find morphological expression under the retarded condition of Amphioxus embryos.

After the eleventh cleavage in Amphioxus a pair of unsegmented coelomic grooves appear along the dorso-lateral regions of the archenteron where the sides of the mesodermal crescent material have become localized. An hour or so later segmental indications appear in a serial order antero-posteriorly. At first 2, then 3 to 4 in rapid succession, and then additional segments in progressively slowing sequence are segregated from the posterior unsegmented mesoentoderm. In terms of tissue mechanics the segments arise in consequence, first, of a differentiation-rate gradient associated with an extremely slow proliferation rate, and secondly, which is an assumption in this case, of a pulse in the proliferation rate.

This is the point I wish to emphasize most of all—that a growth rhythm or pulse is in all probability a general property of protoplasmic growth—that under certain conditions of retardation relative to metabolism, i.e. a retardation in biological time, not absolute time, the pulse is exhibited or expressed as actual protoplasmic or tissue units which commence differentiation independently of the surge that preceded it and of the one next to come; then and only then is segmentation a morphological phenomenon. And the retardations characteristic of Amphioxus development are just those which make possible the critical rhythmic pace. In other words segmentation of the mesodermal component of the developing organism, with consequent induction of segmental organization in the nerve cord, is (or was) made possible by the dilution or otherwise weakening of the ooplasmic crescental determiners of the antecedent type of egg. Selection for an increasingly pronounced structural expression of the latent or incipient mesodermal segmentation could and probably did arise as a result of environmental circumstances.

18

UPSTREAM AND DOWN

AMPHIOXUS has the dual interest of being a contemporary
creature adapted to a particular way of life in the sea,
and of being a primitive, though more or less specialized,
chordate that affords us insight into the chordate past. It will
simplify procedure to discuss first how Amphioxus may have
come to occupy its present status.

The interpretation adopted here is as follows. The ancestral
amphioxids spawned in the sea, liberating small pelagic eggs
that developed freely among the inshore plankton. As critical
sizes were attained they swam on feeding migrations farther
and farther into inland brackish and fresh waters, employing
the segmental body musculature for propulsion, cranial sense
organs for navigation, and the original ascidian or tunicate
filter-feeding apparatus and visceral systems for feeding and
maintenance. Some degree of adaptation to the peculiarities of
freshwater existence must undoubtedly have occurred, but eggs
remained primitive inasmuch as they remained small and pelagic,
could develop only in sea-water, and in all probability as larval
forms required a particular marine algal or diatomic diet; all
of which necessitated a return breeding migration to the sea on
the part of the adult freshwater feeders. Throughout the late
pre-Cambrian, Cambrian, and later times, the marginal lands
of the continents were periodically lifted up and worn down
again, so that at times and for long durations, stream and river
flow was greatly intensified. During one such prolonged period
a parting of the ways must have taken place, because the one
obvious and decisive effect of such a change would be the
elimination of migrations between sea and fresh waters—sufficient power simply had not been developed to make headway
against currents of any appreciable strength. So on the one hand
all those forms, such as the amphioxids, that returned to the sea
to lay minute pelagic eggs became progressively confined to the
sea; while, on the other, part of the freshwater feeding stock

succeeded, if it had not already done so, in laying eggs of a kind that could remain and develop in inland waters and not drift down to the sea. In other words a gate was closed, and on either side of it the divided chordate stock evolved along separate and in distinctive ways. Amphioxids on the seaward side became readapted to a marine life as adult feeders; on the freshwater side the sea became a thing of the past entirely.

How do amphioxids as we now find them fit this concept? In my opinion they fit it well enough to make it plausible, for Amphioxus is anomalous in many ways.

Amphioxids are generally given not only subphyletic class and order rank, which is reasonable in view of their outstanding qualitative distinction, but also a subdivision into two families each embracing two genera, not to mention the forms grouped as Amphioxides. It seems to me, however, that too much emphasis is placed upon the distinguishing differences, and no matter how imposing the classification scheme is made to appear, or how comparable it may seem to be with that of other groups, we are dealing with a single type that varies only within certain very restricted limits. Thus the two genera of the family Branchiostomidae differ mainly in the extent to which the rostral process projects; while the two genera of the Epigonichthyidae differ in the degree of extension of the caudal fin. These may be good diagnostic features, but they contain little significance. On the other hand, the Epigonichthyidae, to which Asymmetron belongs, differs from the Branchiostomidae mainly in the possession of a single asymmetrically placed row of gonads in place of a pair of symmetrically situated rows; this seems to be little more than a retention of a degree of the typical larval asymmetry, possibly associated with reduction in size at sexual maturity; while the relatively large but apparently permanently pelagic forms collectively called Amphioxides are, according to Goldschmidt (1933), neotenic larvae that continue growth without undergoing metamorphosis, i.e. without acquiring the bilateral symmetry of the typical adult, without sinking to the sea floor, and, so far as is known, without ever becoming sexually mature. They may be no more than non-metamorphosing larvae of bottom forms simply drifting to their eventual death, continuing to grow in spite of having failed to make a critical response at a certain time.

In other words, apart from trivial differences in adult structure, and apart from a marked tendency toward neoteny, amphioxids exist at present only as a solitary and non-variable form. The amphioxid is a relic form surviving in isolation as truly as any lungfish. If it were a descendant of a more widespread dominant type of marine chordate, then I believe we would find evidence of such a stock and not just an isolated type, a stock showing much greater structural variation and ecological range. The remarkable limitation in the morphological sense, and the limitation of habit to shallow sandy regions of tropical and temperate coasts alone, suggest that it evolved under other circumstances than its present way of life and is now living in a virtual ecological asylum.

At no stage of its life cycle does Amphioxus swim in a horizontal position, moving through the water like a fish with anterior end foremost. From the time they begin to function as a feeding larva until they settle on the sea floor, a period of growth that may last as long as three months, the larvae live pelagically some distance below the surface of the sea, hanging for the most part in a vertical position maintained by the action of the long ectodermal cilia. During this period the larvae grow from an initial length of about 1 mm to about 8 mm. The Amphioxides larvae grow to about 16 mm. in the western Atlantic, and to about 10 mm. in the Indian Ocean; when larger than this they apparently sink and probably die. There is no indication therefore that the segmented locomotor system has any connexion with life in the open sea, while there is definite indication that the 8–10 mm. length may represent the maximum size that the organism can attain as a pelagic filter-feeder. It is remarkably close to the maximum size attained by larvacean tunicates; and while the tail may well have been put to better use, it is possible that greater employment would produce speed incompatible with efficient operation of the small-scale filtration system.

When the larva abandons its pelagic habit and sinks, it comes to lie on one side or other on the bottom, in which position it remains until its asymmetrically developed single row of gill slits is balanced by the growth of the incipient row of the other side, at least in the case of European Branchiostoma lanceolatum. It is possible, in fact, that the peculiar asymmetry of the pelagic larva, with reference to the gill slits in particular, is a developmental anticipation of the period when it is too heavy to stay aloft and yet too small to burrow effectively and so has to lie on the bottom like a pleuronectid fish. If we call on the theory of recapitulation, in spite of the disrepute into which it has fallen in recent years, there is here a suggestion that the young ancestral amphioxids that failed to enter the downflowing rivers sank to the sea floor and survived as filter-feeders resting as stationary as possible under the circumstances. They would naturally have lain on one side or the other, and an asymmetrically placed mouth and hypertrophy of the gills of that side would have been advantageous and could well have evolved in response to such a habit.

When the symmetrical stage is finally reached, the larva, now resembling the adult in general appearance, buries itself in the sand. As a rule the lancelets lie in the sand in an oblique position with just the anterior end protruding. They function in fact as filter-feeders in much the same way and in the same type of localities as molgulid and polycarpid ascidians, except that they occupy a looser sand than the ascidians can readily tolerate. Locomotion is limited to wriggling through the sand to acquire a better surface location or to regain an old one lost through wave disturbance. And when disturbed they burrow swiftly, usually by wriggling into the sand tail first. They are negatively reactive to light. So that again there is little indication that the body musculature is being employed in any way comparable with its complexity and potentiality. The picture is one of a highly evolved locomotor type secondarily adapted to a sedentary existence.

Under such circumstances a head equipped with navigatory sense organs becomes a positive disadvantage, and I suggest that those amphioxids survived which were able to burrow and stay in place; those that retained an instinct to swim ineffectively into the mouths of rivers were quickly doomed, as were those that simply drifted. In other words a degenerate head with inoperative sense organs became an asset—it eliminated the tendency to migrate against a current and permitted the owner to settle on the sea floor instead. Now in Amphioxus a negatively phototactic eye spot substitutes for whatever navigational sense organs the creature may once have had. This is not implausible, for in terms of developmental physiology the brain and associated sense organs are notoriously easily reduced or partially suppressed, without significant harm to the rest of the organism.

Those that finally survived after their exclusion from the freshwater paradise were those that became fully adapted to life in sand banks in shallow coastal waters. It may be significant that in a bay lying at the mouths of two rivers near Amoy in Southern China, a bank six miles long and but one wide, exposed at ebb tide, yields a catch of more than 1,000 million annually—an abundance suggesting that such is the ideal Amphioxus habitat, and that sand banks at the mouths of rivers were the only places where the exiled chordates could continue to live and feed upon somewhat the same kind of nourishment they had found in inland waters.

Finally, is there any real evidence other than these circumstantial indications that Amphioxus was ever anything but a marine organism? It seems to me that there is and that it lies in the presence and nature of the excretory apparatus.

If Amphioxus in its adult form is a freshwater reject, and if life in fresh water has been an important phase in its past history, it must have had at one time to compensate for or adjust to the low salt concentration of the fresh waters. According to Homer Smith (1939) the primary function of the vertebrate kidney was to bale out the inseeping water as fast as the body fluid acquired it, so that a balance was struck in total salt concentration somewhere between that of fresh water and that of the ancient seas. In simple or disguised or modified form the vertebrate kidney still performs this primary function, whether its owner is now a freshwater, terrestrial, or marine creature. The primitive salt equilibrium of the native marine forms is not regained and the salt concentration in the fluids of the prodigal sons remains diluted. Amphioxids in fresh water would have certainly had to bale out water, and a nephridial system operating between the pharyngeal blood-vessels and the exhalant stream of water is as direct and simple a device as may be conceived. A more elaborate apparatus operating through the coelom and requiring ducts opening far to the rear might well be more efficient, but the need to maintain a balance would have been urgent and the typical vertebrate excretory equipment too slow in attainment. In the meantime such a system as Amphioxus still possesses could have served until it was superseded. It would be of interest to know whether the blood of Amphioxus has the same salt concentration of sea-water or whether it is significantly less. Tunicates have no water-elimination system, and if Amphioxus proves to have one and maintains a salt level below that of its environment, we would have fairly definitive evidence of a freshwater sojourn.

19

STRETCHING OUT

THE transformation of a tunicate tadpole, whether neotenous or not, into an amphioxid type involves other changes besides those of growth as a whole and of segmentation of the musculature. Both the increase in size as such and the elongation associated with the extension of the notochord bring with them other structural changes and relationships.

The increase in number of notochord cells in the embryo, already discussed, alone accounts for a great extension of the notochord as an axial structure, for the increase is expressed as the extension of a single series cells and is for the most part linear. Presumptive embryonic muscle tissue extends in company with the notochord, as in ascidian tadpoles, and both tissues for a while constitute a zone of growth at the posterior end. New chordal cells and new myotomes continue to be added terminally as long as polarized growth continues in the terminal region, until such growth which is primarily in the linear axis ceases; at which time the final and maximum number of myotomes is attained and further increase in length of notochord or musculature arises from cell enlargement and cell intersusception. The region of the embryo which grows to form this combined chordomuscular tail is, in both the ascidian and Amphioxus embryo, the dorso-posterior part, that is, that part which lies posterior to the primary neural region and dorsal to the gut; this is a truism but is important.

In ascidians the embryonic tail grows out from this region before the digestive tube is any more than an endodermal vesicle; although even here the surge of outgrowth involves the adjacent endodermal wall to the extent of drawing out a solid strand of endoderm to accompany the other tissues. This I believe, however, to be only an accidental association of endoderm with the growth activity of the notochord and muscle, and it has no functional value or phylogenetic significance. The strand plays no part in subsequent development and the anterior residual endoderm continues to differentiate into the pharynx and looped intestine characteristic of tunicates in general.

In Amphioxus, however, the retardation in the process of segregation and differentiation of the chordal cells and associated mesoderm causes the general elongation of the tail to become associated in time with a later phase of proliferation of the endoderm. What was a slender solid strand derived from a few endodermal cells in the case of the ascidian tadpole becomes a large extension of the posterior archenteron as a whole in Amphioxus. The presumptive intestine in other words is drawn into the posterior growth of the body and is consequently drawn out as a straight tube instead of coiling as in tunicates.

This may be an over-simple way of looking at what may have in effect amounted to a major adaptive change. Yet there is little doubt that if the presumptive intestinal region of the endoderm became caught up in the posterior growth activity of the essential tissues of the tail, such a tubular extension and straightening of the intestine would inevitably occur. In other words the amphioxid and agnathid digestive tube is straight because of the manner in which the embryo grows, and not because a straight tube is necessarily better than a looped one. It may well be better suited, but greater suitability need not have been the reason for its acquisition.

Apart from the straightening of the tube, the digestive canal as a whole retains the basic tunicate differentiation to a remarkable degree. The hepatic caecum of Amphioxus is clearly the homologue of the caecum of ascidians, and to an even greater degree resembles that of the Larvacea. In the case of the pharynx the general organization and operation of the endostyle and gill-slit feeding mechanism is almost the same in the two types, even to the several histological longitudinal zones of the endostyle itself. Such differences as there are appear to be related to the difference in body size as a whole, and are of considerable importance.

We are concerned here with a comparison, not of the amphioxid pharynx with that of recent adult ascidians, but with a tunicate pharynx such as that of the thaliacean Pyrosoma or of ascidians still in the primary gill-slit stage of growth. The large pharyngeal branchial baskets of the ascidians in general result from the subdivision of the primary gill slits, and without such subdivision the Pyrosoma pharynx appears to represent the largest size to which the system of simple undivided gill slits can attain—at the most a very few millimetres in either axis. At all times the width of a gill slit must not significantly exceed twice the length which a cilium can attain.

Large body size in ascidians, requiring a relatively even larger branchial grid, is dependent upon the subdivision of the primary gill slits into rows of definitive ones of uniform width and shortened axis. In Pyrosoma the individuals constituting the colony do not exceed the small limits of size compatible with a series of primary gill slits in a simple, thin pharyngeal wall. Doliolum retains the primary gill slits as a part of its delicate branchial filter system, but appears to be restricted in consequence to body lengths of a few millimetres, except in cases where the gill slits are reduced proportionately. Salps attain larger dimensions but at the expense of complete elimination of gill slits of any kind. In other words a branchial filter system consisting of primary gill slits operating by means of cilia and supported by a pharyngeal wall of minimal thickness can only attain certain small dimensions of the order of several millimetres. Larger sizes demand modifications.

Amphioxus retains both the primary gill-slit pattern and the ciliary mechanism, and there is internal histological evidence that the mechanical limits of size for ciliary operation have been reached by this form. Whether the longitudinal division of each primary gill slit into two virtually equivalent units by the downgrowth of a tongue bar disqualifies the pairs thus formed from the term 'primary' is hardly relevant. It certainly is a device for doubling the number of slits within a particular band of the pharyngeal wall as growth proceeds, thereby maintaining the apposed edges of a single slit within the critical distance from one another. But the general morphology is still that of a single series. The main problem involved in growth of the whole beyond certain limits is that greatly elongated slits in a thin pharyngeal sheet of tissue are all too likely to gape, especially when water flow is at all considerable. Amphioxus as a whole, and its branchial wall in particular, grows to a size far greater than the size compatible with the originally simple state as exemplified by Pyrosoma, and only as the result of both functional and structural reinforcement of the branchial bars.

Compared with the tunicate structure, the changes are several. Each gill bar extends inwards towards the centre of the pharynx, extending the ciliary face of its two sides; and at the same time the constituent epithelial cells become extremely columnar,

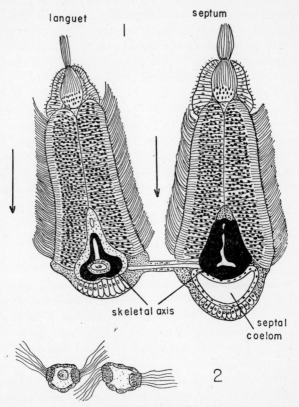

languet septum

skeletal axis

septal coelom

2

FIG. 24. 1, transverse section through gills of Amphioxus, passing through both a septal and languet gill, to show massive construction and presence of skeletal collagen around branchial vessels (after Franz); 2, transverse section through two interstigmatic gill bars of ascidian Fragaroides, at the same magnification as those of Amphioxus (after Maurice).

with consequently longer cilia and therefore a greater reach across the gill aperture. The result is a relatively massive bar of solid tissue extending inwards at right angles to the wall of the pharynx and so better able to withstand spreading pressure effects, while at the same time able to create a relatively stronger water current. Perhaps even more significant, the outer core of each bar consists of a solid collagenous supporting skeletal rod which, with its fellows, joins a dorsal skeletal arch extending the length of the branchial wall. Taken as a whole there is comparatively speaking a great stiffening of the branchial wall and a development of the ciliary current-producing mechanism to about as powerful a state as we can conceive. It is difficult to imagine the same system working effectively in a much larger organism than Amphioxus, or that ciliary power alone could be adapted efficiently for use on a larger scale, apart from the device of complex subdivisions such as we see in the larger forms of ascidians, a device not employed by any others. Growth of the chordate body beyond the size characteristic of Amphioxus in all probability must have involved critical changes in pharyngeal structure.

One of the amphioxid features of outstanding importance is the atrium. All ascidian and thaliacean tunicates possess an atrium; no existing vertebrate has one. Is that of Amphioxus an inheritance from a tunicate ancestor or has it been acquired anew, and why is it absent in the vertebrates proper?

Reviewing the ascidian condition, the atrium is at first, in all except the pleurogonid families, a pair of laterally placed peribranchial sacs. As the young individual grows to the size at which the primary gill slits are subdividing into rows of secondary stigmata, the pair of peribranchial siphons grow toward one another and fuse in a mid-dorsal position. In the highly specialized pleurogonid order the atrium develops from the first as a single mid-dorsal siphon bifurcating into right and left peribranchial sacs; this, however, is clearly a secondary mode of development of a mutatory character, and this order in any case is so set apart and is in general so highly evolved as an ascidian group that it merely shows that the same structure *can* develop in more than one way.

In the thaliaceans the nature of the egg and its development has become so modified by yolk and other factors that it would have been surprising had the primitive developmental procedure of the less specialized ascidians been followed. The atrium develops as a median invagination, but the only question here is whether the fused or single condition of the atrial siphon is inherited from an ascidian ancestral form that had already attained to the fused condition, or whether the fusion has occurred independently after the thaliacean stock diverged from the ancient ascidian. In any case I am convinced that the single siphon is so much more effective for emitting a stream of water to a considerable distance that such fusion would have been acquired if it did not already exist. In the ascidian the atrial siphon serves to send the filtered water, together with occasional excreta, to a distance beyond the region of water intake. In thaliaceans such a function is obviously only incidental, and the siphon serves primarily for jet propulsion, either collectively as in Pyrosoma or for each individual in the case of salps and Doliolum. In these the siphon opens posteriorly instead of dorsally, and the openings of the inhalant and exhalant apertures of the body are accordingly in line with one another, so that inflow and outflow are unimpeded and body contractions both draw water in and force it out behind, thereby forming the food current and the locomotory force.

Now, we have earlier reached the conclusion that the neotenic tadpole, from which the thaliaceans and primitive prevertebrate chordates arose, in all probability possessed a pair of lateral siphons. I believe that posterior fusion of these siphons to form a single atrial opening would have been generally advantageous, and that we can plausibly assume that in the stock that led to the amphioxid and vertebrate line the paired siphons fused posteriorly and the tail evolved in size and importance. The question is, how were these two events related?

Bigelow and Farfante (1948) consider that the atrium in the amphioxid and tunicate is not homologous since it develops in a different way in the two forms. It is possible that the two atrial types are not homologous, as these authors rather categorically state, but homology cannot be rejected on the grounds of differing developmental procedures. The ascidian neural complex, for instance, develops from an invaginating ectodermal neural plate in the embryo, but as an evagination of pharyngeal endoderm in the case of many ascidian buds. Yet the homology remains unquestionably. For the sake of argument therefore, and with no other reason for suspecting lack of homology, we will assume that the tunicate and amphioxid atria represent two forms of one and the same basic structure. Accordingly we

may account for the presence and particular nature of the amphioxid atrium as a derivation from a more primitive tunicate
condition on somewhat the following lines.

In the course of development the tail grows out from a dorso-
posterior position from immediately behind the presumptive
neurosensory vesicle. The pair of peribranchial sacs which later
fuse dorsally in ascidians to form the median atrium arise as
lateral invaginations of the ectoderm slightly dorsal to the
middle level of the trunk. With the general involvement of the
whole posterior region of the embryo in tail outgrowth as it
occurs in Amphioxus, the lateral peribranchial presumptive
areas would be drawn out in a posterior direction in conformance
with adjacent tissues. In such an event they would tend to fuse
eventually in a position ventral to the axial swimming structures; and if it should happen that their first appearance should
be delayed until the posterior growth of the tail is more or less
completed, ventral posterior fusion becomes even more likely.
Whatever the original state may have been, delay in developmental origin combined with the general retardation of development and extension of the tail in Amphioxus would not only
draw the peribranchial sacs posteriorly in such a way that
posterior and ventral fusion becomes likely, but in any case a
new opportunity for fusion in such a location is offered. And
there may have well been an added incentive for such an evolutionary change in the possible use of the exhalant atrial current
as a propulsive force aiding that of the tail and of the same kind
employed exclusively in thaliacean tunicates. In the living
Amphioxus in fact the posterior atrial wall and siphon retain a
musculature remarkably like that of the ascidian atrial siphon,
and which the ascidian uses to clean out the cavity and eject
water to a distance (cf. Hoyle, 1952). In Amphioxus such contractions inevitably have a jet-propulsion effect, whether or not
the animal makes use of it.

The amphioxid atrium, as is well known, arises in the course
of development as long ectodermal folds passing along the
ventro-lateral level of the body (Willey, 1894). These fuse along
their length to enclose an atrial cavity surrounding the branchial
region and the post-branchial gut, as it does in ascidians, remaining open posteriorly as the atriopore, although some distance anteriorly to the anus. These ridges, the metapleural folds,

not only form the atrium, but extend ventrally beyond it as permanent extensions which serve as a pair of bilge keels, undoubtedly stabilizing the animal to some degree while it is swimming.

Willey, although he read the Amphioxus-ascidian connexion in the reverse sequence from what is here proposed, saw clearly

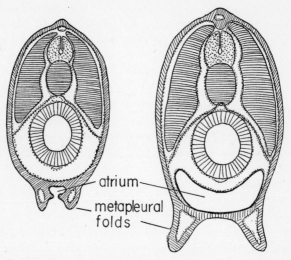

FIG. 25. Cross sections of two stages of Amphioxus to show invagination of atrial cavity and the formation of the meta-pleural folds (after Willey).

that the difference in course of development and nature of the atrium in the two types was primarily a consequence of differences in growth.

The atrial involutions [of an ascidian] occur at a time when the tail is rapidly increasing its length; the body proper, on the contrary, remaining stationary so far as increase in size is concerned, and retaining at this stage approximately the dimensions which it possessed when the tail first began to grow out. Moreover, they occur *before* the appearance of any gill clefts in the wall of branchial sac, so that in the ascidians the gill slits never open directly to the exterior.

In Amphioxus, on the other hand, there is no such delay in the elongation of the body of the embryo, but it goes on continuously till the full complement of myotomes has been formed. The post-anal portion of the body, which we suppose to be the homologue of the tail of the ascidian tadpole, does not appear until a somewhat late period in the development. There is very little of it present in the larva with three gill slits. . . . Not only, therefore, has the elongation of the body of Amphioxus already taken place before the occurrence of the atrial involution, but the primary gill slits have also broken through the wall of the pharynx, and open freely to the exterior before the atrium begins to be closed in.

In Amphioxus, then, the atrial involution has been drawn out into the form of a longitudinal groove because it occurs subsequently to the elongation of the body and the perforation of the gill slits. In the Ascidian embryo the (paired) atrial involution has the form of a simple pit with a circular margin, because it arises before the elongation of the body proper of the embryo and before the perforation of the gill clefts, so that no influence has been at work to draw it out into the form of a groove.

Once again, therefore, a major difference between the ascidian tadpole and the amphioxid appears to be a simple and perhaps inevitable consequence of the basic difference in relative rates of growth and differentiation of the axial and sustaining components of the body.

The retention of the atrium in Amphioxus in all probability is related to the desirability to protect the delicate branchial apparatus from damage by the abrading sand, and to maintain a good outflow of water.

20

JAMOYTIUS AND THE
VERTEBRATE EYE

T HE oldest fossilized vertebrate material consists of fragments of head shields of ostracoderms from the Upper
Ordovician of Canyon City, Colorado. They indicate great
complexity of the outer shell or armour, and micro-sections made
by Bryant (1936) showed that they were not fundamentally
different from the better known pteraspid ostracoderms of the
Silurian and Devonian periods. The successive basal layers of
the exoskeletal tissue did not penetrate the muscular layer of the
body wall but grew in curved lamellar surfaces as if it were enclosed by a limiting membrane.

Gregory (1951) regards the armoured condition of these and
other ostracoderms as the generally primitive condition of the
early vertebrates and on the basis of evidence in both pteraspid
and coelopid ostracoderms considers that a cephalothoracic
shield gave place progressively to a denticular surface like that
of modern sharks and argues that this has been the general
course of events:

the most simple-looking ostracoderm, from the Upper Silurian of
Europe, is Phlebolepis Kiaer, a kind of tadpole-like fish with a small
mouth, a rotund body and a rather short tail. There were small
median dorsal and caudal fin-folds not supported by individual fin-
rays. The body was covered with small separate scales or denticles.
If there be those who still think of evolution as always leading from
the simple to the complex, such persons might well take this innocent-
looking bag as an ideal starting point for all the ostracoderms.

As already mentioned, Gregory favours the evolutionary sequence: basic chordates → ostracoderms → Amphioxus →
ascidians, with the later vertebrates evolving as a separate line
from the ostracoderm stock.

In 1946 two specimens of a very remarkable ostracoderm (?) were described by White from the Silurian (Dowtonian) shale of Lanarkshire, which he named Jamoytius kerwoodi. The two specimens, which were 15 and 18·5 cm. long, persisted only as carbonaceous films on dark shaly flagstone, but strong illumination in suitable liquid has brought out surprising detail. To quote Gregory's summary of this work from *Evolution Emerging* (1951):

Jamoytius was somewhat similar in general outline to Amphioxus, and in other respects it resembled some of the anaspid ostracoderms. It had long horizontal lateral-fin folds, running from behind the very small head to the base of the tapering tail, which, however, was not turned downward as it was in Anaspids. There was a long dorsal spineless dorsal fin and a shorter anal fin. The skin was apparently very thin and without armor. The internal skeleton seems to have been cartilaginous.

Taken altogether this very ancient type tends to connect Amphioxus with the anaspid ostracoderms. It is regarded by White as one of the most primitive known fossil vertebrates and it does indeed appear to lend some support to the older view that the ancestral vertebrates were naked or thin-skinned forms, rather than heavily armored as in the Ordovician Astraspis and Eriptychius.

Gregory concludes: 'Quite conceivably, however, the boneless Jamoytius may well have been on the way toward Amphioxus, while the bony Cephalaspis may have been on or near the line leading to the lampreys.' I have introduced Jamoytius in this manner to indicate not only its general character but also to indicate its present controversial status.

Homer Smith in his recent book *From Fish to Philosopher* (1953) supports Gregory's view whole-heartedly:

Gregory, however, suggests that Jamoytius may be intermediate between the anaspid ostracoderms and Amphioxus, and hence, by implication, secondarily naked. We would supplement Gregory's interpretation by remarking that a single 'naked' ostracoderm carries little weight against the large numbers of armored or heavily scaled forms that are now known and it cannot, in the light of the present evidence, controvert the generally accepted thesis that armor is a basic and primitive character of the earliest vertebrates.

We can admit that armour may well have been generally possessed by the early vertebrates without going so far as to assign it also to the 'earliest' vertebrates. Nor is the abundance of a fossil evidence of anything but successful propagation, mineralization, and subsequent preservation; numbers have little if any bearing on the question of what came first. Palaeontologists naturally tend to think in terms of the material they have to work with, but it is surprising to find a kidney physiologist remaining so impressed by the weight of minerals. White's conclusion that Jamoytius is a primitively and not a secondarily naked form is to my mind much more plausible. In any event every armoured creature that has ever lived has grown individually from an unarmoured egg and larva, and in a general way I believe this has been the course of evolution too.

The Jamoytius fossils belong to a freshwater deposit and are, on any interpretation, of the utmost interest. According to White's original account the body is naked, with no sign of internal calcification; a pair of apparently structureless but relatively enormous eyes occur widely separated along the anterior margin of a depressed, square-cut head. A notochord is recognizable, while a straight intestine runs from about 4 cm. from the middle of the body to a point just in front of the anal fin supports. Myomeres, which are clearly preserved, are of the simplest type found only in the Amphioxus, for not only are they undivided as in Cyclostomes, but they show a single forward flexure which, according to White, 'in life was certainly much less acute than that in Amphioxus'. Fifty to sixty segments are present between the shoulder backwards to where the fossil ends. There is no external trace of branchial apparatus, which may be due to poor preservation; and certainly there is none of the complicated development of exoskeleton connected with a breathing apparatus, such as is shown in the least armoured anaspids.

White considers the forward position of the eyes to be primitive: 'it is certainly the obvious position in creatures with imperfectly developed vision living in clouded waters, and the large, apparently structureless eye spots lend some colour to the idea that its sight was not of a high order'. The unarmoured condition he believes to be primitive and he challenges the view that heavily armoured ostracoderms are primitively so endowed.

The Agnatha did not spring forth, like Pallas Athene, fully armed upon an unsuspecting world, for there was surely an important period during which ossification or calcification was being developed,

and it cannot be doubted that this was preceded by a totally un-
protected phase, since such a peculiarly vertebrate tissue as bone
was not likely to appear until the course of development of the
phylum was well set.

Stensio (1927, p. 333) has placed the period of bone-acquisition
as far back as the 'Lower Ordovician or perhaps even in the Upper

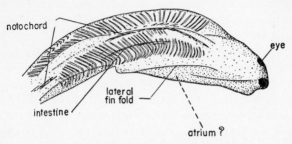

FIG. 26. Jamoytius kerwoodi (after White).

Cambrian'; be that as it may, the preossification period was certainly earlier than the Harding Sandstone where the Canyon City
fragments were found. The presence of a naked form like Jamoytius
in the Ludlovian needs some explanation, for not only was it much
younger than the Canyon City fragments, but it was contem-
poraneous with Thelodius and geologically not much older than the
'Downtonian' fish-fauna with Birkenia, Lasanius, Atilaspis, &c.
Jamoytius cannot, therefore, itself claim ancestral rights over the
Agnatha in general in spite of the suitability of its characters as they
are here interpreted, for they come very near to those of the ideal
chordate ancestor (cf. White, 1935, p. 433), and very much nearer
than, for instance, any of the Anaspida. But with its high degree of
atavism it represents, in my opinion, a conservative element of the
main stock from which the various groups of craniate chordates
arose; for unless we like to suppose that ossification was developed
independently in the Gnathostomes, that class must have originated
at much the same time and from much the same source as the several
groups of Agnatha (cf. Moy-Thomas, 1939, p. 4). The continuation
of this unarmoured group which Jamoytius represents even in Lud-
low times does raise legitimately the question as to whether the
modern cartilaginous Agnatha are as degenerate in their lack of
exoskeleton as is always represented and the possibility of the persistence of an unmodified group such as this cannot be entirely
ignored.

This last seems to me to be a considerable understatement.

We accordingly have in Jamoytius a chordate about three times as long as a full-grown Amphioxus, and of many times the bulk, that lived in fresh water and in all probability had existed as such at least throughout the whole of the Ordovician period. It is obviously in many ways a much more primitive type than its ostracoderm contemporaries, and its presence along-side more advanced and specialized forms is no more or less remarkable than the presence of Amphioxus and Cyclostomes in the world today.

I propose therefore to accept White's opinion that Jamoytius is primitive and not degenerate, and that in spite of its persistence into lower Silurian time it is in all probability a type very close to the basic freshwater chordate stock from which ostracoderms and other vertebrates have evolved.

Lack of ossification or calcification and the general shape and size of the animal suggest that it was sufficiently buoyant and powerful enough to have been an active swimmer not confined to feeding exclusively on bottom fauna or necessarily resting upon the bottom. The forward position of the eyes indicates that the mouth was ventral and considerably subterminal; and in view of the clear impressions left by the myomeres of the trunk and tail, the absence of any detail in the mouth region suggests that neither muscle nor supporting tissue was significantly present. In other words, the mouth in all likelihood consisted of delicate structures such as those of Amphioxus.

Similarly the absence of any detail of branchial structure is equally suggestive. When myomeres, notochord, and post-pharyngeal intestine are so clearly shown, gill slits or gill pouches opening directly to the exterior would probably have been well enough preserved to be recognizable if such had been the case. The relatively great width of the pharyngeal region and the lack of any discernible structure in the fossils seem to me to indicate that the whole anterior part of the body consisted of comparatively delicate tissues which were enclosed by an unbroken external body layer. That is, the feeding and respiratory apparatus was still primarily a ciliary mechanism and was enclosed in an atrium more or less like that of Amphioxus. The outline of Jamoytius in fact suggests the presence of an atrial cavity opening posteriorly about midway between the anterior edge of the body and the anus.

It is difficult to conceive how the branchial-feeding apparatus as we see it in Amphioxus could enlarge to the size implicit in the dimensions of Jamoytius without undergoing important changes concerning the mechanism of creation of the water currents. I doubt if the individual gill slits operated by cilia alone could be enlarged beyond the size attained by the gill slits of adult Amphioxus; at least, the addition of skeletal tissue to give rigidity to the slit walls so that the slit remains no more than twice the length of a cilium must soon have reached a point of diminishing returns. Moreover the work performed by the ciliary margins of the slits would become relatively and progressively inadequate as the body increased in bulk. It seems to me therefore that Jamoytius could only have functioned effectively if the ciliary gill apparatus was reinforced by the action of muscle-tissue associated either with the gill margins or with the floor of the pharynx as in the peculiar larvae of the South African clawed toad Xenopus laevis (Weisz, 1945).

The Xenopus tadpole is interesting, even though it is probably a relatively recent novelty rather than an archaic type, because of the general shape of its body and the manner of its feeding. As a tadpole it grows from about 8 mm. to a maximum of about 8 cm., and so approaches the order of size of Jamoytius. It is unique in having a head which is larger than the abdomen, the result of a tremendous pharynx necessitated by its peculiar mode of feeding upon suspended green and blue green algal material. The body form in fact is remarkably similar to that of Jamoytius, and the locomotory activity associated with feeding is suggestive. From the time feeding begins until the onset of metamorphosis the tadpole is usually suspended in mid-water with its head pointing obliquely downward. The distal third of the tail rapidly oscillates to right and left while the rest of the tail and body remains almost stationary. That is, during feeding, the tail acts to counteract gravity and current but no more than that. Water is taken in to the pharynx by muscular action of the pharyngeal floor. Only when the tadpole is disturbed does the musculature of the trunk and tail as a whole come into play and more powerful thrusts bring about a forward movement of the whole.

I am not suggesting that Jamoytius used its tail like the tadpole of Xenopus, but that it probably fed in much the same manner, virtually poised and motionless, feeding by means of gentle pharyngeal currents upon rich algal suspensions. Only if the mouth were wide and terminal, as in Salpa, would forward motion increase the rate of entry of the food-laden water.

It seems to me that Jamoytius, at least at the size of the two known fossil individuals, in all probability relied upon musculature for the creation of the water current. Yet if the enfolding atrial chamber persisted, as I think it did, it indicates a delicacy of internal tissue and in turn suggests that ciliated epithelia were still of great importance, both for food particle manipulation and for part of the water-current production. Conversion from ciliated slits like those of Amphioxus to the muscle pump system typical of the Cyclostome gills must have been a protracted evolutionary process, and in each life cycle a transition from an exclusively ciliated condition to muscle plus cartilage tissues probably occurred as the individual grew in size. It is possible that some indication of such conversion may be retained during early growth stages of the larval lamprey. The development of this form is all too inadequately known.

White describes the eyes as large structureless masses of pigment. They are structureless inasmuch as there is no sign of skeletal tissue, lens, or eye muscles. If a lens had existed it surely would have become as well preserved as the notochord, and the lack of any indication that it existed forcibly suggests, under the circumstances, that no lens was present. The size of the pigment masses is much larger than would be necessary if the eyes were no more than light-sensitive pigmented areas, and I suggest that the pair of widely separated eyes existed actually in the form of relatively large eye-cups. Whether the opening of the eye cup was relatively large or was a virtual pinhole is difficult even to guess at, but there is little doubt that the vertebrate eye evolved step by step and must have been functionally valuable at all stages. As widely separated cups at the anterior margin of the head they could serve well for general orientation, especially during travel in the horizontal plane, and would compare reasonably well for this purpose with the paired eyes of branchiopods like Artemia or Eubranchipus. That such a stage was a necessary step in the evolution of a continually functional eye is not only logical but is possibly indicated by the development of the eye of the Ammocoete larva of the lamprey.

The lamprey eye has two functional periods, one immediately after hatching and the other following metamorphosis. In the larval form a patch of visual cells is already functional in the primary optic vesicle and persists as 'retina A' until meta- morphosis, although it goes out of function when the tiny larva first burrows in the mud and the eye becomes covered with opaque skin. At metamorphosis the skin becomes transparent, the visual cells of the much-expanded retina ('retina B') are suddenly differentiated and Retina A as an identifiable region becomes indistinguishable from the rest. Intra-ocular muscles or suspensory-ligament fibres never develop, for the pupil is motionless, and no ciliary body forms between choroid and iris. The lens is propped in place only by the vitreous, which seems, according to Walls (1942), to have evolved its semi-solid nature for this original purpose. If the larva did not burrow completely and become temporarily blind the eyes evidently would remain functional from the stage of an uninvaginated optic vesicle, with a flat and useless lens, until it was as fully developed as a lamprey eye becomes.

The problem of the origin of the vertebrate eye has loomed large for a long time; it is basically the problem of the status of each of the parts previous to their present association to form the eye. A detailed review and critical discussion of the various theories have already been given by Walls in his monumental account of the vertebrate eye (1942). According to Walls the embryology of the eye is such that there could have been no complex retina until the chordates had evolved an internal, tubular brain, and accordingly 'the big difficulties which an eye-origin theory must handle are: (a) the inversion of the retina —the fact that the vertebrate visual cells point away from the light; (b) the nature of the visual cell before they become photosensory, and the question of their location at the time they did so; and (c) the question of the status of the lens before it became associated with the retina as a dioptric structure'.

Various investigators since 1874 have seen the beginnings of the vertebrate eye in the anterior pigment spot of Amphioxus, but even by 1890 there was evidence that this so-called 'eye' is not sensory at all, and this now appears to be certain. As for the later theories I cannot do better than quote Walls's own de- scriptions—

Balfour's Theory. It was Balfour, in 1881, who first proposed that the vertebrate retina originated in the skin and was carried inside the animal by the evolution of the neural tube. Several investigators, independently of each other, soon pointed out how well the foveolae opticae fit into this hypothesis. Balfour's theory was the first to account for the inversion of the retina, but it offered no explanation of the lens. . . .

The Placode Theory. The origin of the lens was first explained by Sharp in 1885. He regarded the lens as a modified lateral-line organ which was, like those organs, a sensory ectodermal pit or bud. The 'placode' theory, an extension of Sharp's original idea, proposes that the lens was once the whole eye and that the present retina served as its ganglion, eventually taking over the sensory function itself and releasing the vesicular 'skin' eye to become a lens. Fatal objections to this interpretation of the retina arise from the utter absence of embryological confirmation of any previous connection of retina and lens, and from the lack of any evidence that a self-determining lens placode exists at all as a morphological entity. Nor does the placode theory account for inversion.

Boveri's Theory. Inversion was explained anew by Boveri in 1904 in a theory that made use of the two-celled visual organs of Amphioxus which had been discovered by Hesse in the 'spinal cord' of this so-called grandfather of vertebrates. While Boveri's theory offers no account of the lens, it gives as good an explanation of the retina and its inversion as does Balfour's theory; and both hypotheses are widely taught at the present time. Acceptance of either is impossible, however, unless the mode of development of the rods and cones indicates either that they might have been already photosensory while still in the skin, or that they might have been derived from the photosensory ganglion cells of Hesse's organs or the similar 'Joseph's' cells in the head region of Amphioxus.

Studnicka's Theory. Unfortunately the cytogenesis of the rods and cones supports neither Balfour nor Boveri, but confirms a radically different hypothesis first offered in 1912 by Studnicka, and which has yet to be given consideration in any of the various text-books which afford a little space into the eye-origin problem. Studnicka noticed that if one traces the visual-cell side of the inner layer of the optic cup around the latter and through the optic stalk into the central nervous system, one emerges into the ependymal layer of the brain wall. The ependymal cells lining the cavities of the brain and cord are non-nervous supporting elements which often bear flagella which circulate the cerebro-spinal fluid. Studnicka also laid great stress upon the eye of the young larval lamprey which is precociously

functional while still merely an optic vesicle, as indicating that the
vertebrate eye was originally merely a 'directional' one before it
became capable of forming images. Since the lens is already present
in the tiny lamprey, but in the form of a flat cushion incapable of
dioptric function, Studnicka argued that it must have existed phylogenetically—a vestigial remnant of something else, possibly a sense-
organ—before the retina was devised at all. He also showed that
there are many central nervous sense-organs in vertebrates, including
the median or pineal and parietal eyes, whose receptors are certainly
modified ependymal cells. He has received striking confirmation in
the recent demonstrations of the photosensitivity of the lining of the
diencephala of many forms. . . . But Studnicka never considered in
detail the manner in which rods and cones differentiate, though this
had been carefully worked out by several European investigators.
If he had done so, his theory would surely have seemed much
stronger to subsequent text-writers. For the outer segment, the
receptive organelle, of a vertebrate visual cell develops exactly like
any flagellum. It starts as a filament of centrosomic material rooted
in a diplosome or dumbbell shaped centriole embedded in the future
inner segment, later becoming encrusted and thickened by mitochondria which form the conspicuous spiral filaments making up the
bulk of the outer segment. A closer comparability of visual cells and
ependymal cells could hardly exist.

If the photosensory parts of the rods and cones were once ependymal flagella, it is certain that Boveri's theory must be discarded;
for ependyma, even photosensory ependyma, exists in Amphioxus
side by side with the Hesse's organs and Joseph's cells. It is equally
certain that the vertebrate retina could not have gotten started, as
a photosensitive region of the brain wall, until the latter had become
tubular. Only then was there any need for the ependymal cells to
evolve as elements distinct from nerve cells; and these were primarily
supportive (they still run through the whole thickness of the brain
wall in Amphioxus and the lampreys) then secretory in function
(producing the cerebrospinal fluid) before it became necessary
further to aid in circulation by means of flagella. No flagella, no
sensitivity or photosensitivity; and it can be regarded as certain that
the definitive visual cells were developed within the finished brain
and not, à la Balfour, while the nervous system was still a part of the
skin. . . . The most primitive homologues of rods and cones to which
we can point today are the photosensory flagellated ependymal cells
of the 'infundibular organ' of Amphioxus, which is a crude visual
apparatus seemingly for the detection of the direction of light by
means of shadows cast upon it by the anterior pigment spot.

Much of this is in keeping with the theory we have been developing, and in particular with the paedomorphic ascidian tadpole as we have conceived it to have been, that is, with a closed neural vesicle and tube, and blind as the result of loss of the ascidian ocellus.

The closed neural tube, wide in front and narrow behind, I consider to be a product of embryological or developmental

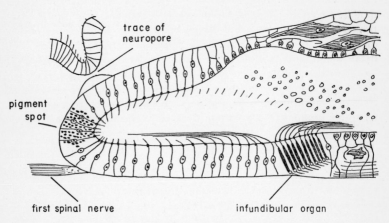

FIG. 27. Sagittal diagram of anterior end of neural tube of Amphioxus (after Franz), showing anterior pigment spot, photosensitive infundibular organ, and flagellated ependymal cells.

fixation subsequently exploited in a phylogenetic sense, and not an embryological relic of an ancestral condition itself; which is the reverse of the interpretations implicit in the theories of vertebrate eye origin just given, with the exception of Walls's own conclusion. Both the general course of chordate evolution so far outlined here and the histological evidence support the hypothesis that the retina evolved after the chordate organism was already established as such, with its neural tube already enclosed.

That the photosensitive elements of the infundibular cells of Amphioxus are related to and apparently extensions of flagellar structure is very evident. The question arises, however, whether, as Walls has concluded, the flagellate ependymal cells are necessary precursors to the photosensitivity.

Relationship of the vertebrate retina with the eye of ascidian larvae has seemingly been ruled out as the result of a belief that the ascidian retina is not inverted. As I have emphasized earlier, I believe the ascidian larval eye to have been lost and the eyes of salps and of vertebrates to have been new acquisitions—but not on the grounds of lack of inversion. The retinal cells of the ascidian eye *are* inverted with regard to the neural cavity, although not in relation to the lens cells. The entire larval eye of the ascidian, no matter in what direction it may appear to face, is a differentiation of the inner wall of the neural vesicle, with the sensory elements directed morphologically, if not actually, towards the lumen. Ependymal cells are not present and there is no indication that the retinal cells evolved from them. On the other hand, the re-establishment of a photosensory organ with the sensory vesicle of the botryllid tadpole larvae discussed earlier is much to the point. Here we have a clear case of an ocellus being lost, and of cells of the dorso-posterior neural wall growing out into the lumen as photosensory elements, finally to penetrate the concavity of the otolith.

In the case of the tadpole embryos of Botryllus and Symplegma (according to Grave, 1932), five processes emerge from the visceral ganglion, each of which is an outgrowth from a ganglion cell. The finger-like terminal endings are clear except for a deep-staining central axis which terminates distally in a deep staining conical point ending in a clear spindle-shaped enlargement; proximally the dark axis in each cell shows continuation with several fibrillae and is associated with basal granules.

I do not suggest that these photosensitive elements are directly related to those of the vertebrate retina. I do believe that the primitive vertebrate brain is a direct descendant of the ascidian neural vesicle. And the botryllid tadpoles show that the neural cells lining the central cavity not only can acquire photosensitivity without previous flagellar differentiation (although the internal structural differentiation is like that of retinal cells and of basal structures associated with flagellar outgrowth in other types) but that retinal cell orientation is just as typically inverted as it is in ascidian ocelli and vertebrate retinas.

In brief, the hollow tubular neural structure precedes sensory developments; retinal differentiation can take place directly in the absence of flagellar differentiation; and the inversion characteristic of the vertebrate retina is apparently an innate tendency from the start. Ependymal cells, however, have come to line the neural cavities of Amphioxus and Cyclostomes as the secretion and circulation of cerebrospinal fluid became more important, and it may have been easier to convert the basal components of the flagellar structure into photosensitive rods than to have evolved the latter without the former. The botryllids merely demonstrate that it could have been done without flagellar aid, not that it was so accomplished.

Accordingly we come to the question how directional optic cups and simple median eyes may have evolved from a potentially photosensitive neural layer.

Studnicka's theory, particularly as shown by Walls's diagrams illustrating it, starts with a thick-walled neural tube with areas of sensory cells, derived from flagellated ependymal cells, occupying ventral and dorsal regions on each side, that is, ventral and dorsal areas of the inner surface that are discontinuous mid-dorsally and mid-ventrally. The pair of dorsal areas, which are relatively small and close together, evaginate as photosensitive sacs destined to become the median eyes. The pair of ventro-lateral areas evaginate as photosensitive optic cups, destined to become the lateral eyes. This of course is virtually the normal developmental course, except that these regions are being considered as functionally photosensitive organs from the beginning. Retinal inversion is the original state and reflects the orientation of the cells lining the neural cavity.

Why two different regions such as the dorsal and the ventro-lateral areas should become so involved is a distinct problem. I suggest that we have here a situation comparable to what we encounter among many invertebrates in one form or another: that the median eyes or photosensitive areas have from the first been associated with orientation in relation to light of an overhead source, relating to negative or positive phototactic behaviour, comparable to the metanauplius median eye of phyllopods or the fused median eye of Cladocera, &c., and that the paired ventro-lateral eyes evolved primarily in relation to orientation and movement in the horizontal plane.

This presupposes a considerable degree of transparency in the tissues in general, so that apart from the barriers or interference of localized pigment, light could penetrate the organism to the photosensitive areas, just as it does now in relation to the infundibular organ of Amphioxus.

The outgrowth of photosensitive optic vesicles on either side of the neural tube towards the sides of the head increases the effective operation of the lateral eyes as a working pair associated with equalization of stimuli for directional purposes. Bulbs or vesicles presumably would serve this purpose to a significant extent, particularly if there was some cutting off of light coming from the opposite side of the anterior head; but the efficiency would greatly increase as soon as a vesicle transformed into an invaginated cup with pigment confined to the outer layer of the cup, so that only rays of light actually entering the mouth of the optic cup would be stimulatory. This I suggest is the condition that existed in Jamoytius.

The remaining question concerns the origin of the lens. Walls remarks:

when everything else in the primitive eye is so plausibly explicable, it really is a shame that we cannot be at all sure how the lens came into existence. The lens placode fits neatly into the set of cephalic lateral-line organs, and from it to develop into a lens is no more remarkable than for one of them to generate the olfactory organ or for another of them the otic placode, to differentiate into the elaborate membranous labyrinth of the internal ear. It would be nice to be able to insist that the lens placode has a real morphological existence and that the lens is therefore a captured lateral-line organ, as Sharp believed; but we cannot do so with clear consciences. . . . Franz . . . suggests that the lens evolved when the neural tube was just closing, in such a position as to concentrate light upon the photosensitive lining of the diencephalon. Its locus somehow escaped involution with the neural tube and later moved laterally to be taken over by the new retina. No ontogenetic conditions support this idea, and like the placode theory it stands or falls with the demonstrability of a self-differentiating lens anlage.

We have already discarded the concept of the process of neurulation having any recapitulatory significance as such, and have assumed the existence of the closed neural tube as our point of departure in this connexion, so that Franz's hypothesis is here not considered.

On the other hand, quite apart from the question whether a retinal cup could capture a lateral line placode if it happened to be close enough, or whether a lens placode is anything but a certain stage in lens development, it is possible to conceive an origin and development of a lens as a direct tissue response to the optic vesicle without invoking at all the concept of mutual co-operation between two originally independent entities.

In the case of both the median and the lateral eyes the primitive photosensitive outgrowths approached the epidermis, for one reason or another, and if there was any tendency for cup formation to occur after contact with the epidermis had been made, simply as the result of further growth, lens formation can be accounted for as a very simple form of induction.

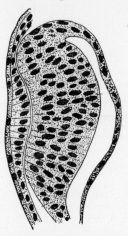

FIG. 28. Developmental stage of optic vesicle and lens of Siredon (after Rabl), showing lens forming in response to non-specific growth stimulus of proliferating retinal tissue.

When a relatively rapidly growing tissue comes in contact with an unspecialized but more slowly growing tissue, the rate of growth of the slower component tends to assume that of the faster. The chemical basis for this is uncertain, except that the stimulus supplied by the faster growing component is of a nonspecific character, but there is no doubt about the fact. It is to be seen clearly for instance in the outgrowth of bud stolons in thaliacean tunicates, where an endodermal outgrowth is a pacemaker and other adjacent tissues conform, and in the development of the medusa bells or entocodons of hydromedusae (Berrill, 1950 *a, b*; 1949).

Accordingly, when the optic vesicles, median or lateral, still in a state of growth, come into contact with unspecialized epidermis, the epidermis of the area of contact undergoes a growth acceleration. For a while the apposed optic and epidermal layers grow as one. This actually is an observational fact in the development of vertebrate eyes in general. Actual contact *is* made, the epidermis immediately exhibits increased growth in the contact area, giving rise at first to a palisade thickening or 'placode'. The phenomenon is exactly comparable to the examples I have just given, and is in keeping with the discovery that optic vesicle stimulus in amphibian embryos is a general one and only the epidermis in its response exhibits specificity.

I suggest therefore that the primitive but functioning optic vesicles came into contact with adjacent epidermis and inevitably induced local epidermal thickening as a result of locally accelerated epidermal growth. This alone would have offered evolutionary opportunities for lens elaboration, for it would, even as an induced 'placode', have tended to refract light into the optic layer whether cup-shaped or not. The difference between median and lateral eyes, both in character and eventual fate, I believe to be a consequence of differences in size. The median eyes were small and made contact as evaginating tissue with only a very small area of epidermis; this epidermis thickened and gave rise to a simple solid lens, but was, at the critical stage of development, of too small an area and too small a number of constituent cells to invaginate as a vesicle. The lateral outgrowth, on the other hand, evaginating from a relatively broad lateral area of neural tube instead of from the narrow contour of the dorsal regions, makes and made contact with a relatively broad area of epidermis; such an epidermal area not only thickened with increase in growth, but consisted of sufficient cells to permit invagination. (For a discussion of invagination, evagination, and segregations in relation to cell numbers cf. Berrill, 1941.) Moreover, if the lateral optic vesicles were growing at a relatively greater rate at the time of contact, the growth stimulus given to adjacent epidermis would be greater and the response correspondingly large.

The lenses of both lateral and median eyes can, in fact, be readily accounted for as simple growth responses to the growing optical outgrowths, at first inevitable consequences and later as rudiments secondarily exploited. In other words the developmental and the evolutionary mechanics of eye-lens formation are virtually the same.

21

THE VERTEBRATE EGG

FOR complete emancipation from the sea, changes in the nature of the egg have been as necessary as changes in the nature of the animal itself, less spectacular perhaps than the changes made necessary at a later time in relation to the emergence of freshwater vertebrates on to the land, but none the less almost if not quite as important.

The confinement of early vertebrates to a freshwater habitat, the presence in a return to fresh water of all existing primitive vertebrates for breeding purposes, and the apparent fate of Amphioxus, indicate that there was no straddling of the border between fresh and salt water. The early chordates evolved into vertebrates at least in part because eggs were laid and developed in fresh water, and this in turn demanded certain qualities in the egg.

The capacity of an egg to develop in fresh water rather than sea-water is a matter of chemistry that need not concern us much. Presumably the mature animals which themselves had adjusted their osmotic balance to the difference between their original salt content and that of the freshwater environment laid eggs which as a result of that process had already become more or less attuned to the lack of external salts. The ease with which the tissues of a marine animal can become adjusted to living in fresh water depends primarily upon the time allowed, great changes being tolerated by many forms if the required rate of change is extremely slow; it depends also upon the presence of a proportionately high proportion, though perhaps very low in absolute concentration, of calcium salts in the fresh water, as Pantin (1931) demonstrated in the case of the estuarine flatworm Gunda. No special problem seems to be raised in this connexion. If young adults grew to sexual maturity in fresh water they could in all probability lay eggs that could develop in fresh water, particularly if the eggs were enclosed in membranes more or less impermeable to salts, as most vertebrate eggs appear to be. The important changes involved in the evolution of a distinctive freshwater vertebrate egg were of another kind.

We can start with the assumption that the eggs of primitive chordates were shed oviparously and were of the same order of size as those of Amphioxus, ascidians, Larvacea, &c., namely, from 0·1 to 0·2 mm. diameter. Eggs of this size inevitably develop into minute larvae which might or might not have found suitable food organisms in the bodies of fresh water in which the parental animals were feeding. It is doubtful in any case. More importantly the minute eggs typical of an Amphioxus would for the most part suffer one of two fates. In completely still water they would sink to the bottom, and being of such small size would tend to be engulfed there in the detritus or mud. If sufficient currents existed to keep the eggs in motion and off the bottom, the same currents would carry them downstream and in one way or another destroy their chances of survival. The primary change in the nature of the egg connected with survival in fresh water is mainly one of size. A larger egg could develop in pockets on the bottom without being smothered or being carried away by gentle currents, and could even be supplied with a glutinous surface for a more specialized anchorage if necessary; and a larger egg would develop into an organism correspondingly larger at the time it commenced to feed on its own, and therefore better able to feed upon the same general kind of food as its parents'. Just as Amphioxus appears to represent a type that lost its head in order to eliminate a tendency to migrate from the sea to the rivers, so the chordates on the inland side of the river barriers laid larger and heavier eggs so that reproduction as well as growth could take place in the inland waters and so eliminate the need to migrate down to the sea to breed. I think there is little doubt that this was the compelling factor. Simply in terms of economy of effort, there would have been favourable selection of those chordates that laid eggs capable of developing in the freshwater feeding areas without being swept away or smothered. An occasional spawning without migration on the part of sexually mature individuals must have been a common physiological accident, and natural selection would quickly operate in favour of any that laid larger eggs than others.

Quite apart from the above approach, we can compare the primitive chordate egg as represented by those of ascidians and Amphioxus with the primitive eggs of vertebrates as represented by those of lampreys, of such fish as Polypterus and the lung fishes, and of most amphibians. Vertebrate eggs such as these are of one and the same order of size, from about 1·0 to 2·5 mm. diameter, that is, about ten times the diameter of the eggs of primitive marine chordates and about 1,000 times the volume. In all cases the cells finally produced are, tissue for tissue, somewhat larger than those of Amphioxus or ascidians, and the individual at the time it begins to feed consists of about 1 million cells in contrast to the several thousand produced by the smaller type of chordate egg (Berrill, 1935a).

Some insight into the general relationship of the two types of eggs, however, can be gained if we compare for instance the developing eggs of urodele and anuran amphibians with those of Amphioxus and ascidians.

In the first place the fate maps are remarkably alike, and in each case crescent-shaped regions represent neural and chordal tissues, together with mesoderm, in bilateral pattern. In the ascidian and Amphioxus egg the mesodermal crescents are visible shortly after fertilization. In anural amphibian eggs the grey crescent, which corresponds to the yellow or mesodermal crescent of the others, appears about one hour after fertilization, but before the first cleavage. In the urodele egg a visible crescent is not detectable.

In the case of the ascidian egg the first cleavage seems always to coincide with the axis established by the crescent; when the blastomeres of the two-cell stage are separated they give rise to what are essentially left or right half embryos. In the anuran egg, of Rana or Bufo, the first cleavage coincides with the crescent-established axis in more than 40 per cent. of cases; isolated blastomeres of the two-cell stage, if not inverted, give rise to virtual right or left half embryos. While there is evidence of somewhat greater plasticity in the anuran egg at the time of the first cleavage, the two types are much alike in so far as the relationship of determination stage to time of first cleavage is concerned.

In Amphioxus, embryos and larvae from right or left 1/2 or 2/4 blastomeres are typical in all but size; anterior or posterior

2/4 blastomeres form partial larvae only. In the case of both urodeles and cyclostomes blastomeres isolated at the two-cell stage develop into complete larvae of smaller size if the cleavage furrow cuts across the middle of the presumptive crescent; otherwise only one part develops normally, while the other does not. With regard to the stage of determination reached by the time of the first cleavage, therefore, the egg of Amphioxus and those of lampreys and urodeles are very similar.

Can we accordingly look upon the primitive vertebrate egg, as represented by those of lampreys and urodeles, as a greatly enlarged version of the egg of Amphioxus, enlarged to at least ten times the diameter or a thousand or more times the volume, in combination with some increase in relative amount of yolk? It does appear that apart from such differences in size and yolk content, the two kinds of eggs at the time of the first cleavage are closely comparable, both with regard to plan of ooplasmic presumptive patterns and to the stage of determination reached at that time. We at least can employ this as our point of departure.

Discussion of this is, however, necessarily restricted for lack of data. For while we have records of the developmental times in relation to temperature in the case of ascidians, Amphioxus, and amphibians, comparable information concerning the development of the lamprey egg is lacking; and while the effect of size of egg upon various aspects of development can be analysed in the case of both ascidians and anuran amphibia, since egg size is greatly variable in these groups, this is not the case either for Amphioxus or lampreys. In other words, while we are more directly interested in the relationship between the amphioxus and lamprey type of egg, we can obtain a more informative comparison between ascidian and amphibian. Three or four examples from each will suffice to show certain significant features.

The small, transparent type of ascidian egg, as for example that of Ascidia, Ciona, Phallusia, &c., cleaves at much the same rate as the similarly sized egg of Amphioxus, at the same given temperature. Thus at temperatures of 24–25° C. the Amphioxus egg divides approximately every twenty-five minutes and the ascidian egg in about thirty-five minutes; the difference is not significant. Most of the relevant data for ascidian and anuran comparison, however, is of records made at 16–17° C., and 18° C. respectively, temperatures close enough to make comparisons valid for the present purpose.

At this general level the egg of Ascidia divides at first at intervals of about one hour; gastrulation (between sixth and seventh cleavage) begins after 7 hours; and neurulation is under way at 10 hours. The egg of Perophora, with a diameter of 0·25 mm., has an initial intercleavage interval of 4 hours and commences gastrulation after about 40 hours. That of Botryllus has a diameter of 0·45 mm., an initial intercleavage interval of 5–6 hours, and gastrulates at about 60 hours. The egg of Ecteinascidia turbinata is the largest of all ascidian eggs, 0·72 mm. diameter; it has an intercleavage interval at first of 9–10 hours, and gastrulates around 110 hours (at 16° C., which in this case is lower than the normal environmental temperature of this species). In all of these cases egg size alone appears to be the variable, and not the relative amount of yolk; in all cases, for instance, gastrulation remains strictly embolic.

When this and similar data are plotted, we get a straight line relationship between rate of cleavage and development as a whole on the one hand and egg diameter on the other. That is to say, the developmental rate for all eggs exceeding 0·2 mm. diameter varies directly with the volume/surface-area ratio, so that the larger eggs cleave and develop at a very slow rate compared with those of smaller size. By extrapolation, an ascidian egg of 1·0 mm. diameter would take as many weeks to develop as that of Ascidia or Ciona takes in days. Whether an amphioxus egg enlarged to the same degree would develop at the same retarded pace we can only guess; I believe that it would.

Accordingly it is somewhat startling to find that the primitive vertebrate eggs, with diameters ranging from 1 to 2 mm., do not suffer this retardation. Those for which we have normal tables are Xenopus laevis (Weisz, 1945), Rana pipiens (Shumway, 1940), and R. sylvaticus (Pollister and Moore, 1937). Xenopus has the smallest and least yolky egg of these, with a diameter of 0·9–1·0 mm., larger than that of Ecteinascidia but close enough for purposes of comparison. According to Weisz the intercleavage intervals at first are about 1 hour; gastrulation commences after 7 hours and is complete at 13; neurulation commences at 15 hours. The cleavage and developmental rate as a whole is in fact almost as rapid as that of ascidian eggs of minimum size in spite of a difference in size of the two types of nearly 10 times in diameter. The larger eggs of Rana species also divide roughly once each hour, but the time elapsing before the onset of gastrulation is relatively long, and the subsequent period of development somewhat retarded, but even here the rates are comparable with those of Xenopus and do not approach the slow pace of the larger ascidian eggs. These comparisons are shown in Table IV.

TABLE IV

Animal	Diameter of egg mm.	Intercleavage interval hours, at 18° C.	Gastrulation onset to end hours from fertilization	Hatching hours from fertilization 18° C.
Xenopus laevis . .	1·0	1	7–13	55
Rana sylvatica . .	2·1	1	19–32	90
Rana pipiens . .	1·6	1	26–44	140
Amphioxus . . .	0·12	$\frac{1}{2}$	6$\frac{1}{2}$–12	(48)
Ascidiella aspersa .	0·15	$\frac{3}{4}$	6–8	26
Perophora listeri . .	0·25	4	30–50	170
Botryllus schlosseri .	0·45	5$\frac{1}{2}$	60–80	190
Ecteinascidia turbinata .	0·72	10	100–140	400

To sum up: the primitive vertebrate egg possesses a general organization and the same type of fate map as the eggs of ascidians and Amphioxus; the stage of chemical determination attained at the time of the first cleavage is approximately the same in Amphioxus, Lamprey, and Urodele, while in this respect the eggs of ascidians and anural amphibia are more alike; the rate of cleavage and morphogenesis of the vertebrate egg is approximately the maximum rate characteristic of ascidian and amphioxid eggs of minimal size and is not at all like that of the larger ascidian eggs. Therefore, while we can with some justification look upon the primitive vertebrate egg as a greatly enlarged version of an Amphioxus egg, we must assume that in some way the pro-vertebrate egg evolved to its relatively large size without suffering from the limitations of a decreasing surface-area/volume ratio. It seems to me that the conclusion must be made that a profound change of a metabolic character occurred during the early evolution of the freshwater chordates which made it possible for the egg to develop rapidly in spite of its large size, and that this advance in the energy system would extend to a marked degree to the whole organism throughout its existence and would not be confined merely to the early phase of development. Possibly the general adjustment of the cells, tissues, and organism as a whole to the low concentration of salts in the water was at least partly responsible.

Spermatozoa are of interest in this connexion. The spermatozoa of marine invertebrates, ascidians, and Amphioxus remain viable in sea-water for many hours. Those of the lamprey and all other freshwater vertebrates are viable for approximately one minute after being shed. Either their limited energy is expended at a remarkably fast rate, or they are imperfectly adapted to existence in fresh water, or perhaps something of each. Whichever it may be, the result has been the inception and evolution of mating behaviour in vertebrates from the beginning of their existence as breeders in fresh water.

If spermatozoa show indications of imperfect adjustment to the freshwater medium, the eggs apparently are so well adapted that much of their evolution as eggs must have taken place in fresh water. All vertebrate eggs that are but partly protected by enveloping jelly and membrane, and cleave holoblastically (that is, are not overburdened with yolk), are laid in fresh water. All vertebrate eggs that are laid in the sea, whether of cyclostomes or fish, are dense with yolk, and most of them are relatively large; individually and as a group they show evidence of readaptation to what has become a secondary environment, with respect to the vicissitudes of larval life.

The larvae of the freshwater vertebrates are in fact as significant as their eggs, as Graham Kerr (1919) has emphasized, for they are as relevant to the evolution of vertebrates as the respective adults. No matter what the final size of the adult form, or the nature of its dermal armour, if the type of egg now laid by lampreys, sturgeon, lungfish, ganoids, and amphibians represents the ancient vertebrate kind, then aquatic vertebrates have as individuals always had to develop from an egg a millimetre or two in diameter, and they have always had to become a small naked larval form before the greater size, complexity, and any sort of dermal protection could be acquired. The nature of the larva at the time of hatching from the egg membrane and its consequent liberation from the place where the egg may have been laid or attached has accordingly always been crucial. Generally speaking the larva at the hatching stage is far from having completed its development even as a closed system. It is not ready to feed, its sensory organs are poorly differentiated, and while the heart has usually commenced to beat and the tail can be employed for somewhat feeble swimming movements, the organism requires a further undisturbed period of development before it is able to fend for itself. It is not equipped to maintain itself either against a flow of water or in any active way against the pull of gravity.

Lamprey larvae, upon hatching, orient by means of their pigmented but lens-less optic cups and burrow at once in the typical ammocoete fashion. They escape displacement by currents, find protection from possible predators, and yield to the force of gravity by the simple expedient of burrowing just beneath the surface of the mud or muddy sand of river-banks. The habit appears to be necessary where currents flow at an appreciable rate, and in so far as the primitive vertebrate seems to have been associated with rivers, a larval type such as that of the newly hatched lamprey both in structure and habit may have well been the original kind. The ammocoete mode of life may have always been a larval phase during which the individual grew to a size which gave it power enough to maintain or control position in a stream. If the manner of existence of Amphioxus is derived from this, then Amphioxus is not only degenerate in possessing an abortive head, but is neotenic as well.

Be this as it may, the aquatic larvae of the great majority of other freshwater vertebrates are of a different character. It is possible that this second type has been derived from the first during the course of evolution, for we have to look upon natural selective factors as operating upon all stages of development and perhaps upon the critical and vulnerable larval phases above all. On the other hand this may represent a dichotomy from the beginning; that almost from the start the newly evolved freshwater vertebrates which had abandoned the seaward breeding migration tended to lay eggs either in the gravelly beds of streams and rivers, or sought out more sheltered bays and backwaters where currents had virtually no existence and where the only hazards for developing eggs were the combination of soft

mud and the pull of gravity, and the presence of small arthropodan predators on the bottom. Taken together, the newly
hatched larvae of sturgeons, lung fishes, ganoids, and amphibians
forcibly suggest that the primitive freshwater fish of Devonian
and earlier times developed holoblastically from eggs of 1 to 2 mm.
diameter into larvae 6 to 8 mm. long, equipped with external
gills and a pair of cement organs on the ventral surface close to
the mouth; and that a period of development, of much the same
duration as that of embryonic development, was passed through
attached to vegetation by cement-organ secretion, and during
which time external gills served the functioning vascular system
while internal gills completed their differentiation. It is likely,
I think, that larvae such as these evolved somewhat later than
the ammocoete type, possibly as part of the Gnathostome emergence itself and in all probability in relation to the comparative
stagnation of inland water of the early Devonian period. Neither
ammocoete nor tadpole should be regarded as representing past
adult conditions, either in habits or structure, but I believe there
is little doubt that the one and then the other have been in their
turn developmental phases of the earliest vertebrates.

22

THE VERTEBRATES

As so often is the case, an end is only a new beginning. The origin and ancestry of the vertebrates becomes the evolution of the vertebrates, and there is no natural place to draw the line. The subject is vast and the literature enormous. What follows is accordingly in brief report. The problems are many.

The Larvae: Ammocoete and Tadpoles

The larval lamprey, or ammocoete, hatches after about three weeks' development, as a transparent eel-like creature about 10 mm. long. Orientating by means of its pair of retina-A eye cups, it swims briefly and soon burrows in the soft mud of the river bottom and banks. Thereafter, until the time of metamorphosis, its developing lateral eyes become covered over by opaque skin and are blind; the pineal eye remains light sensitive but is concerned less with any form of vision than with the diurnal change in pigmentation of the skin, from dark by day to light by night. Active light response comes only from photoreceptors in the tail, which inform a burrowing ammocoete whether its rear end is sticking out of the mud or not, the sensations apparently being carried forward to the brain by the lateral line nerves (Young, 1950). When undisturbed, the larvae are fully embedded in mud, with mouth region barely visible in a small depression. Food is drawn in by the water current produced by the rhythmic movements of the gills, and appears to be drawn mainly from adjacent mud surface where detritus and small organisms are settling.

The particles enter the pharynx with the water current, but before they can disperse and pass out through the gill slits they are intercepted by a large column of flowing mucus pouring into the mid-pharynx, produced by a comparatively short but complex endostyle. The mucus food cord, rotating in the current, passes directly back to the oesophagus. Apart from the relatively

Q

great mucus productivity of the endostyle, and the creation of a feeding current by the action of gill muscles rather than gill cilia, the feeding mechanism as a whole is remarkably similar to that of larvacean and thaliacean tunicates, rather than to the mucus sheet system of the sessile ascidians; compared with the simple endostylar structure of tunicates and Amphioxus it has become considerably elaborated, particularly with regard to increase in

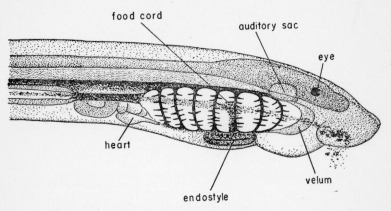

FIG. 29. Freshly hatched ammocoete larva of lamprey, feeding on green algae and detritus, showing endostyle and food cord (after Young).

mucus-secreting layers on each side. At metamorphosis these resorb and the organ becomes a fairly typical vertebrate thyroid with follicles derived not from the mucus-producing cells but from simpler epithelial tissue adjacent to them. Experiments with radioactive iodine show that iodine accumulates in the presumptive thyroid tissue in the ammocoete, and it seems probable that the metabolic function of the thyroid coexists with the endostylar feeding structure and predates the morphological thyroid both in development and evolution. This may well go hand in hand with the fact that the blood carries haemoglobin, whereas that of Amphioxus and Tunicates has no true respiratory pigment and apparently carries no more oxygen than an equivalent amount of sea-water. The great development of the thyroid tissue at the time of metamorphosis, presumably with accompanying increased thyroxin effect, may be a condition not only of metamorphosis itself but of the change from a primarily sessile organism to an active predator.

Atrium

Amphioxus and all tunicates other than the permanently embryonic Larvacea possess an atrial cavity which clearly serves the dual purpose of gill protection and of controlling the nature, course, &c., of the exhalant water current. Its value is obvious, and if the freshwater chordates are descendants of a marine tunicate stock, if Amphioxus has descended from an originally migratory form related to the primitive freshwater chordates, then we must regard the original atrium as a valuable branchial feature that has been lost by these vertebrate descendants.

Ammocoete larvae remain embedded in soft mud at least to the same extent that Amphioxus does in sand, but the gills function well enough without atrial protection or comparable water current modification. So that at least in the case of a way of life such as this where muscle action has taken the place of ciliary for producing water expulsion, the atrium is not essential. On the other hand, in Myxine, the exhalant branchial ducts of either side converge and join posteriorly to form the equivalent of a functional atrium. The gill covers of fish serve much the same end; while the gill chambers of anuran amphibian tadpoles, opening posteriorly by a pair of opercular siphons in Xenopus and by a single one in the others, are virtual functional redevelopments of the atrial cavity and siphon. The feature appears to be of general usefulness in relation to the passage of water through lateral gill systems, in free-swimming forms at least. It is unlikely that it would be disadvantageous to the ammocoete larva, since its only external effect would be to direct the exhalant current to a region more remote from the intake of water at the mouth, unless perhaps the disturbance of silt produced by open gill pouches near the mouth aids the intake of particles. Yet Amphioxus, which feeds in much the same way, retains the structure. If the atrium is a considerable asset to begin with and tends to be reacquired in a functional sense by a number of later forms, why has it been lost? I suggest that it relates to the early stages in the evolution of paired fins.

Lateral Fins

Steady movement of a more or less cylindrical object through water requires keels or fins of some sort if it is to avoid significant rolling motion. A continuous dorsal and ventral fin serves this purpose reasonably well, without the presence of lateral fins, but only as long as the tail is actively and strongly propelling the animal through the water, as a cursory study of amphibian larvae shows very well; rolling tends to occur, however, as soon as the animal is moving passively. For gliding locomotion, or alternate thrust and glide, the median fin apparently confers only minimal stability. Most salps that are towing their chains of buds, for instance, possess a tunic moulded into lateral keels, with concave surfaces between, that give a maximum stability for steady movement; a rolling or rotating progression would endanger the chain trailing behind. Amphioxus for all its usual sedentary habit possesses a pair of small metapleural folds running longitudinally along the ventro-lateral surface of the body commencing near the mouth and ending at the atriopore. These serve as bilge keels, as anti-rolling devices; while numerous smaller longitudinal ridges run lengthways between them along the ventral surface of the atrial wall, serving the same general purpose and resembling the abdominal ridges of the larger whales. The pair of metapleural folds are merely the outermost pair of ridges considerably enlarged.

Now the demands put upon Amphioxus as a swimming chordate must be pretty well at a minimum, yet we must regard these folds and ridges as either of functional and survival value or as persistent features now serving no valuable purpose. In the case of plastic tissue such as these folds are made of, the second alternative seems unlikely.

The question which arises is whether the stabilizing equipment of Amphioxus would be adequate if much greater stress was placed upon it. I am inclined to think not. Moreover the same structure produced on a larger scale in association with a larger organism would be relatively less efficient. The lateral folds contain internal spaces and consist of little more than epidermis, and a reasonable rigidity is maintainable only in relation to a comparatively small size.

As previously described, the Amphioxus atrium develops in the first place as a pair of longitudinal thickenings of the ventro-lateral body wall of the young larvae, which enlarge to form two well-marked folds—the metapleures. Then a pair of small solid longitudinal ridges appear on the inner opposed faces of the folds, and, to quote Willey, it is by the subsequent meeting and coalescence of these subatrial ridges that the atrial cavity becomes enclosed as a small median tube lined by ectoderm . . . at the posterior extremity, the atrial tube does not become closed in, but remains permanently open as the atriopore. It is a curious fact that the fusion of the subatrial ridges to enclose the atrial tube takes place gradually from behind forwards. . .

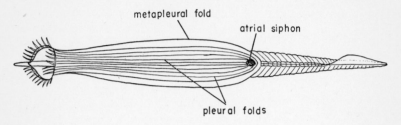

metapleural fold

atrial siphon

pleural folds

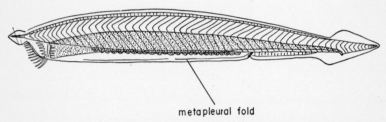

metapleural fold

FIG. 30. Ventral and lateral views of Amphioxus, showing pleural and metapleural stabilizing folds (after Franz).

The functional metapleural folds are only the small ventral-lateral projections of the angles of the more extensive folds formed during the development of the atrium.

As chordates grew larger and more powerful, and greater pressures were put upon the thin marginal folds, more developmental emphasis would have been placed upon the residual metapleural fold and less upon the transverse fusion process. Moreover, the folds, lying as they do at the lower extremities of the myotomes, could be readily filled by myotomic extension to form keels not only of relatively solid tissue, but keels sharing the waves of locomotory muscle contractions of the series of myotomic bodies.

In other words, there seems to be a natural basis for the evolution of lateral fin folds, from which the paired fins have later

differentiated, as Goodrich has so well argued for studies on fin
development in elasmobranchs (1906, 1933), and as the long
continuous lateral fin folds of Jamoytius suggest.

Equilibration

A stabilizing system of fins or keels is advantageous by itself,
even without any sensory-motor controlling devices. Salps, for
instance, are stabilized by shape alone. But in the case of chordates holding a station in flowing streams or moving steadily
through water at the critical speeds for microphagous feeding,
movement must be more closely related to the medium. Sensitivity of the skin to the pattern of water pressures produced by
movement of a more or less streamlined body through the water
must have been an early acquisition to enable efficient responses
to be made by the tail and the emergent lateral fins. There is
little doubt that the lateral line system of the head and trunk of
primitively aquatic vertebrates is a channelled differentiation
of the sensory field exposed to stream flow, and the shallow open
grooves of the cyclostomes may be more primitive in this respect
than the more or less enclosed tubes of other vertebrates, including ostracoderms. In any event, whether the open-groove condition of cyclostomes, larval amphibians, and various specialized
teleosts is primitive or secondary, it must have been at one time
an intermediate evolutionary stage between the more generalized
skin surface sensitivity and the system of canals finally developed.
It has been shown experimentally that the system as a whole is
primarily responsive to the pressures of water against the skin
quite apart from the shock waves produced by other moving
bodies, and that nerve impulses are continuously being trans-
mitted to the brain even when the animal is undisturbed.

In its final form, which the Silurian ostracoderms share with
modern forms, the canals are fully enclosed except for regularly
spaced branch canals opening to the surface and so arranged as
to allow water to pass into the main canals; while at equally
regular intervals along the floor of the canals groups of neuro-
mast cells occur, each group resembling the sensory units of the
labyrinth. Beard in 1884 and Ayers in 1892 both put forward
the view that the sense organs of the internal ear are deeply
sunk neuromasts, and, as Goodrich (1930) states, this view is
supported by much weighty evidence—'they both develop from

similar dorso-lateral placodes, both have sense cells provided with sensory hairs receiving stimuli from a liquid medium (water or endolymph), both tend to sink away from the surface, and both are innervated by fibres from corresponding and related centres in the brain'. The pair of otic sacs invaginating from the larval skin, as simple locally enlarged units of the lateral line system, could have been sensitive to rolling and pitching movements of the head from the very beginning. If evolution followed the course we see in development, there is no stage at which functional value would have been absent. This interpretation is not new, nor has it been challenged, but it leads to certain speculations concerning the relationship of cyclostomes and ostracoderms to other vertebrates.

Young (1950), discussing the analysis made by Harris (1936) of the role of fins in the swimming of fish, writes:

a heterocercal tail is found in almost all the primitive swimming chordates; it is almost a necessity for an animal with a specific gravity in excess of the medium and little flexibility in the vertical plane. The component of positive pitch could be provided by the flattened head or by a continuous fin fold, such as may have been present in early fishes, and adjusted by the limited flexibility which is possible in the fin. The development of movable pectoral fins confers much greater control. Since the useful portions of the fin fold for this purpose would be those well in front and behind the centre of gravity, we can perhaps see the reason why the intervening region has become lost.

It is difficult to see just when the simple otic sac with localized sensory patches, functioning as a statocyst, evolved the system of semicircular canals. All gnathostomes possess the typical three canals, but cyclostomes and cephalaspid ostracoderms lack the horizontal canal (the condition in pteraspids and anaspids is not known). Did the horizontal canal evolve after the two-canal system was already established, or was it lost from an original three-canal system, or have agnathostomes and gnathostomes taken their separate paths from a common but more primitive starting-point? I suspect the last, for it is doubtful whether the horizontal canal could have even become such a positive liability that its elimination was necessary, while on the other hand the formation of the horizontal canal as a belated addition to two already representing the vertical planes is somehow implausible.

If we assume that the otic sac was functional as an organ of equilibration as a simple invaginated sac, then functional continuity must have persisted throughout its elaboration into the typical vertebrate labyrinth. I can see no way in which such an elaboration could take place except along essentially the same path that the otic sac follows during the course of its development in the individual vertebrate embryo and larva. During development three folds evaginate from the wall of the dorsal half of the otocyst, as grooves open throughout their length. Then the walls fuse in the centre of each fold, and break through, leaving the folds connected at each end to the remainder of the dorsal division of the otocyst, which is now the definitive utriculus. There does not seem to be any stage where functional adequacy could not have existed, from simple sensory tracts in the otocyst wall to the crista acoustica at the end of tubes segregated from the wall along the course of the tracts. An evolutionary progression from the one state to the other, following the general line of the developmental sequence, would be mainly a progression in increasing efficiency without any fundamental change in nature. From this standpoint there appears to be no particular difficulty. The problem rather concerns the particular location or orientation of the canals, or of the sensory tracts that gave rise to them. They cannot have evolved in order to analyse space in terms of its three dimensions. This would be not only purposive but too suggestive of mental abstraction. It is more profitable I think to consider the relative location of the canal-tracts as regions locally responding to spacial influences, that is, as special sensory areas evoked by particular movements.

The vertical canals can be considered apart from the horizontal canal, and it is important to realize that while the two vertical canals of one side are at right angles to one another, they do not parallel the long and transverse axes of the body, but each is set at an angle of roughly forty-five degrees to the long axis. In other words the line of the anterior canal of one side is parallel to that of the posterior canal of the other, and but for lateral displacement the two would be in line and the double set would form a cross centred behind the midbrain. If there were a single centrally placed otocyst, uninterrupted by the brain, anterior and posterior vertical canals, or their presumptive tracts, would exist as crossed diagonals relative to the primary axis of the organism. The significant feature I believe is not the right angle that each lateral pair of arms of such a cross makes with the other, but the forty-five degree angle each continuous line makes with the axis of the animal.

Canals, grooves, or tracts of special sensitivity represent local responses reflecting particularly significant movements of fluid within the organ. Three positional features are illuminating: the diagonal or oblique position relative to the longitudinal axis, the location of the ampulla at the posterior ends of the canals, and the confinement of the whole canal system to the dorsal half of the otocyst.

The general dorsal location indicates that sinking rather than rising movements have more meaning, for these are the movements causing fluid to press upwards against the dorsal walls of the otocyst. The posterior position of the ampullae indicate, as is obvious on other grounds, that forward movement is significant; pressures against the anterior wall would occur only as the result of backward movement, which in aquatic vertebrates is almost impossible. The diagonal setting completes the picture; the movements of the body producing the maximum flow along these axes are neither pitching nor rolling but a forward, downward motion with a sharp listing toward one side or the other, the animal moving forward and downward, canting sideways so that the line of travel is out of line with the axis of the head. This is a type of progression rarely if ever seen in a fish or fish-like vertebrate, and the conclusion seems obvious that the main function of the vertical canals has been to enable the owner to avoid this particularly bad form of imbalance; the warnings from right and left maintain a steady balanced forward course, either level or with a downward pitch. Such a system would evolve in a chordate swimming at some distance from the bottom, with a tendency to descend either for food or as the result of pitch produced by a relatively heavy anterior end. And from the first, within a large but simple otic sac, fluid pressure at certain points would be warning signals as distinctive as but less intense than those eventually produced in the crista acoustica of the ampullae. In the course of time the elaboration of the meaningful pressure tracks into morphological grooves and finally into canals would be almost inevitable.

The horizontal canal I believe has a different status and its absence in ostracoderms and cyclostomes and its universal presence in all gnathostomes indicates an early divergence in habits and locomotion. Exclusively related to lateral movements of the head, for the most part in the horizontal plane, it concerns either turning movements of the head resulting in change of direction, or the forward yawing produced by tail action of wide amplitude. The first would be primarily informative of speed and degree of turn, the second function might serve to dampen the lash of the posterior part of the body to an extent which would permit the head to be driven forward without it swinging so much from side to side. The latter seems to me to have been the more important. The lateral line system of the head and trunk as a whole should reflect the changing pressures of water resulting from a turn more than sufficiently, and the relative movement of fluid back along the outer wall of the otocyst I do not think would add significantly to the information centrally received. On the other hand, no matter what the particular form of the propulsive wave may be, whether that of an eel or of a salmon, the less the head yaws with each lateral thrust of the tail the more efficient the forward progression becomes. Control of the degree of head pivoting, in so far as it lies within the capacity of the individual, must surely depend upon sensitivity to it, and the horizontal canals or their antecedent grooves or tracts almost alone could supply the necessary information.

This means I think that the stock which gave rise to the gnathostomes evolved its three-canal system as fast, completely water-borne swimmers; and that ostracoderms, assuming the cephalaspids to be representative in this respect, became comparatively sluggish bottom dwellers either before differentiation of canals was well advanced or while they were plastic enough for the horizontal component to become suppressed. The alternative is that the vertical canals were evolved during a relatively light free-swimming phase that was succeeded by a heavy bottom-dwelling phase before the horizontal canals could come fully into being; and that part of the ostracoderm bottom-dwelling stock became light again, left the bottom and of necessity evolved horizontal canals as a belated addition to those already present. It is possible but does not seem too likely. I prefer to consider the ostracoderms as heavily armoured bottom dwellers that diverged from the main stock, and that gnathostomes evolved from fleeter and less encumbered swimmers. There is in this concept, however, an implication that the vertical canals evolved either sooner or more rapidly than the horizontal, that progression on an even keel took precedence over reduction in yawing, and that the ostracoderm stock descended to the bottom as an alternative to increasing its efficiency at swimming. Increase in current rates during the Ordovician may have forced the issue, presenting a more or less clear-cut choice between mastering the current of fast-flowing streams or escaping to the sanctuaries of the bottom of still waters. White's (1935) account of the Silurian freshwater pond in Herefordshire, only about 9 by 4 feet in area and represented by only a 2-inch deposit of mud shale, which contained about twenty pteraspids and twenty cephalaspids, together with about a dozen acanthodians, all apparently sluggish bottom-scavenging forms, suggests forcibly that the ostracoderms were in a sense fugitives from fast flowing water. And with their heavy rigid head shield extending half way back along the body, and a bottom-dwelling habit, lateral head movement would be restricted by inertia and in any case would not matter very much.

Yet even though ostracoderms may be a side-line of the main chordate advance, as fossils they are all we have that represent the Ordovician and Silurian vertebrates, apart from Jamoytius. In their general internal anatomy they are undoubtedly representative of the group as a whole, and while their exoskeleton may be highly specialized, it still points to a prevailing situation and presents a problem.

Bone

Homer Smith (1943) presents the usual explanation and offers an alternative.

The first vertebrates to appear in abundance in the fossil record, the Silurian and Devonian ostracoderms, the arthrodires, antiarchs, and the earliest shark-like forms bearing jaws, the acanthodians, and even the later advanced fishes, were typically encased from snout to tail in apparently impregnable armor which took the form of bony plates, scutes or scales. Any sample of the vertebrate population of Silurian-Devonian times from Pennsylvania to Spitzbergen, suggests that some death-dealing enemy, swift, merciless and irresistible, lurked in every corner of the world.

Why all this heavy armor? Romer (1933) has pointed out that the only visible enemies of the ostracoderms and early fishes were the eurypterids that shared the continental waterways. Admittedly some of these eurypterids were much larger than the ostracoderms and fishes, and possessed strong claws, but they were primarily sluggish mud-crawlers and unless they struck with their pointed tails; or injected poison, as do their offspring the scorpions, their fearsomeness may have been more apparent than real. The thesis that the armor of the early vertebrates served primarily to protect them from predacious enemies is perhaps open to question. May I offer an alternative suggestion: these vertebrates had an enemy which they could not see, but one which pursued them every minute of the day and night, and one from which there was no escape though they fled from Pennsylvania to Spitzbergen—physico-chemical danger inherent in their new environment. When the first migrant from the sea took up residence in freshwater, its blood and tissues, bearing the physico-chemical imprint of its marine home, were rich in salt: for we may on straight extrapolation assume that at the opening of either Cambrian or Ordovician time the sea had one-half or better of its present salinity. This saline heritage might be in part erased, but it could not wholly be cast aside without reorganizing every nerve and muscle cell. The evolution of a regulated internal environment, if it had not yet begun, was imperatively imminent. For in the new freshwater habitat the salts and proteins of the tissue cells drew water by osmotic pressure so that by degrees the organism tended to pass from excessive hydration to edema and *in extremis* to swell to death. We may confidently assert that were the osmotic infiltration of water not arrested, survival in freshwater would be impossible. The first step towards arresting the infiltration of water would naturally be to insulate the body as far as possible by a waterproof covering. Why not believe that the ever-present armor of the fossilized vertebrates of Silurian and Devonian time was a defense against the osmotic invasion of freshwater rather than against the claws and tailspines of eurypterids?

This approach seems to me to be closer to the truth. Vertebrates at this stage of their evolution certainly could not prey upon one another, and while a eurypterid might seize an armoured bottom-dwelling vertebrate, the armour probably would be effective protection; while those vertebrates with less armour and swimming freely are hardly likely to have been in any danger from such a source. And an impervious exoskeleton of dentine or bone would greatly reduce the area of water absorption and relieve the excretory system of at least part of the load of water elimination. To this extent I think Homer Smith is correct in his point of view. Yet it is, I think, only one aspect of the chemical problem.

Invasion of fresh water from the sea is not exactly a substitution of saltless water for the salt ocean; for fresh water, particularly of the comparatively still waters of shallow lakes and lowland rivers, is generally relatively rich in certain salts, particularly calcium carbonates and phosphates dissolved from adjacent land. While the total salt concentration of fresh water may be very low indeed compared with sea-water, its salt ratio is heavily weighed by carbonates and phosphates and the salt balance is new. The excretory system not only has to bail out excess of water but in some way compensate for excess of phosphates and calcium. In fact since the presence of calcium salt is known to enable such soft bodied forms as the estuarine flatworm Gunda to tolerate the extreme dilution of fresh water, and in general to form more protective protoplasmic surfaces in relation to maintenance of normal internal media, it appears likely, or at least possible, that precipitation of comparatively insoluble calcium phosphates at or beneath the skin surface would do double duty of eliminating excess of the salts from active presence in the body and at the same time gaining significant protection against water inflow. The integument of most arthropods combines both the functions of imperviousness and salt excretion, quite apart from its value as armour or skeleton, and I see no reason why a dentine surface should not have appeared in vertebrates in much the same way, tessellated, of course, to an extent permitting flexibility of the underlying musculature, and expansion during growth.

It is one thing to invoke the devil's protection, it is quite another to keep him under control. If an outer bony layer arose as a result of the conditions just mentioned, the problem thereafter would be to precipitate enough to be of value both as a protective layer and as an elimination without adding weight in excess of what a swimming creature can maintain without having to rest on the bottom. Ostracoderms, as we know them, I suggest are those that went too far too soon with this development, and became adapted in various ways to life on the bottom and in consequence failed to evolve either paired fins, as in pteraspids, or horizontal semicircular canals as in cephalaspids and possibly the others as well. Both of these groups were flattened forms with heavy bony-head shields and obvious adaptation for feeding on the bottom. Only the anaspids possessed a body shape in any way comparable to the fusiform shape of typical fishes.

The relative primitiveness of the two types of vertebrate skeletal material, bone and cartilage, has become a topic of much discussion. Cartilage is always the first to appear during the course of embryonic development and in a general way a cartilaginous skeleton is laid down first, supplying the basic architecture, and is later replaced to a varying extent by bone. And in the earlier days of embryology the individual developmental course was always considered to follow, in sequence at least, the evolutionary course of the species. So it was assumed that the primitive vertebrate skeleton was originally exclusively a cartilaginous one and that bone was a later discovery which more or less displaced it. The cartilaginous nature of the skeleton of the more primitive existing vertebrates, the cyclostomes, elasmobranchs, and to a lesser extent the Chondrostei, seemed to confirm this point of view.

At the hands of palaeontologists in particular, however, this interpretation has been roughly treated. Cyclostomes appear to find their oldest fossil relatives in the bony ostracoderms; the elasmobranchs and others in the more heavily armoured placoderms. The relative lack of bone in these recent vertebrates seems to be secondary, and we are thrown back on to developmental events exclusively for the meaning of cartilage. It should be pointed out, however, that palaeontologists work almost entirely with a selective sampling of the organisms we are interested in. Only those, with extremely rare exceptions, that have mineralized skeletons when alive are likely to have survived in fossil form. The rest, no matter how numerous, have passed into oblivion without leaving a trace, so that, for instance, while the bony ostracoderms are numerous as fossils in Silurian and Devonian deposits, there is no trace of them thereafter, although their non-bony descendants of cyclostomes have swarmed in the fresh waters and shallow seas ever since without leaving a trace of a tail behind them. When all members of a class can be expected to have been ossified, the normal palaeontological practice of working only with the known is the safe and proper procedure, but when a group can be expected to consist of a mixture of ossified and non-ossified forms the procedure is dangerous. In the present context it is I think a fallacy to assume that, because the oldest vertebrate fossils are with one exception all ossified forms, that this was the primitive condition. Both Gregory (1951) and Romer (1942) express this outlook, and Romer in particular has elaborated the thesis 'that bone, not cartilage, was the primitive skeletal material; that cartilage originally was not an adult tissue but a purely embryonic one evolved in connection with the development of internal skeletal elements; and that the presence of cartilage in the adult is indicative not of a primitive condition but of paedogenesis, the retention in the adult of an embryonic stage of skeletal development'. This I believe is a false antithesis.

With Romer's conclusion that cartilage in an existing adult vertebrate is an indication of neoteny there can be little disagreement, but the conclusion that cartilage could never have been an important component of a fully adult vertebrate skeleton I believe is unjustified. He emphasizes that cartilage is ideally adapted for growth, whereas bone, except in the form of dermal plates more or less 'floating free' in the skin, is inflexible, so that the one is employed during growth and the other incorporated only in the final stages. This is true enough, but a somewhat different point of view avoids the difficulty altogether, and I think the following is closer to reality: cartilage evolved as a secretion of connective tissue cells wherever muscle support and attachment was most needed, and formed a fairly typical cartilaginous skeleton from the beginning, as an internal supporting tissue of gills and pharyngeal floor, in relation to the brain as that organ itself evolved, and as a stiffening sheath around the notochord, while keeping pace with the growth of these structures throughout the life of the individual; and that an outer layer of bony material formed partly from a tendency for calcium phosphates to be excreted from the skin and partly as an exploitation of this process as a development of impermeability.

The difficulty of phosphate excretion would tend to increase with increasing body volume, and such a layer would be likely to appear late in the development of an individual, although as long as bone was limited to exoskeletal sites, it would not impede growth of the body as a whole. An expanding superficial coat of bony units of some kind and a growing internal skeleton of supporting cartilage could have gone on evolving side by side without mutual interference or any growth consequences such as appear once bone cells invade previously cartilaginous material. Bone cells in fact appear to be a later acquisition than bone or dentine as an exoskeletal substance, while the later tendency of primitive groups to become progressively less ossified than at first may well reflect an increasing efficiency of the internal renal excretory mechanisms whereby phosphates became more readily controlled.

It is worth while perhaps to give a little more detail of the one ostracoderm, Cephalaspis, that has been worked out with such brilliance by Stensiö, even though it is by no means a primitive or particularly early type. Watson (1951) summarizes the information concerning the nature of the skeleton and his account is given here:

Cephalaspis and its allies are freshwater, bottom-living animals in which the head, branchial region, and a variable length of the anterior part of the trunk are surmounted and surrounded by a co-ossified series of dermal bones. From this head-shield, which is produced laterally, often into long spines, the rest of the body arises abruptly. It is triangular in transverse section, the flat surface being connected with the slightly smaller lateral surfaces by a row of angulated scales; a similar series forms the mid-dorsal ridge, which is drawn up locally into one or two dorsal fins. Posteriorly there is a heterocercal caudal fin. From the hinder surface of the head shield, laterally to the insertion of the body, arises a pair of highly peculiar fins, scale-covered, with an internal musculature, and presumably, although there is not direct evidence on the matter, containing a skeleton. . . . Cephalaspis has a jawless mouth and a paired series of about ten gill slits. Professor Stensiö in 1927 showed that below the dermal bone of the head shield in several cephalaspids there lies a very extensive endocranium whose nature must now be discussed.

This structure contains far more than a neural cranium and is of entirely peculiar nature. It is continuous throughout, and it is impossible to show that it ever consisted of separate elements. In general the bone in this endoskeleton usually consists only of an excessively thin lamella which coats the surface. It forms, for example, continuous bony canals surrounding the cranial nerves and their branches almost from origin to final distribution. It coats canals through which blood vessels pass, and it is limited ventrally by a great, continuous, smooth sheet of bone which extends over the whole of the very widened pharynx. It is so complete that it may fill the cavity of the cornua of the head shield, but in general there is nothing whatever in the way of bone connecting these superficial laminae. As Stensiö has pointed out, the only possible interpretation of this unusual condition is that the bone was laid down as peri-chondral bone on the surface of an extensive mass of a tissue sharply marked off from ordinary connective tissue, which can only have been some form of cartilage, perhaps the muco-cartilage of the ammocoete larva of Petromyzon.

If this interpretation of the cephalaspid condition is correct, as it appears to be, we get a rather clear picture of precipitation of bone salts at the surfaces of a nonvascular tissue, wherever such surfaces are present. It is difficult to see any advantage in the ossification of the lining of channels through which blood-vessels and nerves pass, and I believe we have here evidence in support of the contention that calcium phosphates are in the beginning an inadvertent product of the fresh water and its salts impinging on the internal media of marine ancestry.

Total phosphates fluctuate greatly in both the sea and in bodies of fresh water, but in both cases the mean is somewhere near 0·01 mg. per litre, that is, of the same order of concentration in the two media. With the adaptation of a marine stock to existence in fresh water there is a drop in total concentration of all salts from a value more than half the present concentration of salts in the sea to one that is but a small fraction of that; and an essential part of the process of adaptation, as Homer Smith has emphasized, is a mechanism for the continual bailing out of excess water from the body. The body system in other words is endeavouring to maintain a balance or ratio of salts of the same kind, if of somewhat lower total concentration, as that which it evolved in and inherited from the sea, but it does so in the face of not merely an over-abundant influx of water itself, but of certain salts contained in that water. These are predominantly the carbonates, phosphates, and nitrates of calcium and other elements, and if such salts as these entered the body and tissue fluids of primitive vertebrates with the water in which they were dissolved, their concentration within the body would tend to increase in inverse proportion to the extent that they could be eliminated. The calcium phosphates in particular, because of their extreme insolubility, would tend to crystallize or in some other way come out of solution and thereby become difficult if not impossible to handle adequately by the evolving renal excretory mechanism.

Precipitation presumably would occur to the greatest extent where the flow of body fluids was lowest, and would also tend to occur at already existing surfaces. Bone in its original form, in other words, is something that happened to the vertebrates as a result of the manner in which they handled the oedema problem created by the substitution of fresh water for marine habitat. Bone cells, which apparently came later, may well have been in the first place an organized cellular attempt to distribute the excess of calcium phosphate where it would do least harm, and by further selective processes, to those regions where it would even serve useful ends. The original internal stiffening, however, would have been cartilaginous, primarily a gelated material occupying those internal spaces where connective tissue fluids would be insufficiently supportive or stiffening.

According to this outlook the vertebrate skeleton as a whole evolved more or less along the lines suggested by the course of its development in various vertebrate embryos. The heavily armoured condition of most of the early vertebrates may in fact have been over-developed simply because of inability to eliminate the salts fast enough by other means, and was in no way an adaptation to meet external enemies of a more tangible kind. On this reckoning the cephalaspid and pteraspid ostracoderms, and other forms, became bottom feeders because they were too heavy to be anything else and as such they made the best of the situation.

One other aspect of the phosphate circumstances influencing the evolving early vertebrates concerned the metabolic level in general. Vertebrates utilize phosphorus in connexion with energy transfer much more effectively than do other forms, and employ it to a much greater extent. This may have been a response to an opportunity with excessive quantities of phosphates flowing through the system; those animals that could make the most use of it would gain in every way. They would be less encumbered by insoluble forms of phosphate salts and at the same time would become more efficient and powerful organisms, so that in the end the new and relatively rich phosphate medium itself conferred upon the muscles the power necessary to combat its currents. Moreover, the conversion of endostyle to thyroid, which relates to change in feeding mechanism and habits on the one hand, and to enhanced metabolic level on the other, may be an integral part of the situation just described.

The Brain and Hypophysis

White (1935) gives the following scheme as a possible course of the evolutionary development of the Agnathi.

Agnathous, aquatic, vertebrate animals with paired internal nares, ventral hypophysis, diphycercal tail, paired fin-fold and without armour

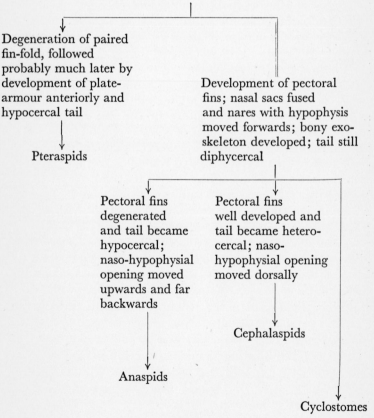

Degeneration of paired fin-fold, followed probably much later by development of plate-armour anteriorly and hypocercal tail

Pteraspids

Development of pectoral fins; nasal sacs fused and nares with hypophysis moved forwards; bony exoskeleton developed; tail still diphycercal

Pectoral fins degenerated and tail became hypocercal; naso-hypophysial opening moved upwards and far backwards

Anaspids

Pectoral fins well developed and tail became heterocercal; naso-hypophysial opening moved dorsally

Cephalaspids

Cyclostomes

All three groups appear to be departures from the main stock which evolved into the gnathostomes, and of which Jamoytius may have been a coextant survivor beyond its time. The point of interest at present, however, is the position of the naso-hypophysial aperture and the single median condition of the nasal sac.

In anaspids, cephalaspids, and modern cyclostomes the naso-hypophysial sac is far back on the dorsal surface of the head, while the olfactory region of the brain is or was an anterior median development. In all gnathostomes the nasal sacs are internal and the olfactory lobes paired. In the pteraspid (?) Aglaspis the nasal sacs are paired and appear to be widely separated at the edge of the broad anterior margin of the head, as though they were sacs similar in kind and position to the olfactory sacs as they first develop in amphibian embryos. This may represent the original condition—as simple chemical-sense direction-finding sacs comparable to the optic cups.

If the fused condition of the sacs and associated olfactory region is secondary, as is generally considered, the fusion may itself be merely the consequence of the relative growth of the upper marginal region of the mouth, the main function of which has been to shift the aperture of the pituitary duct to the upper surface of the head—that is, in the process of being drawn upwards and backwards as part of a relative growth of a large region, the paired sacs drew together into a single invaginative depression with the pituitary duct. I have already suggested that this took place in consequence of the ammocoete habit of burying itself in mud with only the hypophysial and pineal region more or less exposed to the surface. The great displacement posteriorly in the anaspids, cephalaspids, and cyclostomes perhaps indicates a prolonged larval life of ammocoete type in all three groups. The absence of this relative growth of the upper lip, and of its consequences, in all gnathostomes suggests that the ammocoete phase or habit was at the most a fleeting one or was abandoned early in the evolutionary history of the group. I think we should assume, however, quite apart from the question of fusion of nasal sacs and the dorsal position of the hypophysial duct, that functionally the condition in lampreys is reasonably primitive, and that in primitive vertebrates generally the hypophysial duct remained open and conducted water to the lumen of the pituitary.

The lamprey brain, although developed to a lesser degree than that of any other living vertebrate, possesses all of the basic units of vertebrate brains in general. How has it evolved? Amphioxus gives us no help, for if this animal once had some sort of brain and later lost it, what was lost extended as far back as and included the hypophysial region. To return to the tunicates may appear to be a very long step, but in fact the neural complex of a tunicate seems to supply a remarkably good starting-point.

The neural gland of the ascidian and other tunicates has already been discussed, both structurally and in relation to its function, and its homology with the hypophysis, and that of its duct with the hypophysial duct, appears to be established. Its function concerns the testing of water taken into the mouth, with particular reference to the presence of gametes and their dissolved associated chemical products, and with the stimulus releasing the ripe gonads of the animal. It operates by way of the neural ganglion immediately dorsal to it and in contact with it. This neural mass or brain controls the opening and closing of the siphons and appears to be sensitive both to light and to have sensory nerves associated with chemical sense cells at the mouth entrance. It also supplies nerves to the viscera as a whole, to the gonads, the digestive canal, and the heart. In other words the neural ganglion and gland complex governs the organism in a combined neural and chemical manner. In the case of the ascidian it comprises the whole of the governing centre. If the course of events that I have outlined in this book is anywhere near the truth, the ascidian neural complex should lead directly to the type of brain we find in the lamprey in particular and vertebrates in general.

The homology of the neural gland and its duct with the hypophysis and its duct is reasonably well established. What of the ganglionic mass associated with it? That is, can we identify the ascidian brain with a particular region of the vertebrate brain? In my opinion there is no doubt about it. The vertebrate hypophysis connects with the infundibulum of the brain to form the pituitary gland which acts as the chemical master of the organism as a whole and of other endocrine glands in particular. The gland itself, however, now appears to be under the control of the adjacent basal region of the brain, namely, the hypothalamus. The hypothalamus connects directly with the back of the pituitary gland, and according to Mirsky it is the hypothalamus which produces a chemical agent in response to stress, whether from pain, fear, loud noises, or mental or physical stress of any sort, and releases it through the pituitary gland.

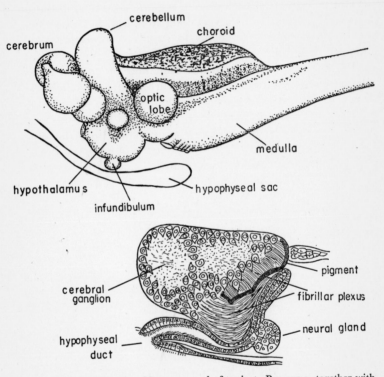

FIG. 31. Side view of brain of Lamprey and of tunicate Pyrosoma, together with hypophyseal duct in each case (after Stensiö, and Neumann).

That is to say, the hypothalamus, working through the pituitary gland, and itself receiving impulses from other parts of the brain, controls the basic activities and reactions of the various organs and tissues. Its operations in conjunction with the pituitary gland appear to be the nervous gateway to all that is most fundamental in the control of the organism as a whole. And in its morphological and chemical relationship with the pituitary and with the body it seems to be the functional equivalent and in fact the homologue of the ascidian neural ganglion. This general relationship is confirmed by the recent work of Palay (1953) on man and monkey. In other words, although its function in the vertebrates has undoubtedly become somewhat circumscribed, the hypothalamus represents the original, primitive brain and is the centre from which later evolutionary expansions have taken place.

That this is so becomes less obvious the greater the development of the superstructure, and conversely it is clearest in the brain of the lamprey. If we disregard the relatively massive medulla as being merely an expansion of the neural tube in relation to local concentrations of nerves, the hypothalamus appears to be the pivot upon which the rest of the brain depends. Optic lobes, thalamus, cerebral hemispheres, and olfactory region all appear as local evaginative growths of neural tissue immediately dorsal to the hypothalamus, and can be regarded as later developments. If we regard the ventral half of the ascidian neural ganglion as giving rise to the hypothalamus and remaining in close association with the hypophysis, we can picture the dorsal and primarily sensory part as giving rise to the olfactory and optic outgrowths and to the co-ordinating thalamic and cerebral regions associated with them. Penfield and others (1952) have demonstrated that the thalamus is the region of the human brain closely associated with consciousness. The interpretation just given would identify this region with the dorsal part of the ascidian brain, just as the ventral part is identified with the hypothalamus. It is significant therefore that the locale of human consciousness, together with the region associated with emotions and response to stress of all kinds, in conjunction with the master gland of the body, can be traced all the way back to the beginning. The centre of consciousness and of nervous and chemical control such as ascidians possess has expanded and become increasingly complex as evolution took place, but it has not shifted or become displaced. The continuity has persisted in spite of all that has been added to the brain in the course of more than 500 million years.

On this note I must end. Whether the flight of imagination outlined in the foregoing pages is correctly orientated or not, it at least has the merit of continuity. It may of course merely indicate an occupational hazard involved in studying sea squirts not wisely but too well. Unfortunately there is little hope that

the morphological argument can find verification in the discovery of actual fossil animals, which would, in the words of
D. M. S. Watson, give 'an intellectual respectability to our procedure'. Most, if not quite all, of the evidence that we can use to
reconstruct this most ancient chordate past must by the nature
of things come from the study of the living. And so a story that
hangs together in a logical way and includes most of the relevant
facts is perhaps all that we will ever possess. Proof may be for
ever unobtainable, and it may not matter, for here is such stuff
as dreams are made on.

BIBLIOGRAPHY

AYERS, H. 1892. 'Morphology of the Vertebrate Ear.' *J. Morph.* **6,** 198.

BACQ, Z. M., and FLORKIN, M. 1935. 'Mise en évidence, dans le complexe "ganglion nerveux-glande dorsale" d'une ascidie ("Ciona intestinalis"), des principes pharmacologiquement analogues à ceux du lobe postérieur de l'hypophyse des vertébrés.' *Arch. Internat. Physiol.* **40,** 422.

BATESON, W. 1884. 'The Early Stages in the Development of Balanoglossus.' *Quart. J. Micr. Sci.* **24,** 207.

—— 1885. 'The Later Stages in the Development of Balanoglossus.' *Quart. J. Micr. Sci.* **25,** 81.

—— 1886. 'Continued Account of the Later Stages of the Development of Balanoglossus.' *Quart. J. Micr. Sci.* **26,** 512.

BEARD, J. 1884. 'Sense Organs of Lateral Line and Morphology of Vertebrate Auditory Organ.' *Zool. Anz.* **7,** 123, 140.

DE BEER, G. R. 1951. *Embryos and Ancestors.* Oxford.

BERRILL, N. J. 1929. 'Digestion in Ascidians and the Influence of Temperature.' *Brit. J. Exp. Biol.* **6,** 275.

—— 1929. 'Studies in Tunicate Development. I. General Physiology of Development of Simple Ascidians.' *Phil. Trans. Roy. Soc.* B, **218,** 37.

—— 1931. 'Studies in Tunicate Development. II. Abbreviation of Development in the Molgulidae.' *Phil. Trans. Roy. Soc.* B, **219,** 281.

—— 1935. 'Studies in Tunicate Development. III. Differential Retardation and Acceleration.' *Phil. Trans. Roy. Soc.* B, **225,** 225.

—— 1935. 'Cell Division and Differentiation in Asexual and Sexual Development.' *J. Morph.* **57,** 353.

—— 1936. 'Studies in Tunicate Development. V. Evolution and Classification.' *Phil. Trans. Roy. Soc.* B, **226,** 43.

—— 1940. 'The Development of a Colonial Organism: Symplegma.' *Biol. Bull.* **79,** 272.

—— 1941. 'Spatial and Temporal Growth Patterns in Colonial Organisms.' *Growth*, 3rd symposium, p. 89.

—— 1947. 'Metamorphosis in Ascidians.' *J. Morph.* **81,** 249.

—— 1948. 'The Nature of the Ascidian Tadpole, with reference to Boltenia Eclimata.' *J. Morph.* **82,** 269.

—— 1948. 'Temperature and Size in the Reorganization of Tubularia.' *J. Exp. Zoo.* **107,** 455.

—— 1949. 'Polymorphic Transformations of Obelia.' *Quart. J. Micr. Sci.* **90,** 235.

—— 1949. 'Growth and Form in Gymnoblastic Hydroids. I.' *J. Morph.* **84,** 1.

—— 1950. 'Budding and Development in Salpa.' *J. Morph.* **87,** 553.

—— 1950. 'Budding in Pyrosoma.' *J. Morph.* **87,** 537.

—— 1950. 'Size and Organization in the Development of Ascidians.' (In) *Essays on Growth and Form*, presented to D'Arcy Wentworth Thompson. Oxford.

BERRILL, N. J. 1951. 'Regeneration and Budding in Tunicates.' *Biol. Rev.*
26, 456.

—— 1952. 'Regeneration and Budding in Worms.' *Biol. Rev.* **27,** 401.

—— and HUSKINS, C. L. 1936. 'The "Resting" Nucleus.' *Amer. Nat.* **70,** 257.

BERTALAFFANY, L. VON, and WOODGER, J. H. 1933. *Modern Theories of
Development.* Oxford.

BIGELOW, H. B., and FARFANTE, I. P. 1948. (In Lancelots) *Fishes of the
Western North Atlantic.* Sears Foundation Marine Research, Yale University.

BOVERI, T. 1892. 'Die Nierenkanaelchen des Amphioxus.' *Zool. Jahrb.
Abt. Anat.* **5,** 429.

BRIEN, P. 1927. 'Contribution à l'étude de la blastogénèse des Tuniciers.'
Arch. Biol. **37,** 1.

—— 1928. 'Contributions à l'étude de l'embryogénèse et de la blastogénèse
des Salpes.' *Rec. Ins. zool.* Torley-Rousseau, Brussels, **2,** 5.

BROOKS, W. K. 1893. *The Genus Salpa.* Baltimore.

BUTCHER, E. D. 1930. 'The Pituitary in the Ascidians (Molgula manhat-
tensis).' *J. Exp. Zool.* **17,** 1.

CARLISLE, D. B. 1951. 'On the Hormonal and Neural Control of the
Release of Gametes in Ascidians.' *J. Exp. Biol.* **28,** 463.

CHABRY, L. 1887. 'Contributions à l'embryologie normale et tératologique
des Ascidies simples.' *J. Anat. Physiol.* **23,** 167.

CHAMBERLAIN, T. C. 1900. 'On the Habitat of the Early Vertebrates.'
J. Geology, **8,** 400.

CONKLIN, E. G. 1905. 'The Organization and Cell Lineage of the Ascidian
Egg.' *J. Acad. Sci. Philadelphia* (2), **13,** 1.

—— 1905. 'The Mosaic Development in Ascidian Eggs.' *J. Exp. Zool.* **2,**
145.

—— 1911. 'The Organization of the Egg and the Development of Single
Blastomeres of Phallusia Mammillata.' *J. Exp. Zool.* **10,** 393.

—— 1931. 'The Development of Centrifuges Eggs of Ascidians.' *J. Exp.
Zool.* **60,** 1.

—— 1932. 'The Embryology of Amphioxus.' *J. Morph.* **54,** 69.

—— 1933. 'The Development of Isolated and Partially Separated Blastomeres of Amphioxus.' *J. Exp. Zool.* **64,** 303.

DALEQ, A. 1932. 'Études des localisations germinales dans l'œuf vierge
d'Ascidie par des expériences de mérogonie.' *Arch. Anat. Univ.* **28,** 223.

—— 1938. Étude micrographique et quantitative de la mérogonie double
chez Ascidiella scabra.' *Arch. Biol.* **49,** 397.

DAMAS, D. 1902. 'Recherches sur le développement des Molgules.' *Arch.
Biol.* **18,** 599.

DAMAS, H. 1944. 'Recherches sur le développement de Lampetra fluvia-
tilis. L.' *Arch. Biol.* **55,** 1.

DAWYDOFF, C. 1948. 'Stomocordes' (In) *Traité de Zoologie,* **11,** 367. P. P.
Grassé. Masson et Cie. Paris.

DELSMAN, H. C. 1912. *The Ancestry of Vertebrates.* Rotterdam.

—— 1912. 'Weitere Beobachtungen ueber die Entwicklung von Diko-
pleura dioica.' *Tidschr. Nederl. Dierk. Ver.* (2) **12,** 197.

DOHRN, A. 1885. *Der Ursprung der Wirbelthiere und das Prinzip des Funktions-wechsels.*

DUNBAR, C. O. 1949. *Historical Geology.* New York.

ELWYN, A. 1937. 'Stages in the Development of the Neural Complex in Ecteinascidia Turbinata.' *Bull. Neur. Inst. New York,* **6,** 163.

FELL, H. B. 1948. 'Echinoderm Embryology and the Origin of Chordates.' *Biol. Rev.* **23,** 81.

GARSTANG, S. L., and GARSTANG, W. 1928. 'On the development of Botrylloides.' *Quart. J. Micr. Sci.* **72,** 1.

GARSTANG, W. 1894. 'Preliminary Note on a New Theory of the Phylogeny of the Chordata.' *Zool. Anz.* **17,** 119.

—— 1922. 'The Theory of Recapitulation: a Critical Restatement of the Biogenetic Law.' *Soc. J. Zool.* **35,** 81.

—— 1928. 'The Morphology of the Tunicata, and its Bearings on the Phylogeny of the Chordata.' *Quart. J. Micr. Sci.* **72,** 51.

GARSTANG, W., and PLATT, M. I. 1928. 'On the Asymmetry and Closure of the Endostyle in Cyclosalpa Pinnata.' *Proc. Leeds Phil. Soc.* **1,** 325.

GASKELL, W. H. 1908. *The Origin of Vertebrates.* London.

GISLEN, T. 1930. 'Affinities between the Echinodermata, Entero and Chordonia.' *Zool. Bidrag J. Uppsala,* **12,** 199.

GOODRICH, E. S. 1902. 'On the Structure of the Excretory Organs of Amphioxus.' *Quart. J. Micr. Sci.* **40,** 138.

GLASER, O., and ANSLOW, G. A. 1949. 'Copper and Ascidian Metamorphosis.' *J. Exp. Zool.* **111,** 117.

GOLDSCHMIDT, R. 1933. 'A Note on Amphioxides from Bermuda based on Dr. W. Beebes' Collections.' *Biol. Bull.* **64,** 321.

GOODRICH, E. S. 1930. *Studies on the Structure and Development of Vertebrates.* Macmillan, London.

GRAVE, C. 1921. 'Amaroucium constellatum (Verrill). II. The Structure and Organization of the Tadpole Larva.' *J. Morph.* **36,** 71.

—— 1935. *Metamorphosis in Ascidian Larvae.* Carneg. Inst. Wash. Publ. No. 452, 209.

—— and NICOL, P. 1939. *Studies of Larval Life and Metamorphosis in Ascidia Nigra and Species of Polyandrocarpa.* Carneg. Inst. Wash. Publ. No. 517, 1.

—— 1944. 'The Larva of Styela (Cynthia) partita: Structure, Activities and Duration of Life.' *J. Morph.* **75,** 173.

GREGORY, W. K. 1951. *Evolution Emerging.* New York.

HARRIS, I. E. 1936. 'The Role of the Fins in the Equilibrium of the Swimming Fish.' *J. Exp. Biol.* **13,** 476 and **15,** 32.

HECHT, S. 1918. 'The Physiology of Ascidia Atra. I. General Physiology.' *J. Exp. Zool.* **25,** 229.

HOGG, B. M. 1937. 'Subneural Gland of Ascidian (Polycarpa tecta): an Ovarian Stimulating Action in Immature Mice.' *Proc. Soc. Exp. Biol.* **35,** 616.

HOYLE, G. 1952. 'The Response Mechanism in Ascidians.' *J. Mar. Biol. Assoc. U.K.* **31,** 287.

—— 1953. 'Spontaneous Squirting of an Ascidian, Phallusia Mammillata.' *J. Mar. Biol. Assoc. U.K.* **31,** 541.

HUBRECHT, A. A. W. 1883. 'On the Ancestral Forms of the Chordata.' *Quart. J. Micr. Sci.* **23,** 349.

HUTCHINSON, G. E. 1930. 'Restudy of some Burgess Shale Fossils.' *Proc. U.S. Nat. Mus.* 78, No. 11.

HÚUS, J. 1937. 'Tunicata: Ascidiaceae.' *Handb. Zool. Kükenthal und Krumbach*, **5** (2nd half), 545.

HUXLEY, J. S. 1921. 'Studies in Differentiation. II. Dedifferentiation and Resorption in Perophora.' *Quart. J. Micr. Sci.* **65,** 643.

—— 1926. 'Studies in Dedifferentiation. II. Reduction Phenomena in Clavelina tepadiformis.' *Pubb. Staz. Zool. Napoli*, **7,** 1.

JULIN, C. 1881. 'Recherches sur l'organisation des Ascidies simples, sur l'hypophyse, etc.' *Arch. Biol.* **2,** 59, 211.

KERR, G. 1919. *Textbook of Embryology*, v. 2. Macmillan, London.

KOWALESKY, A. 1866. *Entwickelungsgeschichte der Einfachen Ascidien*. Mem. Acad. Sci. St. Petersburg.

LACAZE-DUTHIERS, F. J. H. DE. 1874. 'Histoire des Ascidies simples des côtes de France.' *Arch. Zool. Expér.* **3,** 119, 257, 531.

LANDGREBE, F. W., and WARING, H. 1950. 'Biological Assay of the Melanophore Expanding Hormone from the Pituitary.' (In) *Hormone Essay* (C. W. Emmens) New York.

LOHMANN, H. 1933. 'Tunicata.' (In) *Kükenthal und Krumbach. Handb. der Zool.* **5** (2nd half), 1.

METCALF, M. M. 1893. 'The Eyes and Subneural Gland of Salpa.' (In) *The Genus Salpa*, by W. K. Brooks. Baltimore.

MILLAR, R. J. 1951. 'The Development and Early Stages of the Ascidian Pyura squamubosa (Alder).' *J. Mar. Biol. Assoc.* **30,** 27–31.

MINOT, C. S. 1897. 'Cephalic Homologies: A Contribution to the Determination of the Ancestry of Vertebrates.' *Amer. Nat.* **31,** 927.

NEUMANN, G. 1906. 'Doliolum.' *Ergebn. Deutsch. Tiefsee-Exped.* **12,** 93.

—— 1935. 'Pyrosomida and Cyclomyaria (Tunicata).' *Kükenthal und Krumbach, Hand. der Zool.* **5** (2nd half), 226.

PALAY, S. L. 1953. 'Neurosecretory Phenomena in the Hypothalamo-hypophysical System of Man and Monkey.' *Amer. J. Anat.* **93,** 107.

PANTIN, C. F. A. 1931. 'The Adaptation of Gunda ulvae to Salinity.' *J. Exp. Biol.* **8,** 63, 73, 82.

PATTEN, W. 1912. *The Evolution of Vertebrates and their Kin*. Philadelphia.

PENFIELD, W., and RASMUSSEN. *The Cerebral Cortex*. Macmillan, New York.

POLLISTER, A. W., and MOORE, J. A. 1937. 'Tables for the Normal Development of Rana sylvatica.' *Anat. Rec.* **68,** 489.

REVERBERI, G. 1947. 'La distributione delle potenze nel germe di Ascidie allostadis di otto blastomeri, analizzata mediante le combinazione e i traplianti di blastomeri.' *Pubb. Stat. Zool. Napoli* **21,** 1.

RIES, E. 1937. 'Untersuchungen ueber die Zelltod.' *Arch. Entw. Org.* **137,** 327.

ROMER, A. S. 1933. *Vertebrate Palaeontology*. Chicago U. P. Chicago.

—— 1942. 'Cartilage and Embryonic Adaptation.' *Amer. Nat.* **76,** 394.

ROSE, S. M. 1939. 'Embryonic Induction in the Ascidia.' *Biol. Bull.* **77,** 216.

St. Hilaire, Geoffroy E. 1919. *Philosophie Anatomie.* Paris.

Scott, F. M. 1946. 'The Developmental History of Amaroucium Constellatum. II. Organogenesis of the Larval Action System.' *Biol. Bull.* **91,** 66.

Semper, C. 1875–6. *Die Verwandtschaftsbeziehungen der Gegliederten Thiere.* Arbeit. zool. zoot. Inst. Wuerzburg.

Shumway, W. 1940. 'Stages in the Normal Development of Rana sylvatica.' *Anat. Rec.* **78,** 139.

Smith, Homer. 1939. *Studies in the Physiology of the Kidney.* Univ. Kansas.

—— 1953. *From Fish to Philosopher.* Little, Brown, Boston.

Stensiö, E. A. 1927. *The Downtonian and Devonian vertebrates of Spitzbergen.* Pt. 1. Cephalaspidae. Det Norske Vid.-akad. Oslo.

Tung, F. C. 1934. 'Recherches sur les potentialités des blastomères chez Ascidiella scabra. Expériences de translocation, de combination et d'isolement de blastomères.' *Arch. Anat. Micr.* **30,** 381.

Ubisch, L. von. 1939. 'Ueber die Entwicklung von Ascidienlarven nach fruehzeitiger Entfernung der Einzelnen Organbildung Keimbezirke.' *Arch. Entw. Org.* **139,** 438.

Uljanin, B. N. 1884. 'Die Arten des Gattung Doliolum im Golfe von Neapel und den Angrenzenden Meeresabschnitten.' *Fauna und Flora des Golfs von Neapel.* **10,** 1.

Walcott, C. D. 1912. 'Cambrian Geology and Paleontology. II. Middle Cambrian Branchiopoda, Malacostraca, Trilobita and Merostomata.' *Smithsonian Misc. Coll.* **57,** 5, 109, 145.

Walls, G. I. 1939. 'The Origin of the Vertebrate Eye.' *Arch. Ophthalmology,* **22,** 452.

—— 1942. *The Vertebrate Eye.* Cranbook Inst. Sci. No. 19.

Watson, D. M. S. 1951. *Palaeontology and Modern Biology.* Yale U. P. New Haven.

Van Weel, P. V. 1940. 'Beitraege zur Ernaehrungsbiologie der Ascidian.' *Pubb. Staz. zool. Napoli,* **18,** 50.

Weiss, P., and Amprino, R. 1940. 'The Effect of Mechanical Stress on the Differentiation of Scleral Cartilage in Vitro and in the Embryo.' *Growth,* **4,** 245.

Weisz, P. B. 1945. 'The Development and Morphology of the Larva of the South African Clawed Toad, Xenopus laevis.' *J. Morph.* **77,** 163, 193.

—— 1945. 'The Normal Stages in the Development of the South African Clawed Toad, Xenopus laevis.' *Anat. Rec.* **93,** 161.

—— 1947. 'The Histological Pattern of Metameric Development in Artemia Salina.' *J. Morph.* **81,** 45.

Whitaker, D. M. 1933. 'On the Rate of Oxygen Consumption by Fertilized and Unfertilized Eggs. V. Comparisons and Interpretation.' *J. Gen. Physiol.* **16,** 497.

White, E. I. 1935. 'The Ostracoderm Pteraspis Kner and the Relationships of the Agnathous Vertebrates.' *Phil. Trans. Roy. Soc.* B, **225,** 381.

—— 1946. ' "Jamoytius kerwoodi", a new Chordate from the Silurian of Lanarkshire.' *Geol. Mag.* **83,** 89.

WILLEY, A. 1893. 'Studies on the Protochordata. II. The Development of the Neuro-hypophysial System in Ciona Intestinalis and Clavelina lepadiformus, with an Account of the Origin of the Sense-organs in Ascidia mentula.' *Quart. J. Micr. Sci.* (2) **35,** 295.

—— 1894. *Amphioxus and the Ancestry of Vertebrates.* New York.

WILSON, D. P. 1950. 'Larval Metamorphosis and the Substratum.' *Ann. Biol.* **27,** 259.

YONGE, C. M. 1925. 'Studies on the Comparative Physiology of Digestion. 3. Ciona intestinalis.' *Brit. J. Exp. Biol.* **2,** 573.

YOUNG, J. Z. 1950. *The Life of Vertebrates.* Oxford.

INDEX

PRINTED IN
GREAT BRITAIN
AT THE
UNIVERSITY PRESS
OXFORD
BY
CHARLES BATEY
PRINTER
TO THE
UNIVERSITY